INTRODUCTION TO THE THEORY
OF STABILITY

E. A. BARBASHIN

Sverdlov Department of the Institute for Mathematics of the Academy of Sciences of the USSR

INTRODUCTION
TO THE THEORY OF STABILITY

translated from Russian by
TRANSCRIPTA SERVICE, LONDON
edited by T. LUKES

ΙͶͶΝΙ

WOLTERS–NOORDHOFF PUBLISHING GRONINGEN

THE NETHERLANDS

Library of Congress Catalog Card No. 70-90843

ISBN 90 01 05345 9

PRINTED IN THE NETHERLANDS
BY NEDERLANDSE BOEKDRUK INDUSTRIE N.V. – DEN BOSCH

CONTENTS

Chapter 3

Stability of the Solutions of Differential Equations in Banach Space 139

EDITOR'S FOREWORD

Considerable contributions to the theory of stability have been made in the USSR starting with the work of the mathematicians Lurie and Lyapunov about eighteen years ago. In this book readers will find a clear and concise account of this work, to which Dr. Barbashin has himself made original contributions.

T. Lukes

PREFACE

This book is based on a course of lectures given by the author to advanced mathematics students at the "A. M. Gor'kii" Urals State University. The lectures were directed also to scientific workers and engineers interested in applying the methods of stability theory, a circumstance that explains certain features of the contents of the course. On the one hand the author aimed at giving the mathematicians a picture of the present day level of development of stability theory while at the same time pointing out the relation of this theory to other fields of mathematics. The author wished also to acquaint this section of his audience with the most recent methods of investigation, including an account of his own work and of the work of his students. On the other hand, he did not want his audience to go away from the lecture hall with their minds filled only with bare mathematical constructions. Each mathematical fact is therefore considered from the point of view of its applicability and importance to practical problems. Unfortunately, it was not possible to include all such discussion in the book, but the choice of material reflects the above situation well enough.

The first chapter gives an account of the method of Lyapunov functions originally expounded in a book by A. M. Lyapunov with the title *The general problem of stability of motion* which went out of print in 1892. Since then a number of monographs devoted to the further development of the method of Lyapunov functions has been published: in the USSR, those by A. I. Lurie [22], N. G. Chetaev [26], I. G. Malkin [8], A. M. Letov [23], N. N. Krasovskii [7], V. I. Zubov [138]; and abroad, J. La Salle and S. Lefshets [11], W. Hahn [137].

Our book certainly does not pretend to give an exhaustive account of these methods; it does not even cover all the theorems given in the monograph by Lyapunov. Only autonomous systems are discussed and, in the linear case, we confine ourselves to a survey of Lyapunov functions in the form of quadratic forms only. In the non-linear case we do not consider the question of the invertibility of the stability and instability theorems.

On the other hand, Chapter 1 gives a detailed account of problems pertaining to stability in the presence of any initial perturbation, the theory of which was first propounded during the period 1950–1955. The first important work in this field was that of N. P. Erugin [133–135, 16] and the credit for applying Lyapunov functions to these problems belongs to Lurie and Malkin. Theorems of the type 5.2, 6.3, 12.2 presented in Chapter 1 played a significant role in the development of the theory of stability on the whole. In these theorems the property of stability is explained by the presence of a Lyapunov function of constant signs and not one of fixed sign differentiated with respect to time as is required in certain of Lyapunov's theorems. The fundamental role played by these theorems is explained by the fact that almost any attempt to construct simple Lyapunov functions for non-linear systems leads to functions with the above property.

In presenting the material of Chapter 1, the method of constructing the Lyapunov functions is indicated where possible. Examples are given at the end of the Chapter, each of which brings out a particular point of interest.

Chapter 2 is devoted to problems pertaining to systems with variable structure. From a mathematical point of view such systems represent a very narrow class of systems of differential equations with discontinuous right-hand sides, a fact that has enabled the author and his collaborators to construct a more or less complete and rigorous theory for this class of systems. Special note should be taken of the importance of studying the stability of systems with variable structure since such systems are capable of stabilising objects whose parameters are varying over wide limits. Some of the results of Chapter 2 were obtained jointly with the engineers who not only elaborated the theory along independent lines but also constructed analogues of the systems being studied.

The method of Lyapunov function finds an application here also but the reader interested in Chapter 2 can acquaint himself with the contents independently of the material of the preceding Chapter.

In Chapter 3 the stability of the solutions of differential equations in Banach space is discussed. The reasons for including this chapter are the following. First, at the time work commenced on this chapter, no monograph or even basic work existed on this subject apart from the articles by L. Massera and Schäffer [94, 95, 139, 140]. The author also wished to demonstrate the part played by the methods of functional analysis in the theory of stability. The first contribution to this subject was that of M. G. Krein [99]. Later, basing their work in particular on Krein's method, Massera and Schäffer developed the theory of stability in functional spaces considerably further. By the time work on Chapter 3 had been completed, Krein's book [75] had gone out of print. However, the divergence of scientific interests of Krein and the present author were such that the results obtained overlap only when rather general problems are being discussed.

One feature of the presentation of the material in Chapter 3 deserves particular mention. We treat the problem of perturbation build-up as a problem in which one is seeking a norm of the operator which will transform the input signal into the output signal. Considerable importance is given to the theorems of Massera and Schäffer, these theorems again being discussed from the point of view of perturbation build-up but this time over semi-infinite intervals of time.

It has become fashionable to discuss stability in the context of stability with respect to a perturbation of the input signal. If we suppose that a particular unit in an automatic control system transforms an input signal into some other signal then the law of transformation of these signals is given by an operator. In this case, stability represents the situation in which a small perturbation of the input signal causes a small perturbation of the output signal. From a mathematical point of view this property corresponds to the property of continuity of the operator in question. It is interesting to give the internal characteristic of such operators. As a rule this characteristic reduces to a description of the asymptotic behaviour of a Cauchy matrix (of the transfer functions). The results of Sections 5 and 6 will be discussed within this framework.

We should note that the asymptotic behaviour of the Cauchy matrix of the system is completely characterised by the response behaviour of the unit to an impulse. Thus the theorems given in Section 5 and 6 may be regarded as theorems which describe the response of a system to an impulse as a function of the response of the system when acted upon by other types of perturbation. For this reason problems relating to the transformation of impulse actions are of particular importance. Here, the elementary theory of stability with respect to impulse actions is based on the concept of functions of limited variations and on the notion of a Stieltjes integral. This approach permits one to investigate from one and the same point of view both stability in the Lyapunov sense (i.e. stability

with respect to initial perturbations) and stability with respect to continuously acting perturbations.

The last paragraph of Chapter 3 is devoted to the problem of programmed
control. The material of Sections 6 and 7 has been presented in such a way
that no difficulty will be found in applying it for the purpose of solving
the problem of realising a motion along a specified trajectory. To develop
this theory, all that was necessary was to bring in the methods and results
of the theory of mean square approximations.

It should be noted that Chapter 3 demands of the reader a rather more
extensive mathematical groundwork than is required for the earlier
Chapters. In that Chapter we make use of the basic ideas of functional
analysis which the reader can acquaint himself with by reading, for
example, the book by Kantorovich and Akilov [71]. However, for the
convenience of the reader, all the basic definitions and statements of
functional analysis which we use in Chapter 3 are presented in Section 1
of that Chapter.

At the end of the book there is a detailed bibliography relating to the
problems discussed.

The author is grateful to N. N. Krasovskii for his valuable comments and
advice.

The author expresses his sincere thanks to V. A. Tabueva, E. I. Gerash-
chenko, V. L. Gasilov, S. T. Zavalishin, A. F. Kleimenov and L. V.
Kiselev for pointing out a number of defects in the manuscript and to
Yu. K. Sergeez for making an analogue study of some of the results of
Chapter 2.

Chapter 1

THE METHOD OF LYAPUNOV FUNCTIONS

A series of general sufficient conditions for the stability and instability of an undisturbed motion that can be described by a system of ordinary differential equations has been laid down by A. M. Lyapunov. Reducing the problem from one of the stability of an undisturbed motion to one of the stability of a state of equilibrium, he was able to relate the question of the stability or instability of a system to the question of the existence or non-existence of the function $v(x_1, ..., x_n)$, whose time derivative, taken according to the system of differential equations, possesses certain definite properties.

However, the value of Lyapunov functions goes far beyond that of simply establishing whether a system is stable or unstable. A knowledge of the Lyapunov function for an actual automatic control system enables one to estimate the change in the quantity being controlled, the duration of the transient response (control time) of the system, and the quality of the control. Lyapunov functions can be used to obtain estimates of the region of attraction, i.e. the manifold of all initial disturbances which disappear with the passage of time; they can also be used to estimate the effect of disturbances which act continuously. If the Lyapunov function is known one can decide whether or not overcontrol is present, and such functions are useful in solving problems concerned with stability "in the large", i.e. the range of initial disturbances which, with the passage of time, re-main within the bounds of some previously specified domain. In certain cases a knowledge of the Lyapunov function allows one to decide whether there is a periodic solution.

One of the most difficult but interesting aspects of stability theory was concerned with the validity of the converse to Lyapunov's theorems: that is, were the sufficient conditions of stability and instability given by Lyapunov also necessary conditions? This question proved to be an important one not only because one wished to show that the theory was logically complete; the converse to Lyapunov's theorems given by K. P. Persidskii [141], L. Massera [4], E. A. Barbashin [25], I. G. Malkin

[142] and N. N. Krasovskii [7] provided the necessary confidence in the usefulness of the method of Lyapunov functions as a universal means of solving stability problems.

Although the methods of constructing Lyapunov functions given by these authors permit one to establish that these functions exist, these methods are not powerful enough for them to be of use in studying actual systems. A method of constructing Lyapunov functions for an autonomous linear set has been given by Lyapunov himself. The same method also allows one to obtain the Lyapunov function in a sufficiently small neighbourhood about the equilibrium position of a linear system. A considerably more difficult problem is that of constructing such a function in a specified region of the phase space of a non-linear system. Attemps to solve this problem have been made by many mathematicians and engineers and, as a result of their efforts, a wide variety of Lyapunov functions for specific cases have been accumulated for non-linear systems of a special form but, so far, no reliable, simple, well-detailed algorithm has been found for constructing the Lyapunov function for any non-linear system.

In this chapter, in addition to presenting the theorems for stability and instability, we give examples of the use of Lyapunov functions for solving such problems as estimating the control time, the region of permissible disturbances, the region of attraction, etc. In addition, we point out the more frequently used methods of constructing Lyapunov functions for non-linear systems giving appropriate examples of their application.

1. Estimate of the Variation of the Solutions

Let us consider the system of differential equations

$$\frac{dx_i}{dt} = X_i(x_1, \dots, x_n, t), \quad i = 1, 2, \dots, n. \tag{1.1}$$

We shall suppose that the right-hand side of this system (1.1), i.e. the functions $X_i(x_1, \dots, x_n, t)$, are continuous in a certain open region D which may coincide with all space. Let us suppose, in addition, that in any closed region G lying in D, the function $X_i(x_1, \dots, x_n, t)$ satisfies the Lipschitz conditions with respect to the variables $x_1, \dots, x_n$. In this case the theorem guarantees the existence of a unique solution $x_i =$

$x_i(t, x_1^0, ..., x_n^0)$, $i = 1, 2, ..., n$ which satisfies the initial conditions $x_i(t_0, x_1^0, ..., x_n^0) = x_i^0$.

We note that the solution $x = x_i(t, x_1^0, ..., x_n^0)$ can exist only in a certain finite interval, and not for all t, $-\infty < t < \infty$. If the solution is definite for any value of t then we shall call this solution continuable. If the solution does not pass outside the limits of a certain bounded region then it will be continuable [3]. There exist also other more general criteria of continuability; these we shall deduce in Chapter 3.

Later we shall treat the right-hand sides of the system (1.1) as the projection of a varying velocity vector $X(X_1, X_2, ..., X_n)$ and we shall interpret the quantity t as a time. The system (1.1) then specifies the law of motion of the initial point $M_0(x_1^0, ..., x_n^0, t)$ of an $n+1$ dimensional phase space along the trajectory

$$x_i = x_i(t, x_1^0, ..., x_n^0), \qquad i = 1, 2, ..., n.$$

We shall in future frequently write the system (1.1) in vector form, i.e. in the form

$$\frac{dx}{dt} = X(x, t). \tag{1.2}$$

We shall consider the solution of this system to be the vector function $x(t)$ with projections $x_1(t), ..., x_n(t)$, and we shall denote the norm of the vector x by $\|x\|$. In the simplest case the norm of the vector can coincide with the Euclidian length of the vector, i.e. it is defined by the formula

$$\|x\| = \left(\sum_{i=1}^{n} x_i^2 \right)^{\frac{1}{2}}.$$

This is not the only way of defining the norm; we give below two other frequently encountered definitions:

$$\|x\| = \max_i |x_i|$$

$$\|x\| = \sum_{i=1}^{n} |x_i|.$$

It is obvious that having introduced the norm in phase space we can now bring in the idea of the closeness of points in that space and, consequently, the notion of a passage to the limit. It is easy to see that if the sequence of vectors x^m converges to the vector x according to the definition of one of the indicated norms then it converges in the sense of any two other norms. In this case one says that the norms are topologically equivalent. Later on we shall need to make use of the following lemma

Lemma 1.1. *Let $u(t)$ be a continuous function which, for $t > t_0$, satisfies the inequality*

$$0 < u(t) < \delta + \int_{t_0}^{t} (\eta + Lu(t))dt \,, \tag{1.3}$$

where δ, η, L are constants and $\delta \geqslant 0$, $\eta \geqslant 0$, $L > 0$. Then the following inequality holds

$$u(t) < \frac{\eta}{L} (e^{L(t-t_0)} - 1) + \delta\, e^{L(t-t_0)} \,. \tag{1.4}$$

When $t = t_0$, inequality (1.4) is, in fact, fulfilled. In view of the continuity of the function $u(t)$, the inequality (1.4) will be valid also for $t > t_0$ if the difference $t - t_0$ is sufficiently small. Let $t = \tau$ be the closest instant of time at which inequality (1.4) is violated, i.e. the point where it becomes an equality.

If we consider the inequality (1.3) at $t = \tau$, and remember that the inequality (1.3) is valid over the half-interval $t_0 \leqslant t < \tau$, we obtain

$$u(\tau) < \delta + \int_{t_0}^{\tau} \left(\eta + L \left[\frac{\eta}{L} (e^{L(t-t_0)} - 1) + \delta\, e^{L(t-t_0)} \right| \right) dt \,.$$

Integrating and putting in the limits, we obtain the inequality

$$u(\tau) < \frac{\eta}{L} (e^{L(\tau-t_0)} - 1) + \delta\, e^{L(\tau-t_0)} \,,$$

which contradicts our choice of τ.

Having now proved this lemma we shall use it to estimate the variation of the system (1.2) corresponding to a change in the initial conditions and of the right-hand sides of the system.

In addition to the system (1.2) we shall consider the system:

$$\frac{dy}{dt} = X(y, t) + R(y, t) \,. \tag{1.5}$$

In region D, and for $t_0 \leqslant t \leqslant t_0 + T$, let the following inequality be fulfilled

$$\|R(y, t)\| < \eta .\qquad(1.6)$$

Let us examine the solution $x = x(t, x^0)$ of the system (1.2) and the solution $y = y(t, y^0)$ of the system (1.5). We shall suppose that the initial conditions determined by these solutions satisfy the conditions

$$\|y^0 - x^0\| < \delta .\qquad(1.7)$$

We shall now write down the Lipschitz conditions for the system (1.2) in the form of the inequality

$$\|X(y, t) - X(x, t)\| < L\|y - x\| ,\qquad(1.8)$$

where L is a constant.

Theorem 1.1 (concerning the error of the solutions). *Let conditions* (1.6)–(1.8) *be fulfilled; then for* $t_0 \leqslant t \leqslant t_0 + T$ *the estimate is*

$$\|y(t) - x(t)\| < \frac{\eta}{L}(e^{L(t-t_0)} - 1) + \delta\, e^{L(t-t_0)} .\qquad(1.9)$$

To prove this estimate we shall put equations (1.2) and (1.5) in the form of integral equations

$$x(t) = x^0 + \int_{t_0}^{t} X(x, t)dt ,$$

$$y(t) = y^0 + \int_{t_0}^{t} [X(y, t) + R(y, t)]dt .$$

We have

$$\|y(t) - x(t)\| \leqslant \|y^0 - x^0\| + \int_{t_0}^{t} \{\|X(y, t) - X(x, t)\| + \|R(y, t)\|\}\, dt .\qquad(1.10)$$

Using the inequalities (1.6)–(1.8), we obtain

$$\|y(t) - x(t)\| < \delta + \int_{t_0}^{t} \{\eta + L\|y(t) - x(t)\|\}\, dt .$$

The estimate we need now follows directly from lemma 1.1.
Let us take some particular cases. If it is only the initial conditions that

are disturbed and the right-hand sides remain unchanged (this case corresponds to the action of instantaneous disturbances), then we have $\eta = 0$ and estimate (1.9) has the form

$$\| y(t) - x(t) \| < \delta\, e^{L(t - t_0)} .$$

Whence, in particular, it is evident that by making δ sufficiently small it is possible to satisfy the inequality $\| y(t) - x(t) \| < \varepsilon$ on the segment $t_0 \leqslant t \leqslant t_0 + T$, where ε is an arbitrary positive number. This means that the solution of equation (1.2) is a continuous function of the initial data, a fact that may be interpreted as a property of the stability of the solutions of system (1.2) over a finite interval of time. Thus, the property of the stability of the solutions over a finite interval of time is inherent in any system of ordinary differential equations.

If now $\delta = 0$ and $\eta \neq 0$, we have the case of continuously acting disturbances, and estimate (1.9) assumes the form

$$\| y(t) - x(t) \| < \frac{\eta}{L}\, (e^{L(t - t_0)} - 1) .$$

It is clear that for a specified value of ε one can choose η such that over the interval $t_0 \leqslant t \leqslant t_0 + T$ we have

$$\| y(t) - x(t) \| < \varepsilon .$$

This last fact expresses the continuity property of the solution in the functional space of the right-hand sides. In particular, if the right-hand sides of set (1.2) depend continuously upon some parameter λ, then from the estimates obtained it follows that the solution of the system with respect to this parameter is continuous.

If the right-hand sides of system (1.1) are independent of the time t, then we shall call this sytem *autonomous*. Let the system (1.1) now be autonomous and let us suppose, in addition, that all the solutions of system (1.1) are continuable i.e. they are well-defined functions for any instant of time t. Let us consider the point $p(x_1^0, ..., x_n^0)$ in the phase space of the autonomous system and denote the point

$$q(x_1(t, x_1^0, ..., x_n^0), ..., \quad x_n(t, x_1^0, ..., x_n^0))$$

by $f(p, t)$. Thus $f(p, t)$ denotes the position of point p during the interval of time t while it is moving along the trajectory of system (1.1). If t is fixed, then the function $f(p, t)$ effects a mapping of the phase space onto itself. By virtue of the existence and uniqueness theorems for the solutions, and from the estimates we have obtained of the errors of the solutions, this mapping will be reciprocally single-valued and reciprocally continuous. In addition, it is easy to see that the function $f(p, t)$ has the property

$$f(f(p, t_1), t_2) = f(p, t_1 + t_2) .$$ (1.11)

From the property (1.11) (which we shall call the group property of the dynamic system) it follows that the totality of mappings forms a one-parameter group of the mappings of the phase space [3].

2. Definition of Stability. Derivation of Equations for Disturbed Motion

Let us consider the system of differential equations

$$\frac{dy}{dt} = Y(y, t) .$$ (2.1)

We shall separate out of the system (2.1) a certain motion $y = f(t)$ and call it the undisturbed motion.

We shall call the motion $y = f(t)$ stable in the Lyapunov sense if for every $\varepsilon > 0$ one can find $\delta > 0$ such that, from the inequality $\| y(t_0) - f(t_0) \| < \delta$, there follows the inequality $\| y(t) - f(t) \| < \varepsilon$ for $t \geqslant t_0$. Here $y(t)$ denotes any other solution of the system (2.1) determined by the initial conditions $y(t_0)$. The motion $y = f(t)$ is called asymptotically stable in the Lyapunov sense, if it is stable in the Lyapunov sense and if there exists a positive number h such that for $\| y(t_0) - f(t_0) \| < h$ we have

$$\lim_{t \to \infty} \| y(t) - f(t) \| = 0 .$$ (2.2)

If the solution $y(t)$ tends to $f(t)$ as $t \to \infty$ uniformly with respect to t_0, then the asymptotic stability is said to be uniform relative to t_0. If the uniformity with which $y(t)$ tends to the limit is with respect to the initial conditions $y(t_0)$, then we say that the solution $y = f(t)$ is uniformly asymptotically stable with respect to the initial conditions. If the system (2.1) is autonomous, i.e. if the right-hand sides are independent of t, then the asymptotic stability will always be uniform relative to the initial data. This fact was established by Massera [4].

If the motion $y=f(t)$ is stable according to Lyapunov and relation (2.2) is valid for the solutions $y(t)$ determined by any initial data, then we say that the motion $y=f(t)$ is asymptotically stable for any initial data (or asymptotically stable on the whole).

In the system (2.1) let us make the change of variables $x=y-f(t)$. The new system will have the form

$$\frac{dx}{dt} = Y(x+f(t), t) - Y(f(t), t) ;$$

and, introducing the notation

$$X(x, t) = Y(x+f(t), t) - Y(f(t), t),$$

we obtain the system

$$\frac{dx}{dt} = X(x, t),\tag{2.3}$$

where $X(0, t) = 0$ for $t \geqslant t_0$.

The system (2.3) defines the differential equations for disturbed motion. As a result of changing the variables, the motion $y=f(t)$ has become the equilibrium position $x=0$ of the new system. In this way the problem of the stability of the motion $y=f(t)$ has been converted to the problem of stability of the zero solution $x=0$ of the system (2.3).

Let us formulate now a definition of what is meant by the stability of the zero solution $x=0$ of the system (2.3).

The solution $x=0$ of the system (2.3) is called stable in the Lyapunov sense if for any positive number ε one can find a positive number δ such that, from the inequality $\|x(t_0)\| < \delta$ and for $t > t_0$, there follows the inequality $\|x(t)\| < \varepsilon$. If now, in addition, every solution $x(t)$ whose initial conditions are determined by the condition $\|x(t_0)\| < h$ possesses the property $\lim_{t\to\infty}\|x(t)\| = 0$, then the zero solution is called asymptotically stable in the Lyapunov sense. The concepts of uniform asymptotic stability and stability in the large are defined in an analogous way.

3. Lyapunov Functions

Let us consider the function $v(x_1, \ldots, x_n)$, defined in the phase space of the variable $x_1, \ldots, x_n$ and continuous in a certain region D which includes the coordinate origin. Let us suppose also that in the region D the function $v(x_1, ..., x_n)$ possesses continuous partial derivatives.

We shall call the function $v(x_0, ..., x_n)$ positive definite in the region D if, everywhere within region D except for the point O $(0, ..., 0)$, the inequality $v > 0$ is valid. If the inequality $v < 0$ is fulfilled, then we shall say that the function v is negative definite. In both these cases the function can also be referred to as a function of fixed sign.

If in region D the inequality $v \geqslant 0$ or the inequality $v \leqslant 0$ holds, then the function v is said to be of constant sign. In the first case v may also be referred to as a function of positive terms; in the second case, a function of negative terms.

If in the region D the function v assumes values of both positive and negative sign, then in this case v is said to be a function with alternating sign. For example, the function $v = x_1^2 + x_2^2 - x_3^2$ is a function with alternating sign in the space of the variables x_1, x_2, x_3, and the function $v = x_1^2 + x_2^2 + x_3^2$ is positive definite in this space. The function $v = x_1^2 + x_2^2$ is, however, a function of constant sign in the space of the variables x_1, x_2, x_3 (since it vanishes on the Ox_3 axis) and a function of fixed sign in the space of the variables x_1, x_2.

Usually, we shall be dealing with quadratic forms of the variables $x_1, ..., x_n$. Clearly, any quadratic form may be written as

$$v = \sum_{i, k = 1}^{n} a_{ik} x_i x_k , \text{ where } a_{ik} = a_{ki} .$$

Let us compose the matrix of the coefficients of this form:

$$A = \begin{Vmatrix} a_{11} & \cdots & a_{1n} \\ \cdot & \cdots & \cdot \\ a_{n1} & \cdots & a_{nn} \end{Vmatrix}$$

and consider the determinant

$$\Delta_k = \begin{vmatrix} a_{11} & \cdots & a_{1k} \\ \cdot & \cdots & \cdot \\ a_{k1} & \cdots & a_{kk} \end{vmatrix} \qquad k = 1, 2, ..., n .$$

If the inequalities $\Delta_k > 0$ are valid for $k = 1, 2, ..., n$, then the form v will be positive definite.

The converse theorem is true, i.e. the conditions $\Delta_k > 0$, which are called the Silvester criterion [5], are necessary and sufficient for the form v to be positive definite. From the Silvester criterion, it is easy to deduce the necessary and sufficient condition for the form v to be negative definite. This condition can be written down in the form of the inequalities

$$\Delta_1 < 0, \; \Delta_2 > 0, \; \Delta_3 < 0, \; ...,$$

i.e. the determinants Δ_k should alternate in sign, with the sign of Δ_1 negative.

Later we shall study the behaviour of the function $v(x_1, \, ..., \, x_n)$ along the trajectory of the system of differential equations we are studying and proceed from there to deduce the behaviour of the trajectories of the system under consideration. When the functions $v(x_1, \, ..., \, x_n)$ are used for such a purpose they are usually called Lyapunov functions.

We shall now formulate a theorem about the structure of the level surface of the Lyapunov function of fixed sign.

Theorem 3.1. *If the function $v(x_1, \, ..., \, x_n)$ is a function of fixed sign, then there exists a positive number h such that all surfaces $v = c$, where $|c| < h$, are closed surfaces with respect to the point O.*

We note that we call the surface $v = c$ closed with respect to the point O if on any continuous line connecting the point O with a point on the boundary of region D there is at least one point at which $v = c$.

To prove this theorem we shall suppose, to be definite, that $v > 0$ and we shall consider a sphere J_R with its centre at the coordinate origin and with radius, R. Let us suppose that the function v is well defined on this sphere (including its boundary S_R). Thus, for our region D, we shall take the sphere $J_R = J_R \cup S_R$. Since the function v is continuous, then on a closed, bounded set S_R, the boundary of the sphere, this function reaches a minimum value which we shall denote by h.

Let us now join the point O to any point p lying on the boundary S_R of a continuous line $x = x(s)$. Since the function v is equal to zero at the point O, and $v(p) \geqslant h$, and since the function v varies continuously along the continuous curve $x = x(s)$, then function v must at some point on this curve take on the value $v = c$.

Thus, a closed portion of the surface $v = c$ lies inside the sphere J_R; but this does not exclude the possibility that there are other parts of this surface lying outside the limits of this sphere. This possibility is realized, for example, by the function

$$v = \frac{x^2}{(1+x^2)^2} + \frac{y^2}{(1+y^2)^2}.$$

On the other hand, the function

$$v = \frac{x^2}{1+x^2} + y^2$$

provides us with an example of a function whose level line

$$\frac{x^2}{1+x^2} + y^2 = c$$

is unbounded for $c \geqslant 1$, but closed and bounded for $0 < c < 1$ (Fig. 1).

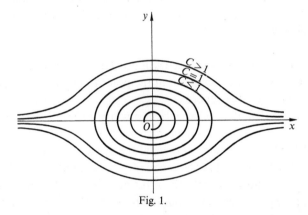

Fig. 1.

However we note that if the positive definite function v increases without limit as $x \to \infty$, i.e. if for any number $A > 0$ one can find a sphere S_R outside which we will have $v > A$, then the level surface of this function will be bounded surfaces.

4. The Stability Theorems of Lyapunov

We shall now give a number of sufficient tests of stability which form the basis of the concept of a Lyapunov function.

Let us consider the system of differential equations

$$\frac{dx_i}{dt} = X_i(x_1, ..., x_n), \qquad i = 1, 2, ..., n, \tag{4.1}$$

the right-hand sides of which $X_i(x_1, ..., x_n)$ are continuous and satisfy the Lipschitz conditions in a certain region D of phase space which in-cludes the point $O(0, ..., 0)$ together with some of its neighbourhood. Let us suppose that the conditions $X_i(0, ..., 0) = 0$ are fulfilled when the point O is a singular point of the system (4.1) or, what amounts to the same thing, the equilibrium position of this system. We shall assume in this case that the right-hand sides of system (4.1) are explicitly independent of t, i.e. we shall consider the system to be autonomous.

Theorem 4.1 (Lyapunov's stability theorem). *If for the set* (4.1) *there exists in the region D a function v of fixed sign whose time derivative v̇ taken on the strength of system* (4.1) *is a function of constant signs whose sign is opposite to the sign of the function v, then the equilibrium position is stable in the Lyapunov sense.*

Let us now prove this theorem. We will use J_ε to represent the interior of a sphere of radius ε whose centre is at the point O, and S_ε to represent the spherical surface of this sphere.

For the sake of definiteness, let v be a positive definite function. Let us suppose that ε is such that J_ε lies in the region D and let l be the minimum value of the function v on the surface of the sphere S_ε. We now choose a positive number δ such that the inequality $v < l$ is fulfilled at the points of the sphere J_δ, and we let p be the arbitrary point of J_δ. Let us consider the trajectory $f(p, t)$ emerging from the point p and assume that it inter-sects the sphere S_ε at some point q. Since

$$\sum_{i=0}^{n} \frac{\partial v}{\partial x_i} X_i \leqslant 0,$$

then the function v does not increase along the trajectory and so that we have $v(q) \leqslant v(p) < l$. On the other hand, since l is the minimum of the function v on S_ε, the inequality $v(q) \geqslant l$ should be fulfilled. This contradic-tion demonstrates that as time increases the point $f(p, t)$ does not pass outside the limits of the sphere S_ε, which proves the theorem.

We shall show now that one can use the same sort of argument that we have just used to prove the theorem to estimate the region of permissible disturbances. The region of permissible disturbances for a given point G is that region E such that all trajectories emerging from its points do not pass outside the limits of the region G. In the case given it is obvious that J_δ will be a region of permissible disturbances for the region J_ε. Thus, to determine the region of permissible disturbances it is necessary to find the minimum value l of the function v on the boundary of the region G and, as the region E, one should take a region in which the inequality $v < l$ is fulfilled.

Theorem 4.2 (The asymptotic stability theory of Lyapunov). *If for the system of differential equations* (4.1) *there exists a function v of fixed sign whose total time derivative found according to the system* 4.1 *will also be of fixed sign which is opposite to that of v, then the equilibrium position will be asymptotically stable.*

Let us prove this theorem. To be definite, let the function v be a positive definite function. Let the number R be such that $\bar{J}_R$ lies inside the region D. It follows from the preceding theorem that the equilibrium position will be stable so that there exists an $r > 0$ such that if the point p lies in J_r then the point $f(p, t)$ will not pass outside the sphere J_R. Let ε be an arbitrarily small positive number. In accordance with the preceding theorem, we again find a number $\delta > 0$ such that from $p \subset J$ it follows that $f(p, t) \subset J_\varepsilon$ for $t > 0$. Let the point p lie inside J_ε. We shall suppose that the point $f(p, t)$ does not fall into the sphere J_δ for $t > 0$. Then the semi-trajectory $f(p, t)$ for $t > 0$ will lie in the spherical layer $\bar{J}_R \setminus J_\delta$. Since $\dot{v} < 0$ everywhere inside this sphere, then there exists a constant $m > 0$ such that $\dot{v} < -m$ at all points of this layer. From the inequality

$$v(f(p, t)) = v(p) + \int_0^t \dot{v}\, dt$$

we quickly derive the inequality

$$v(f(p, t)) < v(p) - mt . \tag{4.2}$$

If t increases without limit, the right-hand side of this inequality becomes negative; this also leads to a contradiction since, on the left-hand side of this inequality, we have the value of the Lyapunov function, and this cannot be negative. Thus, to remove the contradiction, we must assume that the point $f(p, t)$ at some instant of time falls into the sphere J_δ but that the number δ is chosen so that, having fallen into J_δ, the point $f(p, t)$ cannot pass outside the limits J_ε. Since ε was taken as an arbitrarily small number, then it follows that everywhere we have that $\lim_{t \to \infty} f(p, t) = 0$. Thus the theorem is proved.

We shall show now how one can use the same kind of arguments as we used to prove the last theorem to estimate the transient response times. We shall define the transient response time as the time $t(p, \varepsilon)$ needed for the point p moving along the trajectory $f(p, t)$ to fall into a given neighbourhood J_ε of the point O and to remain there for a time $t > t(p, \varepsilon)$.
Let the number l be a minimum of the function v on the sphere S_δ. If $f(p, t_0) \subset J_\delta$ then, for $t \geqslant t_0$, we have $f(p, t) \subset J_\varepsilon$. But the number t_0 can obviously be found from the inequality $v(p) - mt_0 = l$ since, for $t_0 = \{y(p) - l\}/m$ the left-hand side of inequality (4.2) is automatically smaller than l. Thus we obtain the estimate

$$t(p, \varepsilon) < \frac{v(p) - l}{m}. \tag{4.3}$$

In control theory the transient response time is referred to as the control time.
Both the first and second theorems of Lyapunov have a simple geometrical interpretation. The inequality

$$\dot{v} = \sum_{i=1}^{n} \frac{\partial v}{\partial x_i} X_i < 0$$

means that the trajectories of the system (4.1) are directed towards the side where the function v is decreasing, i.e. they intersect the level surface of this function in a direction opposite to the direction of the vector grad v.

5. The Asymptotic Stability Theorem

Let us consider first certain limiting properties of the trajectories.

Definition 5.1. *A point q of phase space is called the ω-limit point of point p if there exists a sequence of times $\{t_n\}$, $t_n \to \infty$ for $n \to \infty$, such that $q = \lim_{n \to \infty} f(p, t_n)$. If $t_n \to -\infty$ then the point $q = \lim_{n \to \infty} f(p, t_n)$ is called the α-limit point of point p.*

Thus, for example, an asymptotically stable equilibrium position is the α-limit point of all points lying in a sufficiently small neighbourhood of this equilibrium point. Points of the limiting cycle about which the spiral curves are coiled (Fig. 2) are also ω-limiting for points belonging to these curves. In both examples the ω-limit points constitute entire trajec-

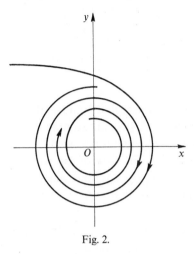

Fig. 2.

tories (in the first case, a singular point; in the second, a limiting cycle). This is not an accident: the following statement is valid.

Theorem 5.1. *The set of ω-limit (α-limit) points of a given point is a closed set consisting of entire trajectories.*

First of all we note that the closure of the set of ω-limit points is a consequence of a well known theorem of set theory. This theorem asserts that a limit point for the limit points of a set is again a limit point of this set. Let us assume now that point q is an ω-limit point for point p; we shall show that the point $f(q, \tau)$ (the number τ can have either positive or negative sign) is also ω-limiting for point p. Indeed, if $q = \lim_{n \to \infty} f(p, t_n)$, then from the group properties of dynamical systems (see Section 1), and from the property of continuity of $f(p, t)$ as a function of p, we obtain $f(q, \tau) = \lim_{n \to \infty} f(p, t_n + \tau)$, which means that the point $f(q, \tau)$ is an ω-limit point of the point p, i.e. all points of the trajectory emerging from q are ω-limit points for p.

A set consisting of entire trajectories is often called an invariant set. The invariant set A possesses the property that $f(A, t) = A$ for any t. If $f(A, t) \subset A$ for $t > 0$, then we say that the set A is positive invariant.

We note that if, for $t > t_0$, the trajectory $f(p, t)$ does not pass outside the bounded part of the space, then the set of its limit points is not simple.

Lemma 5.1. *If there exists a Lyapunov function v bounded from below (from above) by a positive invariant region D, and if the time derivative $\dot{v}$ of this function is a function of negative terms (positive terms) in this region, then all ω-limit points of the given point p lie on a single level surface of the function v.*

In fact, let the point p lie in the region D and let the point $q = \lim_{n \to \infty} f(p, t_n)$ be an ω-limit for point p. First of all we note that the function $v(f(p, t))$ does not increase for $t \to \infty$, and it is bounded from below so that the limit $v_0 = \lim_{t \to \infty} v(f(p, t))$ exists. In view of the continuity of function v, we have also $v(q) = \lim_{n \to \infty} v(f(p, t_n))$, but since $v(f(p, t))$ varies monotonically we have, obviously, that $v(q) = v_0$, which proves the lemma.

Theorem 5.2. *If there exists a positive definite function v such that $\dot{v} < 0$ outside M and $\dot{v} \leqslant 0$ on M, where M is a set which contains no entire trajectories apart from the point O, then the equilibrium position O is asymptotically stable.*

Let us prove this theorem. It is obvious that the equilibrium position—the point O—is stable in the Lyapunov sense since the conditions of theorem 4.1 are fulfilled. By virtue of this stability, there exists for a given positive number ε a positive number δ such that if $p \subset J_\delta$, then $f(p, t) \subset J_\varepsilon$ for $t > 0$. Since, for $t > 0$, the trajectory $f(p, t)$ does not pass outside the limits of the sphere $\bar{J}_\varepsilon$, then the set Ω of ω-limit points of the point p is not empty. If Ω coincides with the point O, then the theorem is proved since we will have $\lim_{t \to \infty} f(p, t) = 0$.

Let us assume that the set Ω contains at least one point q which differs from point O. From lemma 5.1, it follows that

$$v(q) = v(f(q, t)) = \lim_{t \to \infty} v(f(p, t)) \neq 0 \, .$$

Thus, all the ω-limit points of p lie on the same level surface $v = v(q)$. From theorem 5.1, it follows that the set Ω is closed and consists of entire trajectories. Thus, since v stays constant along these trajectories, we must have $\dot{v} = 0$ on the whole set Ω. The theorem stipulates that the set Ω should be contained within the set M; but the set M contains no entire trajectories. The contradiction we have obtained proves the theorem.

We note that the validity of theorem 5.2 follows from theorem 4.2 so that theorem 5.2 is an extension of the Lyapunov theorem for asymptotic stability. Using theorem 5.2 one can decide the question of asymptotic stability with the help of a Lyapunov function whose derivative is a function of constant signs. In actual examples involving non-linear systems it is just such Lyapunov functions that one most often succeeds in constructing. We should note that it is easy to verify the requirement of the theorem that there should be no entire trajectories on the set M. Indeed, if, for example, the equation of $\varphi(x_1, ..., x_n) = 0$ is the equation of the surface M, then the condition

$$\frac{d\varphi}{dt} = \sum_{i=1}^{n} \frac{\partial\varphi}{\partial x_i} X_i \neq 0$$

is obviously a sufficient condition for the absence of entire trajectories on the set M because, if this condition is fulfilled, the integral curves pierce the surface M.

6. Instability Theorems

Let us discuss now the instability theorems. Theorems 6.1 and 6.2 are due to A. M. Lyapunov and theorem 6.3 was proved by N. N. Krasovskii [7].

Theorem 6.1. *If there exists a function v whose time derivative is of fixed sign and such that in any neighbourhood of the point O the function v is not a function of constant signs with sign opposite to $\dot{v}$, then the zero solution of the system* (4.1) *is unstable.*

Let the conditions of the theorem be fulfilled in the sphere J_ε. We shall suppose for the sake of definiteness that the function $\dot{v}$ is positive definite and proceed to consider an arbitrarily small neighbourhood J_δ of the point O. We shall show that there exists a point p whose trajectory for $t > 0$ passes outside the limits of J_ε. According to the provisions of the theorem, there is in J_δ a point p at which $v(p) = v_0 > 0$. In view of the continuity of the function v, there exists a number η such that inside J_η we have $|v| < v_0$. Since the function $\dot{v}$ is positive definite, then $v(f(p, t))$ increases with t and we know that the point $f(p, t)$ does not fall inside J_η. Let us assume that the point $f(p, t)$ does not pass outside the bounds of J_ε. Since, in the region $\bar{J_\varepsilon} \setminus J_\eta$, $\dot{v}$ has a positive minimum m, then the following inequality is valid

$$v(f(p, t)) = v(p) + \int_0^t \dot{v} \, dt > v(p) + mt \, . \tag{6.1}$$

We see from this that with increasing t the function $v(f(p, t))$ increases without limit although, on the other hand, as a continuous function, v must be bounded inside the spherical layer $\bar{J_\varepsilon} \setminus J_\eta$. This contradiction proves the theorem.

Theorem 6.2. *If there exists a function v such that its time derivative has the form*

$$\frac{dv}{dt} = \lambda v + w \, , \tag{6.2}$$

where λ is a positive constant and w either vanishes identically or is of constant sign, and if in the latter case the function v is not of constant sign with sign opposite to w in the neighbourhood of the point O, then the zero solution of the system (4.1) *is unstable.*

Let us suppose, to be definite, that $w \geqslant 0$ and that in an arbitrarily small neighbourhood J_δ we select a point p at which $v(p) = v_0 > 0$. We shall show that with increasing t the point $f(p, t)$ falls outside the limits of any neighbourhood J_ε in which the provisions of the theorem are fulfilled. Treating the functions $v(f(p, t))$ and $w(f(p, t))$ as functions of time, we can determine $v(f(p, t))$ from the differential equation (6.2) according to the Cauchy formula:

$$v(f(p, t)) = e^{\lambda t} \left[\int_0^t e^{-\lambda t} w \, dt + v_0 \right] .$$

From the condition $w \geqslant 0$, we have

$$v(f(p, t)) \geqslant v_0 e^{\lambda t} \, .$$

Since $\lambda > 0$, then, with increasing t, the function $v(f(p, t))$ increases without limit; this means that the point $f(p, t)$ must go outside the bounds of the region J_ε.

Theorem 6.3. *If there exists a function v which is a function of negative sign in an arbitrary neighbourhood of the point O such that*

$$\frac{dv}{dt} > 0 \ outside \ M, \quad \frac{dv}{dt} \geqslant 0 \ on \ M$$

where M is a set which does not contain entire trajectories (apart from the point O), then the equilibrium position is unstable.

Just as we did in proving theorem 6.1, in an arbitrarily small neighbourhood J_δ we shall choose a point p at which $v(p) = v_0 > 0$ and we shall then choose a sphere J_η at all points of which the inequality $v < v_0$ holds. Let us assume now that the point $f(p, t)$ does not go outside the limits of a certain sphere $\bar{J}_\varepsilon$. Since $f(p, t)$ does not fall in J_η, then for all $t > 0$ the point $f(p, t)$ will lie inside the spherical layer $\bar{J}_\varepsilon \backslash J_\eta$ so that the non-empty set Ω of the ω-limit points of the point p will also lie in this spherical layer. However, according to lemma 5.1, the set Ω lies on the surface $v = c$, and according to theorem 5.1 the set Ω is closed and consists of entire trajectories. Thus, on Ω we have $\dot{v} = 0$ from which it follows that $\Omega \subset M$; this last statement contradicts the statement of the theorem since the set M does not contain entire trajectories.

In conclusion we note that various generalizations of these theorems are possible. Thus, for example, one can dispense with requirement that the Lipschitz conditions are fulfilled for the right-hand sides of the system (4.1), or even with the requirement that the right-hand sides should be continuous. All the theorems of Sections 4–6 will be unconditionally valid if the right-hand sides of the system (4.1) are sectionally continuous. One may also remove the requirement of continuity and differentiability of the Lyapunov function if one substitutes other requirements which follow in an obvious way from the proofs of these theorems. These possibilities are examined more fully in a monograph by N. N. Krasovskii [7]. This monograph includes a fundamental investigation of the conditions required for the validity of the converse of the Lyapunov theorems, of theorems 5.2 and 6.3, and of many other theorems relating to the method we have been discussing.

7. Examples

Example 1. Let us consider the system of equations

$$\dot{x} = ax^3 + by, \quad \dot{y} = -cx + dy^3 \tag{7.1}$$

and try to find a Lyapunov function for it in the form $v = F_1(x) + F_2(x)$. In this case, we have $v = F_1'(x) \times (ax^3 + by) - F_2'(y)(cx - dy^3)$. We require once again that the function $\dot{v}$ should have the same functional structure as the function v, i.e. we require that $bF_1'(x)y - cF_2'(y)x = 0$ should be fulfilled identically. Dividing the variables, we obtain

$$\frac{cx}{F_1'(x)} = \frac{by}{F_2'(y)},$$

and hence each of these fractions·should be a constant which could be, for example, $\frac{1}{2}$.

Thus, we obtain $F_1(x) = cx^3$ and $F_2(y) = by^2$, i.e. $v = cx^2 + by^2$. For the derivative $\dot{v}$, we obtain the expression $v = 2acx^4 + 2bdy^4$. If $a < 0$, $d < 0$, $bc > 0$, we find, under the conditions for which theorem 4.2 is applicable, that the equilibrium position will be asymptotically stable. If $a = 0$, $b > 0$, $d < 0$, $c > 0$, then the zero solution will be stable in the Lyapunov sense, because this follows from theorem 4.1. However, in the given case, there is also asymptotic stability as this follows from theorem 5.2. Indeed, in the given case, the set $y = 0$, i.e. the axis Ox, serves as the set M. It is easy to see that there are no entire trajectories of the system (7.1) on the axis Ox. In fact, if such a trajectory did lie on the axis Ox, then we would have identically $y = 0$, $\dot{y} = 0$ along it and, from the second equation of system (7.1), we would deduce that $x = 0$. Thus, there is only one entire trajectory on the axis Ox: the singular point $O(0, 0)$. If $bc < 0$, $ad < 0$ or $a > 0$, $b > 0$, $c > 0$, $d > 0$ then, under the conditions for which theorem 6.1 is applicable, we find also that the zero solution will be unstable. By virtue of theorem (6.3), there will also be instability when $a = 0$, $bc < 0$, $d \neq 0$. We note that the method of constructing the Lyapunov function demonstrated here is called the method of division of variables [18].

Example 2. Let us consider now the equation for the oscillations of a pendulum.

$$I\ddot{\varphi} + n\dot{\varphi} + Mgl \sin \varphi = L, \tag{7.2}$$

where I is the moment of inertia, $n\dot{\varphi}$ is the moment of the frictional force, $Mgl \sin \varphi$ is the moment of the gravitational force, L is the external couple, M is the mass, g is the acceleration due to gravity, l is the distance of the centre of mass of the pendulum up to the axis of rotation, φ is the angle of deviation of the pendulum from the vertical.

Dividing through by I and introducing the notation

$$a = \frac{n}{I}, \quad b = \frac{Mgl}{I}, \quad N = \frac{L}{I},$$

we write the equation in the form

$$\ddot{\varphi} + a\dot{\varphi} + b \sin \varphi = N, \tag{7.3}$$

or in the form of the system

$$\dot{\varphi} = \omega, \quad \dot{\omega} = -b \sin \varphi - a\omega + N. \tag{7.4}$$

It is obvious that the system (7.4) will have an equilibrium position which can be determined from the equation

$$\omega = 0, \quad -b \sin \varphi - a\omega + N = 0$$

from which it follows that an equilibrium position exists if the equation $\sin \varphi = N/b$ has a solution φ_0. Thus, for an equilibrium position to exist, it is necessary that the inequality $|N| \leq b$ be fulfilled. Introducing the new variable $x = \varphi - \varphi_0$, we reduce equation (7.3) to the equation

$$\ddot{x} + a\dot{x} + b(\sin(x + \varphi_0) - \sin \varphi_0) = 0, \tag{7.5}$$

for which the equilibrium state will be the state $x = 0$, $\dot{x} = 0$. A system, equivalent to equation (7.5), has the form

$$\dot{x} = y, \quad \dot{y} = -b(\sin(x + \varphi_0) - \sin \varphi_0) - ay. \tag{7.6}$$

We note that, in the absence of friction, equation (7.2) possesses a first integral (the energy integral)

$$E = \frac{I\omega^2}{2} + Mgl(1 - \cos \varphi) - L\varphi = c. \tag{7.7}$$

For $n = 0$, the first integral can be found from equation (7.3) by making the substitution $\omega = \dot{\varphi}$. The physical meaning of the first integral is that it gives the total energy of the pendulum, this energy remaining constant while the pendulum oscillates, so long as no energy dissipation occurs.

If there is friction present (at the point of suspension of the pendulum, resistance of the medium, *etc.*) then energy dissipation does occur. The quantity E will no longer be constant along the trajectory but will diminish, i.e. it will behave in the same way as the Lyapunov function of the system (7.6). Making the change of variables in (7.7) $x = \varphi - \varphi_0$, $y = \omega$, we will consider the new function

$$v = \frac{ly^2}{2} + Ib\left(\cos \varphi_0 - \cos(x + \varphi_0) - x \sin \varphi_0\right).$$

It is evident that v differs from E only by a constant. By virtue of system (7.6), we obtain $\dot{v} = -Iay^2$. If $\cos \varphi_0 > 0$, then for sufficiently small x the function v will be positive definite.

In fact, from Taylor's formula it follows that

$$F(x) = \cos \varphi - \cos(x + \varphi_0) - x \sin \varphi_0 = \frac{\cos(x^* + \varphi_0)}{2} x^2 ,$$

where $|x^*| \leqslant |x|$; it is obvious that for x sufficiently small the sign of the function $F(x)$ is the same as the sign of $\cos \varphi_0$.

We note further that $\dot{v}$ vanishes only on the axis Ox so that the set M occurring in the formulation of theorem 5.1 will be the line $y = 0$ or a segment of this line. It is easy to see that there are no entire trajectories on the line $y = 0$, apart from the singular points whose abscissa satisfy the equation

$$\sin(x + \varphi_0) - \sin \varphi_0 = 0 .$$

To apply theorem 5.1 one should take as the set the interval of the axis Ox included between the nearest singular points to the origin. The region included within the line $v = c$ which passes through the nearest point will obviously possess the property that all its points are attracted towards the point $(0, 0)$.

It is evident that in the case $\cos \varphi_0 < 0$, the point $(0, 0)$ is an unstable equilibrium position.

8. Linear Systems

Let us consider the following system of linear differential equations with constant coefficients

$$\frac{dx_i}{dt} = \sum_{k=1}^{n} a_{ik} x_k, \qquad i = 1, 2, \ldots, n. \tag{8.1}$$

Let $\lambda_1, \ldots, \lambda_n$ be the roots of the characteristic equation of system 8.1, i.e. the roots of the equation

$$\begin{vmatrix} a_{11} - \lambda & \ldots & a_{1n} \\ \ldots\ldots\ldots\ldots \\ a_{n1} & \ldots a_{nn} - \lambda \end{vmatrix} = 0. \tag{8.2}$$

The following statements are true [8]:
(1) If all the roots of equation (8.2) have negative real parts then the zero solution of system (8.1) is asymptotically stable.
(2) If there is one root amongst the roots of equation (8.2) with a positive real part then the zero solution of system (8.1) is unstable.
(3) If equation (8.2) has no roots with a positive real part but some of its roots have zero real parts then the system is both stable (but not asymptotically) and unstable.

Thus, the question of the stability of the zero solution of system (8.1) reduces to one of investigating the nature of the roots of equation (8.2). Multiplying out the determinant of (8.2), we obtain the equation

$$f(\lambda) = \lambda^n + a_1 \lambda^{n-1} + \ldots + a_n = 0. \tag{8.3}$$

From the coefficients of the polynomial $f(\lambda)$ we form the matrix

$$\begin{pmatrix} a_1 & 1 & 0 & 0 & 0 & 0 \ldots \\ a_3 & a_2 & a_1 & 1 & 0 & 0 \ldots \\ a_5 & a_4 & a_3 & a_2 & a_1 & 1 \ldots \\ \ldots\ldots\ldots\ldots\ldots\ldots\ldots \end{pmatrix}.$$

In the notation of this matrix we suppose that $a_m = 0$ if $m > n$. Consider the determinants

$$\Delta_1 = a_1, \quad \Delta_2 = \begin{vmatrix} a_1 & 1 \\ a_3 & a_2 \end{vmatrix}, \quad \Delta_3 = \begin{vmatrix} a_1 & 1 & 0 \\ a_3 & a_2 & a_1 \\ a_5 & a_4 & a_3 \end{vmatrix}, \ldots, \Delta_n = a_n \Delta_{n-1}.$$

For all the roots of equation (8.3) to have negative real parts it is necessary and sufficient that the following inequalities be fulfilled

$$\Delta_k > 0 \quad \text{for} \quad k = 1, 2, \ldots, n. \tag{8.4}$$

This statement is called Hurwitz's theorem; an example of a proof of Hurwitz's theorem can be found in the monograph by Chetaev [26]. The conditions (8.4) are often called the Routh–Hurwitz conditions.

For an equation of the second degree

$$\lambda^2 + a_1 \lambda + a_2 = 0$$

the Routh–Hurwitz conditions have the form

$$a_1 > 0, \quad \begin{vmatrix} a_1 & 1 \\ 0 & a_2 \end{vmatrix} > 0$$

or, what amounts to the same thing, $a_1 > 0$, $a_2 > 0$.

For an equation of the third degree

$$\lambda^3 + a_1 \lambda^2 + a_2 \lambda + a_3 = 0$$

and the Routh–Hurwitz conditions are written in the form

$$a_1 > 0, \quad \begin{vmatrix} a_1 & 1 \\ a_3 & a_2 \end{vmatrix} > 0, \quad a_2 \begin{vmatrix} a_1 & 1 \\ a_3 & a_2 \end{vmatrix} > 0.$$

It is obvious that these conditions are equivalent to the conditions

$$a_1 > 0, \quad a_2 > 0, \quad a_1 a_2 > a_3.$$

In future we shall need the following results taken from linear algebra. Let us consider the quadratic form

$$v = \sum_{i,k=1}^{n} b_{ik} x_i x_k$$

where $b_{ik} = b_{ki}$. Using B to denote the matrix formed from the coefficients b_{ik}, and x to denote the vector with projections $x_1, \ldots, x_2$, we can write

$$v = (x, Bx),$$

where (x, Bx) denotes the scalar product of the vectors x and Bx.

If the vector x is a function of time, then the form v will also be a function of time and the following rule of differentiation will hold:

$$\frac{dv}{dt} = \left(\frac{dx}{dt}, Bx \right) + \left(x, B \frac{dx}{dt} \right). \tag{8.5}$$

If the matrix B is symmetric, then for the vectors x and y we have the relation

$$(x, By) = (B^* x, y), \tag{8.6}$$

where B^* is the transposed matrix.

We note further the following well-known fact: if the matrix T is a non-singular matrix, i.e. a matrix with a non-zero determinant, then the matrices B and TBT^{-1} (similar matrices) have identical eigenvalues.

Let us write the system (8.1) in matrix form

$$\frac{dx}{dt} = Ax, \tag{8.7}$$

and find the derivative of the quadratic form $v = (x, Bx)$ according to this equation. According to (8.5) we have

$$\frac{dv}{dt} = (Ax, Bx) + (x, BAx).$$

Using relation (8.6), we obtain

$$\frac{dv}{dt} = (x, [A^* B + BA] x). \tag{8.8}$$

We now require that the form v shall satisfy the equation

$$\frac{dv}{dt} = w, \tag{8.9}$$

where $w = (x, Cx)$ is a given quadratic form. Comparing (8.8) and (8.9), we obtain a matrix equation for determining the matrix B

$$A^* B + BA = C. \tag{8.10}$$

Equation (8.10) enables us to find the matrix of the form v in accordance with the given matrix of the form w. Equation (8.10) is of particular interest because it permits us to find a Lyapunov function expressed in terms of a quadratic form of a given derivative. Equation (8.10) places the matrix C in correspondence with every matrix B, and this correspondence is linear. Thus, one can define the linear operator $F(B) = A^* B + BA$ in the space of n-th order square matrices. The problem of whether equation (8.10) is solvable reduces to the problem of finding the inverse operator to operator F, since $B = F^{-1} C$. Since F operates in a finite-dimensional space (n^2

dimensions), then for the inverse operator to exist it is necessary and sufficient that none of the eigenvalues of F should be zero.

Theorem 8.1. *If the roots of the characteristic equation of the system* (8.7) *are such that the sum* $\lambda_i + \lambda_k$ *does not vanish for any* i, k *then, regardless of the choice of the preassigned quadratic form* w, *there exists a unique quadratic form* v *which satisfies equation* (8.9).

Let us prove this theorem. According to definition, the eigenvalue of the operator F is a number μ such that the equation $F(B) = \mu B$ is a solution of the non-zero matrix B. This equation may be written in the form $A^*B + BA = \mu B$; from which it follows that $(A^* - \mu E)B = -BA$.

We shall show that the matrices $A^* - \mu E$ and $-A$ have at least one eigenvalue in common. If this were not so then the characteristic polynomials $g(\lambda)$ and $f(\lambda)$ of these matrices would not have common divisors so that one could find polynomials $g_1(\lambda)$, $f_1(\lambda)$ such that the relation $g_1(\lambda)g(\lambda) + f_1(\lambda)f(\lambda) = 1$ held. Let $h(\lambda) = g_1(\lambda)g(\lambda)$. According to the Caley–Hamilton theorem ([5] – p. 74), we have $h(A^* - \mu E) = 0$ and $h(-A) = E$. On the other hand it is easy to see that the relation $h(A^* - \mu E)B = Bh(-A)$ holds, although this leads us to the opposite conclusion that $B = 0$.

Thus, amongst the eigenvalues $\lambda_i - \mu$ of the matrix $A - \mu E$ there exists at least one that is equal to $-\lambda_k$ (here λ_i, λ_k denote the eigenvalues of the matrix A). Thus, $\mu = \lambda_i + \lambda_k$ and, by virtue of the provisions of the theorem, $\mu \neq 0$. From which we have proved that the operator F has an inverse and that equation (8.10) has a solution.

9. Construction of Lyapunov Functions in the Form of Quadratic Forms for Linear Systems of Differential Equations

We shall now prove a number of theorems concerning the existence of Lyapunov functions for linear systems. The results given below were obtained by A. M. Lyapunov who constructed the functions in the form of homogeneous forms of the m-th order. Restricting ourselves for simplicity to quadratic forms, we shall, however, extend Lyapunov's formulation a little. The extension consists in abandoning the requirement that the function w should have fixed sign in considering equation (8.9) (Yu. I. Alimov [9]).

Theorem 9.1. *If all the roots of the characteristic equation have negative real parts then regardless of the choice of the preassigned quadratic form w, being a function of negative signs which vanishes on a set M containing no entire trajectories apart from the point O, there exists one and only one quadratic form v satisfying equation (8.9) and this form will necessarily be positive definite.*

Since $\lambda_i + \lambda_k$ does not vanish then, according to theorem 8.1, a form v satisfying equation (8.9) must exist. It remains to show that v is positive definite. Let us assume that at a certain point $p(x_1^0, \ldots, x_n^0)$ the inequality $v(x_1^0, \ldots, x_n^0) < 0$ is fulfilled. In view of the uniformity of the function v, the inequality $v(kx_1^0, \ldots, kx_n^0) < 0$ must hold for any positive k. This means that in any neighbourhood of the point O there are points at which v is negative. When $w = 0$ the set M contains no entire trajectories. It follows from theorem 6.3 (replacing v by $-v$ and w by $-w$) that the equilibrium position is unstable, but this contradicts our assumption since the provisions of the theorem ensure asymptotic stability. Let us assume now that at some point, $v(p) = 0$. Since $\dot{v} \leqslant 0$, and along the trajectory $f(p, t)$ the equality $v = 0$ cannot be fulfilled identically, there is a point $q = f(p, t)$ at which $v(q) < 0$, which again leads to a contradiction. Thus, everywhere, except at the point O, we have $v(p) > 0$, and the theorem is proved.

Theorem 9.2. *If amongst the roots of the characteristic system of equations (8.1) there is one with a positive real part, and if there are no i, k for which the quantity $\lambda_i + \lambda_k$ vanishes, then regardless of the choice of the function w, being a function of positive signs that vanishes on a set M containing no entire trajectories, there exists one and only one quadratic form v satisfying equation (8.9) and this form will not be a function of negative signs.*

According to theorem 8.1, the form v does indeed exist; it only remains to show that it assumes positive values. Let us assume that everywhere, except at the point O, the inequality $v < 0$ is fulfilled; but if that is so the conditions for which theorem 5.2 is applicable will be satisfied (again we replace v by $-v$ and w by $-w$), from which it follows that the zero solution of the system (8.1) is asymptotically stable. However, because of the assumption in that theorem concerning the roots of the characteristic equation of system (8.1), the system must be unstable. If at some point, $v(p) = 0$, then since $\dot{v}$ cannot be zero along the trajectory of the point p, we arrive at the conclusion that there is a point q on this trajectory for which $v(q) > 0$, which is in agreement with the statement of the theorem. This proves the theorem because the fact that it is possible for points to exist for which $v(q) > 0$ is simply a statement of our theorem.

Note. We shall show that theorem 9.2 is not true if the condition $\lambda_i + \lambda_k \neq 0$ is fulfilled. Let us consider the case where, included amongst the roots of equation 7.2, there is a zero root. In this case, the determinant $|A|$ made up of the coefficients of the system (8.1), is equal to zero and the system of equations

$$\sum_{k=1}^{n} a_{ik} x_k = 0, \qquad i = 1, 2, ..., n, \tag{9.1}$$

will have the zero solution $x_k = x_k^0$, $k = 1, 2, ..., n$. No matter what the choice of function v, at the point $Q(x_1^0, ..., x_n^0)$ we obtain

$$\frac{dv}{dt} = \sum_{i=1}^{n} \frac{\partial v}{\partial x_i} \sum_{k=1}^{n} a_{ik} x_k^0 = 0,$$

so that $\dot{v}$ will not be a function of fixed sign. Moreover, where $\dot{v} = 0$, the set contains entire trajectories, since Q is a singular point.

Theorem 9.3. If amongst the roots of the characteristic equations of system (8.1) there exist just one root with a positive real part then, regardless of the choice of the quadratic form w, being a function of positive signs which vanishes on the set M containing no entire trajectories, one can always find a quadratic form v and a positive number α such that the relation

$$\frac{dv}{dt} = \alpha v + w, \tag{9.2}$$

will be fulfilled, and the function v will not be a function of negative signs.

To prove this theorem let us side by side with the system (8.7) consider also the system

$$\frac{dx}{d\tau} = \left(A - \frac{\alpha}{2} E \right) x. \tag{9.3}$$

The characteristic equation of this system will have the form

$$\left| A - \left(\frac{\alpha}{2} + \rho \right) E \right| = 0 . \tag{9.4}$$

It is evident that the roots of the characteristic equation of system (8.7) are connected with the roots of system (9.3) through the relation $\lambda_i = \rho_i + \frac{1}{2}\alpha$. Let us choose α to be so small that the following two conditions are fulfilled.

(1) $\mathrm{Re}\, \lambda_i > 0$ follows from $\mathrm{Re}\, \rho_i > 0$

(2) $\rho_i + \rho_k \neq 0$ for any integral i and k.

It is obvious that the first condition is easily satisfied if one chooses a sufficiently small value of α. Noting that $\rho_i + \rho_k = \lambda_i + \lambda_k - \alpha$, we can choose α so that it does not coincide with any of the finite set of numbers $\lambda_i + \lambda_k$, with the result that the second condition also is satisfied.

According to theorem 9.2, there exists a function v which assumes positive values and is such that, by virtue of the system (9.3), $dv/dt = w$. Since

$$\frac{dv}{d\tau} = \left(A - \frac{\alpha}{2} E \right) x\, \mathrm{grad}\, v = Ax\, \mathrm{grad}\, v - \frac{\alpha}{2} x\, \mathrm{grad}\, v ,$$

and since by Euler's theorem for homogeneous functions

$$x\, \mathrm{grad}\, v = \sum_{i=1}^{n} \frac{\partial v}{\partial x_i} x_i = 2v ,$$

we have

$$w = \frac{dv}{d\tau} = \frac{dv}{dt} - \alpha v ,$$

where dv/dt is the derivative of the function v taken in accordance with system (8.7). Thus, relation (9.2) is proved.

10. Estimates of the Solutions of Linear Systems

Let us introduce first an important inequality from the theory of quadratic forms. We consider the quadratic form $v = (x, Bx)$ and set out to find the smallest and largest values of this quadratic form on the sphere

$$x^2 = \sum_{i=1}^{n} x_i^2 = r .$$

According to the rules for solving relative extremal problems, one should seek an extremal of quadratic form, $w = v - \lambda(x^2 - r^2)$.
At extreme points the following condition should be fulfilled

$$\operatorname{grad} w = \operatorname{grad} v - 2\lambda x = 0 .$$

Since grad $v = 2Bx$, the necessary extremal conditions lead us to the equation

$$Bx = \lambda x . \tag{10.1}$$

This equation has a non-zero solution only in the event that λ is a root of the equation

$$|B - \lambda E| = 0 . \tag{10.2}$$

Since the matrix B is symmetric, its eigenvalues must be real. Let λ_1 denote the smallest eigenvalue of matrix B, and λ_n the largest.
Multiplying equation (10.1) from the left and from the right by x, we obtain $v = (Bx, x) = \lambda x^2$, i.e. $v = \lambda r^2$. Thus, making λ the largest and smallest eigenvalues, we arrive at the inequality

$$\lambda_1 r^2 \leqslant v \leqslant \lambda_n r^2 , \tag{10.3}$$

which is valid for all points of space.
Taking $r^2 = 1$, we reach the conclusion that λ_1 is the minimum value of the function v on a unit sphere, and λ_n is the maximum value.
Let us turn now to the problem of estimating the solutions of a system of linear differential equations [10].
We shall consider the system of differential equations

$$\frac{dx}{dt} = Ax , \tag{10.4}$$

and shall suppose that all the eigenvalues of matrix A are negative real numbers. According to theorem 9.1, there exists a positive definite quadratic form $v = (x, Bx)$ such that, by virtue of the system (10.4), we will have

$$\frac{dv}{dt} = -r^2 , \quad \text{where} \quad r^2 = \sum_{i=1}^{n} x_i^2 . \tag{10.5}$$

On the other hand, from the inequality (10.3) one deduces the inequality

$$-\frac{v}{\lambda_n} \geqslant -r^2 \geqslant -\frac{v}{\lambda_1} , \tag{10.6}$$

where λ_1, λ_n are respectively the smallest and largest eigenvalues of the form v. Thus, from relations (10.5) and (10.6), there follows the inequality

$$- \frac{v}{\lambda_1} \leqslant \frac{dv}{dt} \leqslant - \frac{v}{\lambda_n},$$

which can be written in the form

$$- \frac{dt}{\lambda_1} \leqslant \frac{dv}{v} \leqslant - \frac{dt}{\lambda_n}. \tag{10.7}$$

Integrating (10.7) from zero to t, and using v_0 to denote the value of function v at the initial point of the trajectory p, we obtain

$$v_0 e^{-t/\lambda_1} \leqslant v \leqslant v_0 e^{-t/\lambda_n}.$$

Making use of inequality (10.6), we obtain a final estimate of r^2 along the solution of the system (10.4):

$$\frac{v_0}{\lambda_n} e^{-t/\lambda_1} \leqslant r^2 \leqslant \frac{v_0}{\lambda_1} e^{-t/\lambda_n}. \tag{10.8}$$

The inequality (10.8) can be used to estimate the transient response time. In fact, solving the equation

$$\frac{v_0}{\lambda_1} e^{-t/\lambda_n} = \varepsilon^2$$

for t, we obtain $t = - \lambda_n \ln (\lambda_1 \varepsilon^2 / v_0)$.

Thus, the transient response time $t(p, \varepsilon)$, i.e. the time required for r to become, and to remain, smaller than ε, satisfies the inequality $t(p, \varepsilon) \leqslant - \lambda_n \ln (\lambda_1 \varepsilon^2 / v_0)$.

11. Stability Theorems According to the First Approximation

Side by side with the system

$$\frac{dx_i}{dt} = \sum_{k=1}^{n} a_{ik} x_k + X_i(x_i, \ldots, x_n), \qquad i = 1, 2, \ldots, n, \tag{11.1}$$

let us consider also the system

$$\frac{dx_i}{dt} = \sum_{k=1}^{n} a_{ik} x_k, \qquad i = 1, 2, \ldots, n. \tag{11.2}$$

We shall suppose that $X_i(0, ..., 0) = 0$ and

$$\sum_{i=1}^{n} X_i^2 (x_1, ..., x_n) \leqslant A^2 \left(\sum_{i=1}^{n} x_i^2 \right)^{1+\alpha}, \tag{11.3}$$

where $\alpha > 0$ and A is a positive constant. The system (11.2) will be called the system of the first approximation.

We seek now to determine the conditions for which the stability or instability of the zero solution of system (11.1) follows from the stability or instability of the system of the first approximation.

Lemma 11.1. *Let w be a fixed-sign quadratic form and v be an arbitrary quadratic form. In a certain neighbourhood of the origin, the function*

$$w + \sum_{i=1}^{n} \frac{\partial v}{\partial x_i} X_i$$

will be a function of fixed sign, the sign being the same as that of w.

According to (10.3), we have

$$\rho_1 r^2 \leqslant w \leqslant \rho_n r^2 \,,$$

where ρ_1 is the smallest and ρ_n is the largest of the eigenvalues belonging to the form

$$w \quad \text{and} \quad r = \left(\sum_{i=1}^{n} x_1^2 \right)^{\frac{1}{2}}.$$

Since

$$\sum_{i=1}^{n} \left(\frac{\partial v}{\partial x_i} \right)^2$$

is also a quadratic form, we have

$$\Delta_1^2 r^2 \leqslant \sum_{i=1}^{n} \left(\frac{\partial v}{\partial x_i} \right)^2 \leqslant \Delta_n^2 r^2 \,,$$

where Δ_1^2, Δ_n^2 are eigenvalues of this form. From the Schwartz inequality, and from (11.3), it follows that

$$\left| \sum_{i=1}^{n} \frac{\partial v}{\partial x_i} X_i \right| \leqslant \left(\sum_{i=1}^{n} \left(\frac{\partial v}{\partial x_i} \right)^2 \right)^{\frac{1}{2}} \left(\sum_{i=1}^{n} X_i^2 \right)^{\frac{1}{2}} \leqslant A \Delta_n r^{\alpha+2} \,.$$

Let us suppose that w is a negative definite form. We have

$$w + \sum_{i=1}^{n} \frac{\partial v}{\partial x_i} X_i \leqslant (\rho_n + A\Delta_n r^\alpha) r^2 .$$

If we choose a neighbourhood in which

$$A\Delta_n r^\alpha < |\rho_n| ,$$

we obtain the required inequality

$$w + \sum_{i=1}^{n} \frac{\partial v}{\partial x_i} X_i < 0 \quad \text{when} \quad r \neq 0 .$$

If $w > 0$, we obtain

$$w + \sum_{i=1}^{n} \frac{\partial v}{\partial x_i} X_i > (\rho_1 - A\Delta_n r^\alpha) r^2 > 0 \quad \text{when} \quad r \neq 0 ,$$

if, only, $A\Delta_n r^\alpha < \rho_1$.

Theorem 11.1. (The stability theorem of the first approximation). *If the roots of the characteristic equation of a system of the first approximation have negative real parts then the zero solution of the system* (11.1) *is asymptotically unstable.*

According to theorem 9.1, a positive definite quadratic form v does indeed exist whose derivative, by virtue of system (11.2), is equal to $-r^2$. By virtue of the system (11.1), the derivative of the function v has the form

$$\frac{dv}{dt} = -r^2 + \sum_{i=1}^{n} \frac{\partial v}{\partial x_i} X_i$$

and, according to lemma 11.1, it also will be negative definite. Asymptotic stability now follows from theorem 4.2.

Theorem 11.2. (The instability theorem of the first approximation). *If amongst the roots of the characteristic equation of a system of the first approximation there is just one with a positive real part, then the zero solution of system* (11.1) *will be unstable.*

According to theorem 9.3, there exists a quadratic form which assumes positive values and satisfies the relation

$$\frac{dv}{d\tau} = r^2 + \alpha v , \qquad \alpha > 0 ,$$

where $dv/d\tau$ is the derivative of v taken on the strength of system (11.2). Taking the derivative of the function v on the strength of system (11.1), we obtain

$$\frac{dv}{dt} = r^2 + \alpha v + \sum_{i=1}^{n} \frac{\partial v}{\partial x_i} X_i ,$$

but from lemma 11.1 it follows that

$$r^2 + \sum_{i=1}^{n} \frac{\partial v}{\partial x_i} X_i$$

will be a positive definite function. Instability follows from theorem 6.2. Let us discuss a few examples.

1. Let us consider the equation for the oscillations of a pendulum

$$\ddot{x} + a\dot{x} + b \sin x = 0 .$$

To this equation there corresponds the system

$$\dot{x} = y, \quad \dot{y} = -b \sin x - ay . \tag{11.4}$$

The singular points of this system have coordinates $x = k\pi$ (k is any integer), $y = 0$. Making use of the expansion

$$\sin x = x - \frac{x^3}{3!} + \dots ,$$

the system of the first approximation is

$$\dot{x} = y, \quad \dot{y} = -bx - ay , \tag{11.5}$$

which has a characteristic equation of the form

$$\lambda^2 + a\lambda + b = 0 .$$

If $a > 0$, $b > 0$, then the roots have negative real parts and the zero equilibrium position will be stable with respect to the first approximation. Let us now investigate the stability of the point $(\pi, 0)$. Using the expansion

$$\sin x = -(x - \pi) + \frac{(x - \pi)^3}{3!} - \dots ,$$

we will write down the system of the first approximation:

$$\dot{x} = y, \quad \dot{y} = b(x - \pi) - ay .$$

Transferring the coordinate origin to the point $x = \pi$, $y = 0$, we obtain the system

$$\dot{x} = y, \quad \dot{y} = bx - ay .$$

In this case the characteristic equation has the form

$$\lambda^2 + a\lambda - b = 0 .$$

For $a > 0$, $b > 0$, the roots of this equation will be real and of different signs so that the point $(\pi, 0)$ is an unstable point.

2. Let us consider now the equation of a pendulum to which an external couple has been applied (see Section 7):

$$\ddot{x} + a\dot{x} + b \sin x = L . \tag{11.6}$$

We shall consider the case when $|L| < b$. In this case one can put $L = b \sin x_0$, whereupon equation (11.6) assumes the form of the system

$$\dot{x} = y, \quad \dot{y} = -b(\sin x - \sin x_0) - ay . \tag{11.7}$$

The singular points are defined by the equations $y = 0$, $\sin x = \sin x_0$; consequently, the coordinates X_0, Y_0 of the singular points will have the form

$$X_0 = (-1)^k x_0 + k\pi, \quad Y_0 = 0, \qquad k = 0, 1, 2, \dots .$$

Making use of the Taylor series expansion of $\sin x$ in the neighbourhood of the point X_0, we write down the system of the first approximation:

$$\dot{x} = y, \quad \dot{y} = -b \cos X_0 (x - X_0) - ay . \tag{11.8}$$

After transferring the coordinate origin to the point $x = X_0$, $y = 0$, we obtain the system

$$\dot{X} = Y, \quad \dot{Y} = -b \cos X_0 X - aY .$$

The characteristic equation $\lambda^2 + a\lambda + b \cos X_0 = 0$ of this system has roots with negative real parts if $a > 0$, $b \cos X_0 > 0$. If it is stipulated that $a > 0$ and $b > 0$, then the condition for stability will have the form $\cos X_0 > 0$.

3. Let us consider the system

$$\dot{x} = y - xy^2, \quad \dot{y} = -x^3 . \tag{11.9}$$

The system of the first approximation has the form $\dot{x} = y$, $\dot{y} = 0$, from which it follows that $y = y_0$, $x = y_0 t + x_0$. Thus, the zero solution of the system of the first approximation is unstable. However, since both roots of the characteristic equation are equal to zero, we cannot, on the basis of theorem 11.2, come to any conclusion about the stability of the zero solution of system (11.9). Moreover, the zero solution of the complete system will actually be asymptotically stable. Indeed, by virtue of the system (11.9), the derivative of the Lyapunov function $v = \frac{1}{4}x^2 + \frac{1}{2}y^2$ has the form $\dot{v} = -x^4 y^2$ so that it must be a function of negative signs. It is easy to convince oneself that the coordinate axes $x = 0$, $y = 0$, on which the function $\dot{v}$ vanishes, contain no entire trajectories apart from the zero equilibrium position. Thus, theorem 5.2 is applicable, and asymptotic stability follows.

12. Stability on the Whole

Let us consider the system

$$\frac{dx}{dt} = X(x) \tag{12.1}$$

with the condition $X(0) = 0$.

Definition 12.1. *The zero solution of system* (12.1) *is said to be stable in the large* (*or stable for any initial disturbance*) *if it is stable in the Lyapunov sense and if every other solution* $x(t)$ *of the system possesses the property* $\|x(t)\| \to 0$ *when* $t \to \infty$.

We shall say that the Lyapunov function v is infinitely large if for any positive number A there exists a positive number R such that outside the sphere $\Sigma_{i=1}^{n} x_i^2 = R$ the inequality $v > A$ holds.

Thus, for example, a positive definite quadratic form will be infinitely large since, by virtue of (10.3), we will have $\lambda_1 r^2 \leqslant v \leqslant \lambda_n r^2$, where $\lambda_1 > 0$ and r is the radius vector of the point.

The function

$$v = \frac{x^2}{1+x^2} + y^2$$

is positive definite but not infinitely large since, when $y=0$ and $x \to \infty$, the function v does not tend to infinity.

The level surface of an infinitely large function is bounded. To show this, let us consider any level surface $v=c$. For a given c we can find a sphere of radius R outside which we will have $v > c$, and consequently, the surface $v=c$ will always lie inside this sphere.

Theorem 12.1. (asymptotic stability on the whole). *If there exists a positive definite infinitely large function v having a negative definite derivative throughout all space, then the zero solution of the system is asymptotically stable for any initial disturbance.*

This theorem has a converse and is a particular case of the following more general theorem [6].

Theorem 12.2. *Let there exist an infinitely large positive definite function v such that $dv/dt < 0$ outside M and $dv/dt \leqslant$ on M, where the set M contains no entire trajectories (apart from the zero equilibrium position). The zero solution of system* (12.1) *will then be stable in the large.*

To prove this theorem, let p be an arbitrary point in phase space. From p we trace out the semi-trajectory $f(p, t)$ $(t > 0)$. Since, according to the provisions of the theorem $dv/dt \leqslant 0$, we have $v(f(p, t)) \leqslant v_0$. Since the set $v(p) \leqslant v_0$ is bounded, the semi-trajectory $f(p, t)$ lies in a bounded region and consequently possesses ω-limit points. From lemma 5.1 it follows that the complete ω-limit set lies on a single level surface $v = v_\omega$.

Let us consider two cases. If $v_\omega = 0$, then the level surface $v = 0$ is the coordinate origin. Consequently, the whole ω-limit set of the trajectory $f(p, t)$ coincides with the origin and we have $\lim_{t \to \infty} x(t) = 0$. Since, from the inequality $dv/dt \leqslant 0$, ordinary stability in the Lyapunov sense follows (see theorem 4.1), then we again obtain asymptotic stability on the whole.

Let us suppose now that $v_\omega \neq 0$. On the surface $v = v_\omega$ lies the ω-limit set Ω of the point p consisting of entire trajectories. It is evident that along these trajectories we will have $\dot{v} = 0$, so that the set Ω lies in M. But according to the provisions of the theorem, M contains no entire trajectories: therefore the supposition that $v_\omega \neq 0$ leads to a contradiction, and the theorem is proved.

We note now that if the set M had contained entire trajectories then from the proof of the theorem it would follow that all the trajectories of the system (12.1) are attracted by a certain set lying in M. This set is invariant, i.e. it consists of entire trajectories. (This assertion is due to La Salle [11]).

Theorem 12.3. (Stability in the large of the zero solution of a linear system). *If the zero solution of a linear system is asymptotically stable in the Lyapunov sense then it is stable on the whole.*

In fact the zero solution will be asymptotically stable in the Lyapunov sense only when all the roots of the characteristic equation of the system have negative real parts. According to theorem 9.1, for any negative definite quadratic form w one can find a positive definite form v such that $\dot{v} = w$. Since the form v is infinitely large, then the conditions of theorem 12.1 apply.

13. Aizerman's Problem

Side by side with the second order linear equation

$$\ddot{x} + a\dot{x} + bx = 0 \tag{13.1}$$

let us consider also the non-linear equation

$$\ddot{x} + a\dot{x} + f(x) = 0, \quad f(0) = 0 . \tag{13.2}$$

If $a > 0$ and $b > 0$, the zero solution of the equation is asymptotically stable on the whole. The condition $b > 0$ may be regarded as the condition that the straight line $y = bx$ is located in the first and third quadrant of the coordinate plane. We now put to ourselves the following question: if the graph of the single-valued function $y = f(x)$ is also located in the first and third quadrant, will the zero solution of equation (13.2) be asymptotically stable on the whole? In other words, do the conditions $a > 0, f(x)x > 0$

ensure asymptotic stability on the whole or are some additional conditions necessary?

In order to decide this question we shall consider the Lyapunov function

$$v = y^2 + 2 \int_0^x f(x)dx .$$

By virtue of the system

$$\dot{x} = y, \quad \dot{y} = -f(x) - ay$$

the derivative of the function v has the form $\dot{v} = -2ay^2$. For v to be positive definite it is necessary for the condition $f(x) x > 0$ to be fulfilled. If $a > 0$, then $\dot{v}$ is a function of negative signs. It is evident that $\dot{v}$ vanishes on the line $y = 0$, which contains no entire trajectories apart from the equilibrium position.

Thus, for theorem 12.2 to be applicable all that is necessary now is to ensure that the function v is infinitely large. For this it is sufficient to require that the condition

$$\int_0^x f(x)dx \to 0$$

is fulfilled for $|x| \to \infty$, or the more right condition $f(x)/x > \varepsilon > 0$ for $x \neq 0$. We see that, in general, the fulfilment of the generalized Hurwitz–Routh conditions $a > 0$, $f(x)x > 0$ is insufficient for one to decide whether or not the property of stability on the whole is present.

Let us now discuss this question from a more general point of view. Along with the linear system

$$\frac{dx_1}{dt} = \sum_{k=1}^{n} a_{1k}x_k + bx_1,$$

$$\left. \begin{array}{l} \\ \\ \end{array} \right\} \tag{13.3}$$

$$\frac{dx_i}{dt} = \sum_{k=1}^{n} a_{ik}x_k, \quad i = 2, ..., n,$$

let us consider the non-linear system

$$\frac{dx_1}{dt} = \sum_{k=1}^{n} a_{1k}x_k + f(x_1),$$

$$\left. \begin{array}{l} \\ \\ \end{array} \right\} \tag{13.4}$$

$$\frac{dx_i}{dt} = \sum_{k=1}^{n} a_{ik}x_k, \quad i = 2, ..., n, \quad f(0) = 0 .$$

Suppose that we know that the zero solution of system (13.3) is asymptotically stable for all b satisfying the condition

$$\alpha < b < \beta .$$

The question now is, will the zero solution of system (13.4) be stable in the large if the following condition is fulfilled?

$$\alpha < \frac{f(x_1)}{x_1} < \beta . \tag{13.5}$$

In other words, if the graph of the curve $y = f(x)$ lies between the straight

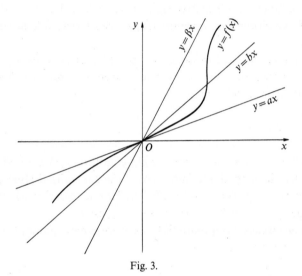

Fig. 3.

lines $y = \alpha x$ and $y = \beta x$ (Fig. 3), then will this be sufficient to ensure that the zero solution of the system (13.4) will be stable on the whole? This problem was first formulated by M. A. Aizerman [12] and it stimulated a large number of investigations by mathematicians and engineers.

The first example showing that the fulfilment of the generalized condition (13.5) is not enough for stability on the whole to be present in the case of a system of two equations was constructed by H. H. Krasovskii [13]. V. A. Pliss [14] carried out an intensive study of a third order system and showed that the fulfilment of condition (13.5) even in a more stringent form, i.e. in the form

$$\alpha_1 < \frac{f(x_1)}{x_1} < \beta_1, \quad \text{where} \quad \alpha_1 > \alpha, \ \beta_1 < \beta,$$

may not ensure stability on the whole.

We give below some examples of an investigation of the stability in the large of non-linear systems. These examples are all connected in one way or another with the Aizerman problem. We note, however, that the most interesting aspect of these examples is the demonstration they give of Lyapunov functions for non-linear systems.

14. Examples

Example 1 (I. G. Malkin [15], N. P. Erugin [16]). Along with the system

$$\left. \begin{array}{l} \dot{x} = ax + by, \\ \dot{y} = cx + dy, \end{array} \right\} \tag{14.1}$$

let us consider also the system

$$\left. \begin{array}{l} \dot{x} = f(x) + by, \\ \dot{y} = cx + dy. \end{array} \right\} \tag{14.2}$$

Using the results of section 9, we construct the Lyapunov function for system (14.1) as a quadratic form starting out from the condition

$$\dot{v} = -2(a+d)(bc-ad)x^2.$$

If we suppose that $v = \alpha x^2 + 2\beta xy + \gamma y^2$, it is easy to find the undefined coefficients α, β, γ. After computation we find the function

$$v = (dx - by)^2 + adx^2 - bcx^2. \tag{14.3}$$

The Hurwitz–Routh conditions for system (14.1) have the form $a+d<0$, $ad-bc>0$, and it is obvious that these conditions ensure that v is a fixed-sign function and $\dot{v}$ is a function of negative signs.

Taking function (14.3) as a basis, we now construct the Lyapunov function for the system (14.2). This system (14.2) differs from (14.1) by the fact that in place of ax we have the non-linear function $f(x)$. In (14.3) the coefficient a appears with x^2. If we regard the expression ax^2 as being twice the integral $\int_0^x ax\,dx$, then by analogy it seems reasonable to take for the Lyapunov function of system (14.2) the function

$$u = (dx - by)^2 + 2d \int_0^x f(x)dx - bcx^2. \tag{14.4}$$

Taking the derivative of the function u, we obtain, by virtue of system (14.2),

$$\dot{u} = -2 \left(\frac{f(x)}{x} + d \right) \left(bc - \frac{f(x)}{x} d \right) x^2.$$

Since

$$u = (dx - by)^2 + 2 \int_0^x (df(x) - bcx)dx,$$

then the condition that function u is of fixed sign has the form

(a) $d\dfrac{f(x)}{x} - bc > 0$ for $x \neq 0$.

Condition (a), together with the condition

(b) $\dfrac{f(x)}{x} + d < 0$ for $x \neq 0$

ensures that $\dot{u}$ is a function of negative signs. It is evident that when $\dot{u} = 0$ the set $x = 0$ does not contain entire trajectories. For the function u to be infinitely large it is sufficient that the condition

(c) $\displaystyle\int_0^x [df(x) - bcx]dx \to \infty$ for $|x| \to \infty$

be fulfilled. On the basis of theorem 12.2, conditions (a), (b), (c) ensure stability on the whole of the zero solution of system (14.2).
Krasvoskii [13] showed that if (c) is not fulfilled then there can be a loss of stability for any initial disturbances.
Along with system (14.1) let us consider further the system (Krasovskii [17])

$$\left.\begin{array}{l} \dot{x} = f(x) + by, \\ \dot{y} = \varphi(x) + dy. \end{array}\right\} \tag{14.5}$$

Taking the Lyapunov function in the form

$$v = (dx - by)^2 + 2 \int_0^x [df(x) - b\varphi(x)]dx$$

and taking into account that by virtue of (14.5) we have

$$\dot{v} = -2 \left(\frac{f(x)}{x} + d \right) (b\varphi(x) - df(x))x,$$

we obtain the sufficient conditions for stability on the whole in the form

(a) $(b\varphi(x) - df(x))x > 0$ for $x \neq 0$

(b) $\dfrac{f(x)}{x} + d < 0$ for $x \neq 0$

(c) $\displaystyle\int_0^x [df(x) - b\varphi(x)]\,dx \to \infty$ for $|x| \to \infty$.

Example 2 (E. A. Barbashin [6]). Let us consider the equation

$$\ddot{x} + \varphi(\dot{x}) + g(\dot{x})f(x) = 0,\tag{14.6}$$

which is equivalent to the system

$$\left.\begin{aligned}\dot{x} &= y \\ \dot{y} &= -g(y)f(x) - \varphi(y).\end{aligned}\right\}\tag{14.7}$$

To construct the Lyapunov function we shall make use of the method of the division of variables [18]. We shall seek the function v in the form $v = F(x) + \Phi(y)$. By virtue of the system (14.7), we have

$$\dot{v} = F'(x)y - \Phi'(y)[g(y)f(x) + \varphi(y)] .$$

Let us now require that $\dot{v}$ shall have the same structure as v, i.e. we require that the equation

$$F'(x)y - \Phi'(y)g(y)f(x) = 0$$

be fulfilled identically. Dividing the variables, we obtain

$$\frac{F'(x)}{f(x)} = \frac{\Phi'(y)g(y)}{y} ,$$

which is valid if each of the expressions on the two sides are equal to a constant, for example, unity. From this it at once follows that

$$F(x) = \int_0^x f(x)\,dx , \qquad \Phi(y) = \int_0^y \frac{y\,dy}{g(y)} ,$$

i.e.

$$v = \int_0^x f(x)\,dx + \int_0^y \frac{y\,dy}{g(y)} \quad \text{and} \quad \dot{v} = -y\frac{\varphi(y)}{g(y)} .$$

The stability conditions of the zero solution are written in the form

(a) $f(x)x > 0$ for $x \neq 0$,

(b) $g(y) > 0$ for $y \neq 0$,

(c) $\varphi(y)y > 0$ for $y \neq 0$,

(d) $\displaystyle\int_0^x f(x)dx \to \infty$ as $|x| \to \infty$,

(e) $\displaystyle\int_0^y \frac{y\,dy}{g(y)} \to \infty$ as $|y| \to \infty$.

Example 3. In the equation

$$\ddot{x} + \varphi(x)\dot{x} + f(x) = 0,$$

Having carried out the change of variables (the Lienard transformation)

$$y = \dot{x} + \int_0^x \varphi(x)dx,$$

we obtain the system

$$\dot{x} = y - \int_0^x \varphi(x)dx,$$

$$\dot{y} = -f(x). \tag{14.8}$$

Making use of the Lienard function

$$v = y^2 + 2\int_0^x f(x)dx$$

and taking into account the fact that

$$\dot{v} = -2f(x)\int_0^x \varphi(x)dx,$$

we obtain the following sufficient conditions for stability on the whole

(a) $f(x)x > 0$ for $x \neq 0$

(b) $\varphi(x) > 0$ for $x \neq 0$

(c) $\displaystyle\int_0^x f(x)dx \to \infty$ as $|x| \to \infty$.

Example 4 (N. N. Krasovskii [9]). Let us consider the equation

$$\ddot{x} = f(x, \dot{x})$$

which is equivalent to the system

$$\dot{x} = y,$$
$$\dot{y} = f(x, y).$$

Taking the Lyapunov function in the form

$$v = y^2 - 2 \int_0^x f(x, 0)dx$$

we obtain

$$\dot{v} = 2[f(x, y) - f(x, 0)]y.$$

The conditions of stability on the whole have the form

(a) $f(x, 0)x < 0$ for $x \neq 0$

(b) $[f(x, y) - f(x, 0)]y < 0$ for $y \neq 0$

(c) $\int_0^x f(x, 0)dx \to \infty$ as $|x| \to \infty$.

Example 5 (E. A. Barbashin [20]). Let us consider the equation

$$\ddot{x} + a\ddot{x} + \varphi(x) + f(x) = 0, \tag{14.9}$$

where $\varphi(0) = f(0) = 0$, $a > 0$, function $f(x)$ is continuously differentiable, and function $\varphi(x)$ is continuous for all values of the argument. Later on we shall need to make use of the function

$$w(x, y) = aF(x) + f(x)y + \Phi(y),$$

where

$$F(x) = \int_0^x f(x)dx,$$

$$\Phi(y) = \int_0^y \varphi(y)dy.$$

Introducing the notation $y = \dot{x}$, $z = \dot{y} + ay$, equation (14.9) leads to the system

$$\dot{x} = y, \quad \dot{y} = z - ay, \quad \dot{z} = -\varphi(y) - f(x). \tag{14.10}$$

Let us consider the function

$$v = aF(x) + f(x)y + \Phi(y) + \tfrac{1}{2}z^2 = w(x, y) + \tfrac{1}{2}z^2 .$$

We have

$$\dot{v} = \left[f'(x) - a\,\frac{\varphi(y)}{y} \right] y^2 .$$

Let the following conditions be fulfilled

(a) $f(x)x > 0$ for $x \neq 0$,

(b) $a\,\dfrac{\varphi(y)}{y} - f'(x) > 0$ for $y \neq 0$,

(c) $\lim\limits_{r \to \infty} w(x, y) = \infty$,   where $r = (x^2 + y^2)^{\frac{1}{2}}$.

From condition (b) it follows that $\dot{v} < 0$ for $y \neq 0$ and $\dot{v} = 0$ for $y = 0$. We shall show that there are no entire trajectories on the plane $y = 0$ apart from the zero equilibrium point. Indeed, if there were such a trajectory then along it we would have $y \equiv \dot{y} \equiv 0$. From the second equation of system (14.10) it would follow that $z \equiv 0$ and $\dot{z} \equiv 0$, from the third (since $\varphi(y) = 0$), the identity $f(x) \equiv 0$ follows. Taking into account the continuity of $f(x)$, condition (a) leads us to the identity $x \equiv 0$. Thus, the movement may be only a zero movement.

We shall show now that the function w is positive definite. We have

$$w(x, y) = \frac{(2\Phi(y) + yf(x))^2}{4\Phi(y)} + \frac{4aF(x)\,\Phi(y) - y^2 f^2(x)}{4\Phi(y)} .$$

We note that $\Phi(y) > 0$ for $y \neq 0$. Indeed, since $f(x)$ changes sign at the point $x = 0$, $f'(x)$ assumes positive values for certain values of x; as can be seen from condition (b), these values do not exceed the lower bound of the values $\varphi(y)/y$, which ensures that $\varphi(y)/y$ is positive or, what amounts to the same thing, that $\Phi(y)$ is positive.

We shall show further that the function

$$u(x, y) = 4aF(x)\,\Phi(y) - y^2 f^2(x)$$

is positive for $x \neq 0$, $y \neq 0$. In fact we have

$$u(x, y) = 4 \int_0^x \int_0^y f(x) \left[a\,\frac{\varphi(y)}{y} - f'(x)y \right] dy\,dx .$$

Condition (b) ensures that the inner integral is positive, and condition (a) that the function $u(x, y)$ is positive. Thus, $w(x, y)$ is a positive definite function of the arguments x and y and consequently function $v(x, y, z) = w(x, y) + \frac{1}{2}z^2$ is a positive definite function of the arguments x, y, z.

Thus, the conditions of applicability of theorem 12.2 are met, from which it follows that conditions (a), (b), (c) must ensure the stability on the whole of the zero solution of system (14.10).

Example 6 (E. I. Zheleznov [21]). We consider the equation

$$\ddot{x} + a\ddot{x} + f(x)\dot{x} + cx = 0 . \tag{14.11}$$

Introducing the new variables

$$y = \ddot{x} + a\dot{x} + \int_0^x f(x)dx ,$$

$$z = \dot{x} + ax ,$$

we obtain the system

$$\dot{x} = z - ax , \quad \dot{y} = -cx, \quad \dot{z} = y - F(x) , \tag{14.12}$$

where

$$F(x) = \int_0^x f(x)dx .$$

Let us consider the function

$$v = \int_0^x F(x)dx - xy + \frac{a}{2c} y^2 + \frac{z^2}{2} .$$

We evaluate the derivative of v, using (14.12) and obtain

$$\dot{v} = - \left[a \frac{F(x)}{x} - c \right] x^2 .$$

The conditions (a) $a > 0$, $c > 0$, (b) $af(x) > c + \varepsilon$, where $\varepsilon > 0$, ensure stability on the whole of the zero system (14.12).

In fact, from condition (b) it follows from the theorem of mean values that

$$a \frac{F(x)}{x} - c > \varepsilon > 0 ,$$

from which we obtain the result that the derivative $\dot{v}$ is a function of negative signs.

In order to demonstrate that v is a function of fixed signs let us put this function in the following form:

$$v = \frac{(ay-cx)^2}{2ac} + \frac{\int_0^x \left(a\,\frac{F(x)}{x} - c\right)x\,dx}{a} + \frac{z^2}{2}.$$

Condition (b) obviously ensures that the integral in the expression for v is positive and condition (a) ensures that both terms are positive. It is also easy to prove that there are no entire trajectories on the plane $x=0$.

Example 7 (E. A. Barbashin [18]). Let us construct the Lyapunov function for the system

$$\dot{x}_i = \sum_{k=1}^n p_{ik} f_k(\sigma_k), \qquad i=1, 2, \ldots, n,$$

where $f_k(\sigma_k)\sigma_k > 0$ for $\sigma_k \neq 0$, $\sigma_k = \Sigma_{m=1}^n a_{km} x_m$, $k=1, 2, \ldots, n$, the a_{km} are constants, the p_{ik} may be functions of the coordinates, of the parameters or of time.

Let us consider the function

$$v = \sum_{i=1}^n \int_0^\sigma f_i(\sigma)d\sigma.$$

It is obvious that this function will be positive definite and it is also clear that

$$\dot{v} = 2 \sum_{m,k=1}^n b_{km} f_k(\sigma_k) f_m(\sigma_m),$$

where

$$b_{km} = \tfrac{1}{2} \sum_{i=1}^n (a_{ki} p_{im} + a_{mi} p_{ik}).$$

Thus, v will be negative definite, or a function of negative signs if this same property is possessed by the form

$$\sum_{m,k=1}^n b_{km} u_k u_m.$$

The Silvester criterion, and the criterion that a function shall be a function of negative signs, are easily transposed in the case of quadratic forms with variable coefficients, so that these criteria can be used successfully here.

We note that the list of interesting examples could have been lengthened considerably. A detailed bibliography can be found in a report by Barbashin [18]. An essential criterion of the value of the Lyapunov function is the requirement that the sufficient conditions of stability ensuing from the Lyapunov function that is obtained should, in the linear case, also be necessary conditions.

We will not discuss the interesting problem here of the absolute stability of non-linear systems. The reader will find a complete account of such problems in the monographs by A. I. Lur'e [22], A. M. Letov [23], M. A. Aizerman and F. P. Gantmakher [24].

Chapter 2

STABILITY OF CONTROL SYSTEMS WITH VARIABLE STRUCTURE

1. Preliminary Remarks. Statement of the Problem

In this chapter we shall be considering the stability of automatic control systems having a variable structure. In variable structure systems stability is attained by means of a step-wise variation of certain system parameters. The characteristic feature of the passage of the transient response through such systems is that after a certain time a sliding mode of behaviour is established in the system.

1. Before we concern ourselves with the details of this problem, let us consider briefly some of the basic ideas of automatic control theory. In any automatic control system it is usually possible to identify an object which is the subject of the control and a controlling device, or controller. The purpose of the controller is to generate a control signal which acts

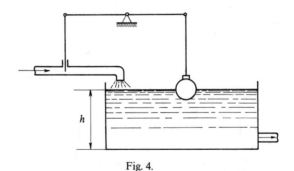

Fig. 4.

upon the object in such a way that the process being controlled always gives the desired indicator reading. Thus, for example, Fig. 4 illustrates a very simple system for controlling the level of liquid in a tank.

Here, the quantity being controlled is the level of the liquid h. By varying the cross sectional area of the feed pipe, the controller regulates the quantity of liquid x supplied to the tank per unit time in accordance with the magnitude of h. As far as the object is concerned (i.e. the tank), signal x is the input and signal h is the output signal. In this case, the output signal h is fed back to the controlling device with the aim of determining the magnitude of the control signal x; in other words, the system we are considering possesses negative feedback.

In principle, an automatic system can perform the following tasks:
(1) It can maintain the output signal of the object at the same constant level (a stabilizing automatic system).
(2) It can vary the control signal in accordance with a predetermined function of time (a programmed automatic system).
(3) It can vary the control signal as a function of a varying controlling action (an automatic servo-system) which is not known in advance.

An automatic system may be divided into separate units or elements (the object, the controller, etc.), each of which converts an input signal x (from the point of view of that section) into an output signal y. Mathematically, the relation between the input and the output may be expressed by the equation $y(t) = Ax(t)$, where A is an operator defined in the space of the input signals x.

The operator A is usually given in the form of a differential equation. For example, in a linear system, the relation between $y(t)$ and $x(t)$ may be given in the form of a linear differential equation

$$P(D)y(t) = Q(D)x(t),$$

where $P(D)$, $Q(D)$ are polynomial functions of D, and D is a differential operator, i.e. $D = d/dt$.

Starting from zero initial conditions for $y(t)$, we find that for the Laplace transforms of the functions $x(t)$, $y(t)$, i.e. for the functions

$$X(p) = \int_0^\infty e^{-pt} x(t)\,dt, \qquad Y(p) = \int_0^\infty e^{-pt} y(t)\,dt$$

the following relation is valid:

$$Y(p) = \frac{Q(p)}{P(p)} X(p).$$

The function $L(P) = Q(P)/P(P)$ is usually called the transfer function of the unit. It is clear that the transfer function completely determines the

form of the differential equation describing the unit. Consequently, if
one also takes into account the initial conditions for the output signal $y(t)$,
then, given the transfer function for the unit, one can completely determine the operator A.

It is usual to describe an automatic control circuit with the aid of a block
diagram with the appropriate transfer functions written in. For example,
Fig. 5 is a block diagram of a simple servo-system in which ψ represents
the desired response signal and φ the output signal. The output signal is
fed back *via* an inverse feedback connexion to the input of the system
where it is subtracted from the signal ψ. The signal $x = \psi - \varphi$ is applied to
the object whose transfer function is $K/L(p)$. The purpose of the servo-
system in this case is to track the desired response signal ψ, i.e. the system
works in such a way that the signal at the output φ differs by as little as
possible from the signal ψ. It is clear, therefore, that x should be as small
as possible.

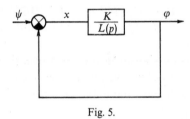

Fig. 5.

Treating the transfer function as an operator, we obtain the relation
$Kx/\{L(p)\} = \varphi$; from which it follows that

$$L(p)x = L(p)\psi - Kx .\tag{1.1}$$

Equation (1.1) may be regarded as a differential equation provided that
the symbol p is taken to represent a differential operator.
Writing (1.1) in the form

$$x = \frac{L(p)}{L(p)+K}\,\psi ,$$

one can see intuitively that to reduce the absolute magnitude of the signal
x, i.e. to increase the accuracy of the tracking, it is necessary to increase
the parameter K. This parameter is usually called gain of the system.

2. We should note that the servo-system we are discussing is continuously exposed to disturbing actions which affect the magnitude of the signal x. Let us suppose that as a result of the action of such a disturbance, the new value of x is $x = x_1 + \Delta x$. The quantity x_1 also satisfies equation (1.1), and we have

$$L(p)x_1 = L(p)\psi - Kx_1 ,$$

since the desired response signal ψ remains the same. It is easy to see that the equation for the deviation or error of x, i.e. for the quantity Δx is

$$L(p)\Delta x = -K\Delta x . \tag{1.2}$$

If the zero solution of equation (1.2) is asymptotically stable in the Lyapunov sense, the servo-system will operate reliably, i.e. with the passage of time the error Δx tends asymptotically to zero. Thus, to investigate the properties of a servo-system, one should examine the stabilizing system specified by equation (1.2). For equation (1.2) to possess the property of asymptotic stability it is necessary and sufficient that the roots of the equation $L(\lambda) + K = 0$ should have negative real parts.

Thus, if the system is to track accurately, K should be made large, while if the system is to be stable with respect to noise it is necessary that the Routh–Hurwitz conditions be fulfilled for the polynomial $L(\lambda) + K$. We shall show that already for a third order system these requirements are contradictory. Assume $L(\lambda) = \lambda^3 + a\lambda^2 + b\lambda + c$. The Routh–Hurwitz conditions for the polynomial $L(\lambda) + K$ have the form $c + K > 0$, $b > 0$, $ab > c + K$. We see that if K is too large the third condition may be violated.

The question that now arises is, can one remove the contradiction by making K not only large but of variable sign? Can one not choose such a law of sign variation for the quantity α ($|\alpha| \leqslant 1$) that the equation

$$L(p)x = -\alpha K x$$

becomes stable? We shall see later that this can indeed be done.

It turns out that the transient response of servo-systems having a coefficient α that alternates in sign passes over to a sliding mode of behavior at a certain instant of time. The response then becomes independent of the system parameters and depends only on the magnitude of K. This important property, usually referred to as the roughness of the system, has made this type of system of particular interest to engineers. In future we shall call any system whose operation is based on the principle of a step-wise change in the parameters, a system with variable structure.

The basic results of the theory of sliding modes are due to Dolgolenko [27], Neimark [28], and Flugge–Lotz [29]. The advantages of varying gain systems were pointed out in 1957 by Letov [30].

An investigation of the theory of the stability of variable structure systems was carried out under the direction of Barbashin in Sverdlovsk [31–48], and also under the direction of Emelianov in Moscow [49–61]. A somewhat different approach to these systems can be found in the work of Garret [62].

3. Consider now the system of differental equations

$$\frac{dx_i}{dt} = X_i(x_1, ..., x_n), \qquad i = 1, 2, ..., n . \tag{1.3}$$

Suppose that on a certain surface S given by the equation $s(x_1, ..., x_n) = 0$ the right-hand sides of system (1.3) allow the presence of discontinuities of the first kind. This means that at any point $(x_1^0, ..., x_n^0)$ of the surface S and for any function $X_i(x_1, ..., x_n)$ there exist finite limits $\lim_{s \to +0} X_i$, $\lim_{s \to -0} X_i$ which cannot coincide. Let the surface S divide the phase space E of system (1.3) into two parts, E_1 and E_2. Consider a vector F with projections $X_1, ..., X_n$ and introduce the notation $F^+ = \lim_{s \to +0} F$, $F^- = \lim_{s \to -0} F$. Clearly, the vectors F^+ and F^- are well-defined at the points of the surface S and moreover $\lim_{s \to +0} \dot{s} = F^+ N$ and $\lim_{s \to 0^-} s = F^- N$, where N is the vector-gradient of the function $s(x_1, ..., x_n)$ at the corresponding point of the surface S.

The points of the surface S may be divided into the following three groups [63]. To the first group belong those points of surface S at which $\lim_{s \to +0} \dot{s} \cdot \lim_{s \to -0} \dot{s} > 0$. At these points the vectors F^- and F^+ are directed with the same sense away from surface S. If a point of phase space which is moving along a trajectory of system (1.3) falls onto a point of this first group, then it very soon moves off the surface S and crosses over to another part of the space E. In this region the trajectories "sew" the surface (Fig. 6, segment BC).

The second group of points on S is defined by the inequalities $\lim_{s \to +0} \dot{s} > 0$,

$\lim_{s \to -0} \dot{s} < 0$. These points must rapidly move off the surface S along one of the trajectories of system (1.3) emerging from the given point (see Fig. 6, segment CD). The question as to which particular trajectory the point will move along in order to make its escape from the surface S should also be decided because, in the given case, the answer can be non-unique. It is often reckoned that the point will leave the surface in the direction of whichever of the two vectors F^+ and F^- gives the largest absolute value for its projection along the normal N.

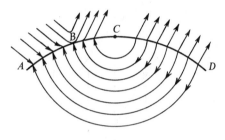

Fig. 6.

Finally the third group of points consists of those points on the surface S for which $\lim_{s \to +0} \dot{s} \leqslant 0$ and $\lim_{s \to -0} \dot{s} \geqslant 0$. In this case the trajectories of system (1.3) either pass into the surface S or they run along this surface. In the case when the image point after a finite interval of time falls onto surface S, the motion does not end there; the image point starts to slide along the surface and continues to slide until it passes outside the limits of the sliding region (section AB in Fig. 6).

The three groups of points on the switching surface are separated from each other, in general, by an $(n-2)$-dimensional manifold. At the points of this manifold either $\lim_{s \to +0} \dot{s} = 0$ or $\lim_{s \to -0} \dot{s} = 0$, or both of these equalities are fulfilled simultaneously.

Let us discuss the points belonging to the third group in a little more detail. Assume that point M lies in the sliding region on the surface S and consider the vectors F^- and F^+ which emerge from this point. Let us join the ends of these vectors by a straight line and find the point of intersection P of this straight line with the tangential plane drawn at the point M (Fig. 7). In future we shall always assume as a starting hypothesis [63] that at point M the sliding velocity vector coincides with the vector $\overrightarrow{MP}$. This working rule, which has been confirmed in practice, enables us to derive the differential equations for the sliding process.

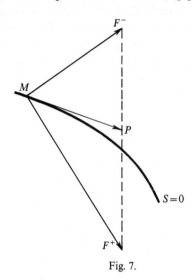

Fig. 7.

2. Stabilization of a Second Order System

Consider the second order equation

$$\ddot{x} + a\dot{x} + bx = \alpha Kx . \tag{2.1}$$

Here a, b are arbitrary constants, K is a positive constant, and α satisfied the condition $|\alpha| \leqslant 1$. We wish to find that law of variation of α which will ensure asymptotic stability for the zero solution of equation (2.1).
Having put equation (2.1) in the form

$$\dot{x} = y, \quad \dot{y} = -bx - ay - \alpha Kx , \tag{2.2}$$

we shall try to find α, starting out from the following arguments. Let $v(x, y)$ be any function of the variables x and y. For example, this function might be the potential of a vector field in the phase space of the variables x and y. We shall choose the value of α that will give the greatest rate of decrease of the function v along the trajectory of system (2.2) [66, 79]. Since

$$\dot{v} = \frac{\partial v}{\partial x}\, y - \frac{\partial v}{\partial y}\,(bx+ay) - \alpha K \frac{\partial v}{\partial y}\, x\,,$$

and since only the last term depends on α, then min $\dot{v}$ is attained by setting

$$\alpha = \text{sign}\,\frac{\partial v}{\partial y}\, x\,. \tag{2.3}$$

If, for example, $v = \frac{1}{2}Bx^2 + Axy + \frac{1}{2}y^2$, we obtain

$$\alpha = \text{sign}\,(Ax+y)x\,. \tag{2.4}$$

Thus, in considering the system (2.2), we shall assume that α is determined by the relation (2.4). System (2.2) can also be written in the form of the two systems:

$$\dot{x} = y, \quad \dot{y} = -bx - ay - Kx\,, \tag{2.5}$$

with $x(Ax+y) > 0$, and

$$\dot{x} = y, \quad \dot{y} = -bx - ay + Kx\,, \tag{2.6}$$

with $x(Ax+y) < 0$.

The straight lines $x = 0$ and $s = Ax + y = 0$ divide the phase plane into four parts, G_1, G_2, G_3 and G_4 specified, respectively, by the inequalities (G_1): $x > 0, s > 0$; (G_2): $x < 0, s > 0$; (G_3): $x < 0, s < 0$; and (G_4): $x > 0, s < 0$.

The lines $x = 0$ and $Ax + y = 0$ are switching lines on which the transition from trajectories belonging to one system to trajectories belonging to the other system is accomplished. Since, for $x = 0$, we have $\dot{x} > 0$ if $y > 0$, and $\dot{x} < 0$ if $y < 0$, then, by virtue of the two systems (2.5) and (2.6), the line $x = 0$ is intersected by the trajectories in a clock-wise direction, i.e. all the points of the line $x = 0$ (except the point where $y = 0$) are "sewing" points. Let us investigate now the points of the straight line $s = Ax + y = 0$ which in future we shall call the straight line S. In order to find the conditions which will make S a straight line of sliding let us in accordance with system (2.2) find $\dot{s}$ on this straight line:

$$\dot{s} = -(A^2 - aA + b + \alpha K)x\,.$$

For $x > 0$, we have

$$\lim_{s \to +0} \dot{s} = -(A^2 - aA + b + K)x\,,$$

$$\lim_{s \to -0} \dot{s} = -(A^2 - aA + b - K)x\,,$$

and for $x < 0$

$$\lim_{s \to +0} \dot{s} = -(A^2 - aA + b - K)x,$$

$$\lim_{s \to -0} \dot{s} = -(A^2 - aA + b + K)x .$$

Since the conditions for the existence of sliding have the form

$$\lim_{s \to +0} \dot{s} \leqslant 0 \quad \text{and} \quad \lim_{s \to -0} \dot{s} \geqslant 0 ,$$

they are, for the case we are considering, equivalent to the conditions

$$A^2 - aA + b + K \geqslant 0, \quad A^2 - aA + b - K \leqslant 0, \tag{2.7}$$

which may be written in the more compact form:

$$|A^2 - aA + b| \leqslant K . \tag{2.8}$$

Thus, condition (2.8) is a necessary and sufficient condition for the existence of a sliding mode in system (2.2). It is clear that it is always possible to ensure that this condition is fulfilled by choosing a sufficiently large value for the gain K.

Let us now investigate the system (2.2) in each of the regions G_i, $i = 1, 2, 3, 4$. In regions G_1 and G_3 we have $\alpha = 1$, and system (2.5) is operative. The characteristic equation of this system has the form

$$\lambda^2 + a\lambda + b + K = 0 . \tag{2.9}$$

If K is sufficiently large, the roots of this equation will be complex with the result that the integral curves will be spirals and the coordinate origin will be a singular point of the "focus" type. If $a > 0$, the image point will approach the coordinate origin along the trajectory, the origin in this case being an asymptotically stable equilibrium point (Fig. 8). If $a < 0$, then the points of phase space will move away from the origin.

In regions G_2 and G_4 system (2.6) is in force; its characteristic equation has the form

$$\mu^2 + a\mu + b - K = 0 . \tag{2.10}$$

If K is sufficiently large, the roots of this equation

$$\mu_1 = -\frac{a}{2} + \sqrt{\frac{a^2}{4} - b + K}, \quad \mu_2 = -\frac{a}{2} - \sqrt{\frac{a^2}{4} - b + K},$$

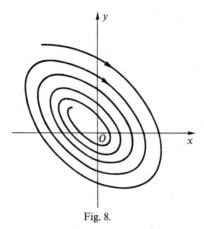

Fig. 8.

will be real and of opposite sign. In this case the origin will be a singular point of the "saddle" type. Amongst the integral curves of system (2.6) there will be the two straight lines $y=\mu_1 x$ and $y=\mu_2 x$, a fact that can be demonstrated simply by substituting the functions $y=\mu_1 x$ and $y=\mu_2 x$ into the equation

$$\frac{dy}{dx} = -b\frac{x}{y} - a + K\frac{x}{y},$$

which is equivalent to system (2.6). The remaining integral curves, which are hyperbolic in form, approach these integral straight lines which play the part of asymptotes (Fig. 9).

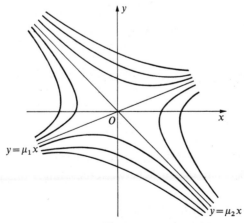

Fig. 9.

We note that the graph of the function $f(\mu) = \mu^2 + a\mu + b - K$ will be a parabola intersecting the μ-axis at the points $\mu = \mu_1$ and $\mu = \mu_2$ (Fig. 10). If the inequality $\mu_2 \leqslant \mu \leqslant \mu_1$, is fulfilled, then $f(\mu) \leqslant 0$. If we assume now that $A > 0$ and suppose in addition that $\mu = -A \geqslant \mu_2$, we obtain $f(-A) = A^2 - aA + b - K \leqslant 0$. Thus, the second of the inequalities (2.7) will be

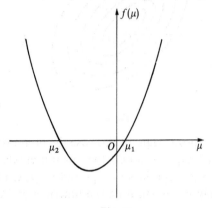

Fig. 10.

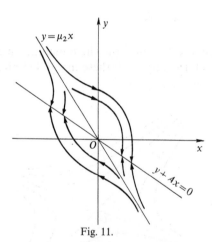

Fig. 11.

satisfied if $-A \geqslant \mu_2$, i.e. if the angle between the switching line S and the x-axis is smaller than the angle between the straight line $y = \mu_2 x$ and the x-axis.

The first of the inequalities (2.7) can always be satisfied by choosing a sufficiently large value of K. Thus, by choosing a sufficiently large value for

K, and by choosing A so that it satisfies the condition $0 < A \leqslant -\mu_2$, one can always ensure that sliding is present at all points of the straight line S.

It can be seen from Fig. 11, which gives a phase portrait of system (2.2), that any point of phase space moving along the trajectories of system (2.2) falls onto S. Having fallen onto S, the image point begins to slide along this line to the coordinate origin. Indeed, using the rule for determining the sliding velocity vector given at the end of the preceding section, it is not difficult to show that the differential equation for the sliding process has the form $\dot{x} + Ax = 0$. In fact, it follows from this rule that the vectors F^- and F^+ emerging from point M (see Fig. 7) have identical projections on the axis Ox, each equal to the ordinate y of that point. From this it follows that the sliding velocity vector $\overrightarrow{MP}$ is also equal to y, so that $\dot{x} = y$. On the other hand, the abscissa x and the ordinate y of the point M are connected by the relation $Ax + y = 0$, which yields the required differential equation $\dot{x} + Ax = 0$. It follows from this equation that for $A > 0$ sliding will take place in a direction towards the coordinate origin in accordance with with the law $x = x_0 e^{-A(t-t_0)}$.

The block diagram for the system corresponding to equation (2.1) is shown in Fig. 12. Here, since the stabilising system we are considering corresponds to a servo-system, we suppose that $\psi = 0$ and $\varphi = -x$. The transfer function $L(p)$ has the form $L(p) = p^2 + ap + b$. The factor α is generated in unit F in accordance with the values of x and of its derivatives; in unit N, x is multiplied by α.

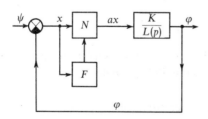

Fig. 12.

In conclusion we shall show that when $a > 0$ one can apply the method of Lyapunov functions to the investigation of the stability of the system we have been considering. Let us first consider the function $v = (b + K)x^2 + y^2$, whose derivative taken according to system (2.2), has the form $\dot{v} = -2ay^2 + 2K(1 - \alpha)xy$.

In regions G_1 and G_3 we have $\alpha = 1$ and, consequently, $\dot{v} = -2ay^2$. In regions G_2 and G_4 we have $\alpha = -1$, whence we obtain $\dot{v} = -2ay^2 + 4Kxy$; but since in these regions $xy < 0$, we obtain $\dot{v} \leqslant 0$ everywhere on the phase plane. Assume $|b| < K$. The set of points $y = 0$ at which $\dot{v} = 0$ obviously does not contain entire trajectories so that we can apply theorem 12.2 of Chapter 1, whence it follows that the zero equilibrium position is asymptotically stable on the whole. An analysis of the proof of this theorem shows that one can ignore the discontinuity of the derivative on the switching line S and the non-uniqueness in the negative direction of the time axis.

Let us consider now the function $v = bx^2 + y^2 + \alpha Kx^2$. This function has discontinuities on the straight line S; if $0 \leqslant K < b$, v will be positive definite and infinitely large; if $K \geqslant b$, it is not difficult to see that if these properties are to be maintained the condition $A > \sqrt{K - b}$ must be fulfilled. It is easy to see that by virtue of system (2.2) we obtain $\dot{v} = -2ay^2$ outside the switching line S. On the other hand, when a trajectory of the system crosses the switching line the function v suffers a stepwise decrease of $2Kx^2$. Appealing again to the arguments used in proving theorem 12.2 of Chapter 1, we come to the conclusion that any point of phase space either falls directly onto the coordinate origin or falls first onto the line S and then slides along it to the origin.

Alimov [64] derived some possible generalizations of theorem 12.2; these include problems where the right-hand sides of the equations are discontinuous.

3. Stabilization of a Third Order System. Conditions for the Existence of the Sliding Mode

Consider the third order equation

$$\dddot{x} + a\ddot{x} + b\dot{x} + cx = -\alpha Kx,$$ (3.1)

where a, b, c are arbitrary constants, K is a positive constant and α satisfies the condition $|\alpha| \leqslant 1$.

We will consider the function $v = Cx^2 + Ey^2 + z^2 + 2Dxy + 2Axz + 2Byz$ and choose a law of variation of α that will ensure the maximum rate of decrease of v along the trajectory of the system

$$\dot{x} = y, \quad \dot{y} = z, \quad \dot{z} = -cx - by - az - \alpha Kx, \tag{3.2}$$

equivalent to equation (3.1).
Since

$$\dot{v} = \frac{\partial v}{\partial x} y + \frac{\partial v}{\partial y} z - \frac{\partial v}{\partial z} (cx + by + az) - \alpha K \frac{\partial v}{\partial z} x,$$

and since only the last term depends on α, it is clear that α should be found from the formula $\alpha = \text{sign}(\partial y/\partial z)x$ or, what amounts to the same thing, from the formula

$$\alpha = \text{sign}(Ax + By + z)x. \tag{3.3}$$

The block diagram for the stabilizing system we are discussing is illustrated in Fig. 12. Suppose the desired-response signal ψ is equal to zero and that $L(p) = p^3 + ap^2 + bp + c$. An investigation of a servo-system with variable structure has been carried out by Barbashin *et al.* [31] for a non-zero ψ and second order system. Barbashin and Tabueva [33], and also Barbashin, Tabueva and Eidinov [34], have investigated the same problem for a third order system.

We shall derive now the conditions which will ensure the existence of sliding at any point of the plane S specified by the equation

$$S = Ax + By + z = 0. \tag{3.4}$$

Theorem 3.1. *For a plane S to be a sliding plane it is necessary and sufficient that the following conditions be fulfilled*

$$A = B^2 - aB + b,$$

$$|(B - a)^3 + a(B - a)^2 + b(B - a) + c| \leqslant K. \tag{3.5}$$

If we put $r = B - a$, then the conditions (3.5) can be written in the form

$$B = a + r, \quad A = Br + b, \quad |f(r)| \leqslant K,$$

where we have introduced the notation $f(r) = r^3 + ar^2 + br + c$. We shall now prove this theorem. In system (3.2), let us change the variables by introducing the coordinate $s = Ax + By + c$. The new system will have the form

$$\left.\begin{array}{l} \dot{x} = y, \\ \dot{y} = -Ax - By + s, \\ \dot{s} = -(A(B-a)+c+\alpha K)x+(A-B^2+aB-b)y+(B-a)s. \end{array}\right\} \quad (3.6)$$

On the plane $s=0$, we obtain two lines:

$$(A(B-a)+c+K)x-(A-B^2+aB-b)y = 0, \qquad (3.7)$$

$$(A(B-a)+c-K)x-(A-B^2+aB-b)y = 0, \qquad (3.8)$$

which divide this plane into regions in which the following two quantities have constant sign: $R_1 = \dot{s}$ for $\alpha = 1$, and $R_2 = \dot{s}$ for $\alpha = -1$. For S to be a sliding plane it is necessary and sufficient that the conditions sign $R_1 = -$ sign x and sign $R_2 =$ sign x be fulfilled, as follows from section 1 of this Chapter. Since the signs of R_1 and R_2 depend only on x, it is necessary that the coefficient of y in equations (3.7) and (3.8) be equal to zero. Thus, the necessity of the first of our conditions (3.5) is proved. If condition (3.5) is fulfilled then, on the plane $s=0$, we obtain

$$\dot{s} = -[f(B-a)+\alpha K]x \qquad (3.9)$$

whence it follows that in the presence of sliding the inequalities

$$f(B-a)+K \geqslant 0 \quad \text{and} \quad f(B-a)-K \leqslant 0,$$

must be fulfilled. These inequalities are equivalent to the single inequality $|f(B-a)| \leqslant K$.

It is easy to see that conditions (3.5) which we have just proved to be necessary conditions for the existence of sliding are also sufficient conditions. We note the following: if the first of the conditions (3.5), i.e. the condition $A = B^2 - aB + b$ is not fulfilled then, on the plane S, a sector is formed near the line $x=0$ which is bounded by the lines (3.7) and (3.8). It is easy to see that at the points of this sector the trajectories of system (3.2) will sew the surface S. However, with a sufficiently large value of K the sector can be made as narrow as one pleases. The image point of the system slides along the plane S until it reaches the boundary of the sector, after which it moves away a little from this plane only to fall on S once more a short interval of time later. It then continues to slide and again reaches the sector boundary. One can show [34] that in the presence of this violation of the sliding conditions the property of stability is in a certain sense preserved. However we will postpone detailed discussion of this until section 7 where we shall be considering the non-linear case.

We shall derive now the differential equations for sliding. Applying the rule given in section 1 for determining the sliding velocity vector, and noting that the vectors $F^+\,(y,\,z,\,-cx-Kx-by-az)$ and $F^-\,(y,\,z,\,-cx+Kx-by-az)$ have identical projections on the Ox- and Oy-axes, we arrive at the conclusion that the projection of the sliding velocity vector on the Ox-axis is equal to y, and that on the Oy-axis is equal to z. Thus, the projections of the velocity vectors are given by the equations $\dot{x}=y$, $\dot{y}=z$. But since we have $z=-Ax-By$ on the plane S then, eliminating z, we obtain the following system of differential equations describing the sliding process.

$$\dot{x}=y,\quad \dot{y}=Ax-By. \tag{3.10}$$

It is clear that system (3.10) will be asymptotically stable if, and only if, the conditions $A>0$ and $B>0$ are fulfilled. We shall in the future assume that these conditions are everywhere fulfilled.

Finally, we should note that system (3.10) describes an ideal sliding process: the description of an actual sliding process must be considerably more complicated since, because of switching delays, the presence of inertia, etc., the image point oscillates continually about the plane S during the time it is moving towards the coordinate origin [65].

4. Stabilization of a Third Order System. The Stability of the System

With account of conditions (3.5), we rewrite the system (3.6) in the form

$$\left.\begin{array}{l}\dot{x}=y\\[4pt]\dot{y}=-Ax-By+s,\\[4pt]\dot{s}=-[f(B-a)+\alpha K]x+(B-a)s,\end{array}\right\} \tag{4.1}$$

and make the change of variables $t=\rho\tau$, $X=x$, $Y=\rho y$, $R=\rho^2 s$, where $\rho=K^{-\frac{1}{3}}$.

The new system will have the form

$$\left.\begin{array}{l}\dfrac{dX}{d\tau}=Y,\\[12pt]\dfrac{dY}{d\tau}=-A\rho^2 X-B\rho Y+R,\\[12pt]\dfrac{dR}{d\tau}=-\alpha X-\rho^3 f(B-a)X+\rho(B-a)R.\end{array}\right\} \tag{4.2}$$

Let K be a sufficiently large positive number so that ρ can be treated as a small parameter.
Along with system (4.2), we shall consider also the simplified system

$$\frac{dX}{d\tau} = Y, \quad \frac{dY}{d\tau} = R, \quad \frac{dR}{d\tau} = -\alpha X. \tag{4.3}$$

Let us investigate the motion of system (4.3) in the region $R > 0$. Since $\alpha = \operatorname{sign} X$ in this region, system (4.3) assumes the form

$$\frac{dX}{d\tau} = Y, \quad \frac{dY}{d\tau} = R, \quad \frac{dR}{d\tau} = -X. \tag{4.4}$$

We shall now examine the properties of the motions of system (4.4) throughout the phase space of the variables X, Y, R.

Lemma 4.1. *If the initial point* (X_0, Y_0, R_0), *where* $R_0 > 0$, *does not lie on the straight line* $X = -Y = R$, *then the solution of system* (4.4) *defined by this point possesses the property*

$$\lim_{\tau \to \infty} X(\tau) = \lim_{\tau \to \infty} Y(\tau) = \lim_{\tau \to \infty} R(\tau) = -\infty.$$

If the condition $X_0 = -Y_0 = R_0$ *is fulfilled, then system* (4.4) *possesses the property*

$$\lim_{\tau \to \infty} X(\tau) = \lim_{\tau \to \infty} Y(\tau) = \lim_{\tau \to \infty} R(\tau) = 0.$$

In fact, it follows from the third equation of system (4.4) that R decreases with increasing time. Let us suppose that $\lim_{\tau \to \infty} R(\tau) = L$ and let $L > -\infty$. For non-zero L, it follows from the first and second equations of the system that $|Y(\tau)| \to \infty$ and $|X(\tau)| \to \infty$ as $\tau \to \infty$, but from the last equation we deduce that $\lim_{\tau \to \infty} R(\tau) = -\infty$, which leads to a contradiction. If $L = 0$, then we will have $R(\tau) > 0$, from which it follows that $Y(\tau)$ is an increasing function. Let us suppose that $\lim_{\tau \to \infty} Y(\tau) = L_1$. If L_1 is not equal to zero, it follows immediately from the first equation of system (4.4) that $\lim_{\tau \to \infty} |X(\tau)| = \infty$ but from the third equation we obtain $\lim_{\tau \to \infty} R(\tau) = -\infty$, which again leads to a contradiction. Thus we must have $L = L_1 = 0$, but if $L_1 = 0$, then $Y(\tau)$ must be negative and consequently $X(\tau)$ must decrease. If $\lim_{\tau \to \infty} X(\tau) = L_2 \neq 0$, we again arrive at a conclusion that is inconsistent with the supposition that $\lim_{\tau \to \infty} R(\tau) \neq -\infty$.

We are faced, therefore, with two alternatives: either $\lim_{\tau \to \infty} R(\tau) = -\infty$ or $\lim_{\tau \to \infty} X(\tau) = \lim_{\tau \to \infty} Y(\tau) = \lim_{\tau \to \infty} R(\tau) = -\infty$. In the first case we also have $\lim_{\tau \to \infty} X(\tau) = \lim_{\tau \to \infty} Y(\tau) = -\infty$. In the second case the solution of system (4.4) must satisfy the inequalities

$$X(\tau) > 0, \quad Y(\tau) < 0, \quad R(\tau) > 0.$$

It is not difficult to show that in this case the image point arrives at the coordinate origin only along the integral straight line

$$X = -Y = R \tag{4.5}$$

of system (4.3) with $\alpha = 1$. There are no other trajectories of system (4.3) along which the image point can directly reach the coordinate origin without first encountering the plane $R = 0$. Indeed, for $\alpha = 1$, the solution of (4.3) has the form

$$X = c_0 e^{-\tau} + \varphi_1(\tau), \quad Y = -c_0 e^{-\tau} + \varphi_2(\tau), \quad R = c_0 e^{-\tau} + \varphi_3(\tau),$$

where $\varphi_i(\tau)$ is an unbounded function. By an appropriate choice of the initial data these unbounded functions may be excluded from the solution, in which case we obtain the unique particular solution $X = c_0 e^{-\tau}$, $Y = -c_0 e^{-\tau}$, $R = c_0 e^{-\tau}$ corresponding to the integral straight line (4.5). It is easy to verify that with $\alpha = -1$ none of the trajectories of system (4.3) arriving at the coordinate origin conserve the sign of X. The lemma is therefore proved.

Lemma 4.2. *If a point $M(\tau)$ moves from the position $M_0, (X_0, Y_0, R_0)$ along a trajectory of system (4.4) then it cannot be in the region $|X| > \delta$, $R > 0$ for more than R_0/δ units of time.*

Indeed, from the last equation of (4.4) we have $R < R_0 - \delta \tau$, where τ is measured from the instant at which the inequality $|X| \geqslant \delta$ begins to be fulfilled. If $\tau_1 > R/\delta$, then $R(\tau_1)$ must already have become a negative quantity and the point $M(\tau_1)$ must be outside the region we are considering. Thus, during the time interval $0 \leqslant \tau \leqslant \tau_1$, the point $M(\tau)$ falls either into the region $|X| < \delta$ or onto the plane $R = 0$.

We note that if the initial point $M_0(X_0, Y_0, R_0)$ satisfies the conditions $X_0 > \delta$, $Y_0 > 0$, the point $M(\tau)$ can only fall onto the plane $R = 0$. From this it follows that any point of phase space may fall into the region $|X| < \delta$, but not more than twice.

Lemma 4.3. *If the conditions* $|X_0| < \delta$, $|Y_0| < \delta$, $0 < R_0 < \delta$ *are fulfilled, then the solution of system* (4.4) *defined by the initial point* $M_0(X_0, Y_0, R_0)$ *satisfies the inequalities* $-2\delta < X(\tau) < 5\delta$, $-\delta < Y(\tau) < 4\delta$, $0 < R(\tau) < \delta$, *in the region* $R > 0$.

It is clear that the last of the inequalities that are to be proved follows immediately from the third equation of (4.4). It will be shown now that the following inequality holds

$$-\delta < Y(\tau) < 4\delta .\qquad\qquad(4.6)$$

Suppose $Y_0 > 0$. Since $X(\tau)$ and $Y(\tau)$ can only be increasing functions, we shall use τ_0 to denote the instant of time when $X(\tau_0) = \delta$, and τ_0 the instant when $Y(\tau_0') = \delta$. The time at which the point $M(\tau)$ meets the plane $R = 0$ will be denoted by τ_1.

By virtue of lemma 4.2, if $\tau_1 = \infty$ then $|X(\tau)| < \delta$ for all positive values of τ_1; if also $\tau_0' = \infty$ then inequality (4.6) will be valid. Two cases are possible. In the first we assume that $\tau_0 \leqslant \tau_0'$. From the second equation of system (4.4) with $\tau \geqslant \tau_0'$ it follows that $Y(\tau) - Y(\tau_0') \leqslant R_0(\tau - \tau_0')$. However, since by virtue of lemma 4.2 we have $\tau - \tau_0' < \tau_1 - \tau_0' = 1$, we obtain $Y(\tau) < 2\delta$ for all τ in the interval $\tau_0' \leqslant \tau \leqslant \tau_1$.

In the second case we assume that $\tau_0' < \tau_0$ and evaluate the difference $\tau_0 - \tau_0'$. Again we invoke the second equation of (4.4) and obtain

$$\delta < Y(\tau) < R_0(\tau - \tau_0') + \delta \quad \text{for} \quad \tau > \tau_0' .\qquad\qquad(4.7)$$

The left-hand side of this inequality yields the estimate

$$\delta(\tau - \tau_0') + X(\tau_0') < X(\tau_0) ,$$

from which it follows that $\tau_0 - \tau_0' < 2$. The right-hand side of inequality (4.7) yields the estimate $Y(\tau) < \delta(\tau - \tau_0 + \tau_0 + \tau_0') + \delta < 4\delta$ since, according to lemma 4.2, $\tau - \tau_0 < 1$.

Let us now examine the case when $Y_0 < 0$. If $Y(\tau)$ does not change sign, then inequality (4.6) is fulfilled. If $Y(\tau)$ changes sign at the instant τ_3, then two cases are again possible. In the case when $|X(\tau_3)| < \delta$, and for $\tau > \tau_3$, the point $M(\tau)$ satisfies the conditions discussed above. If $X(\tau_3) < -\delta$ then, according to lemma 4.2, the point $M(\tau)$ cannot find itself outside the zone $|X| < \delta$ for more than one unit of time, but during this time $Y(\tau)$ can increase by not more than δ. Consequently, the point

$M(\tau)$ again falls into the region $|X| < \delta$, $|Y| < \delta$, whereupon $Y(\tau)$ will already be positive and so will satisfy estimate (4.6).

We shall show now that the following inequality holds up to the time when the point $M(\tau)$ falls onto the plane $R = 0$:

$$-2\delta < X(\tau) < 5\delta .\tag{4.8}$$

Indeed, if the point $M(\tau)$ moves into the region $X > \delta$ it will not return to the zone $|X| < \delta$ and must fall onto the plane $R = 0$. In this case, from the first equation of (4.4) it follows that

$$X(\tau) - X(\tau_0) < Y(\tau)(\tau - \tau_0)$$

when $\tau_0 \leqslant \tau \leqslant \tau_1$. From lemma 4.2 it follows that $\tau - \tau_0 < 1$, and from inequality (4.6) we have $0 < Y(\tau) < 4\delta$. Thus, when $\tau > \tau_0$, $-\delta < X(\tau) < 5\delta$. If the point $M(\tau)$ leaves for the region $X < -\delta$ at time τ_4, it either falls onto the plane $R = 0$ without returning to the zone $|X| < \delta$ or it returns to this zone. In the first case we obtain $-\delta(\tau - \tau_4) < X(\tau) - X(\tau_4)$, from which it follows that $X(\tau) > -2\delta$. In the second case point $M(\tau)$ will return to the region $|X| < \delta$, $|Y| < \delta$ and the situation we have discussed will hold. We note that in the second case the minimum value of $X(\tau_3)$ satisfies the inequality $X(\tau_3) > -2\delta$. The lemma is therefore proved.

In future we shall need the following general result. In conjunction with the equation

$$\dot{x} = X(x, t)\tag{4.9}$$

consider the equation

$$\dot{y} = X(y, t) + R(y, t) ,\tag{4.10}$$

where x, y are n-dimensional vectors, $X(x, t)$ and $R(y, t)$ are vector functions. Suppose that in a certain region D of phase space in the interval $t_0 \leqslant t \leqslant t_0 + T$ the following conditions are fulfilled

$$\|X(y, t) - X(x, t)\| \leqslant L\|y - x\|\tag{4.11}$$

and

$$\|R(y, t)\| \leqslant M\|y\| .\tag{4.12}$$

Let us further suppose that in this interval of time the solution $x(t)$ of system (4.9) satisfies the inequality

$$\|x(t)\| \leqslant \varepsilon .$$

Lemma 4.4. *If conditions* (4.11) *and* (4.12) *are fulfilled then the time interval* $t_0 \leqslant t \leqslant t_0 + T$ *the following estimate holds*

$$\| y(t) - x(t) \| \leqslant \frac{M\varepsilon}{M + L} \left(e^{(M + L)(t - t_0)} - 1 \right), \tag{4.13}$$

where $x(t)$ *and* $y(t)$ *are the solutions of equations* (4.9) *and* (4.10), *respectively, determined by identical initial conditions.*

Indeed, if we start out from the inequality

$$\| y(t) - x(t) \| \leqslant \int_{t_0}^{t} \left[\| X(y, t) - X(x, t) \| + \| R(y, t) \| \right] dt ,$$

we obtain

$$\| y(t) - x(t) \| \leqslant \int_{t_0}^{t} \left[L \| y(t) - x(t) \| + M \| y(t) \| \right] dt .$$

Since

$$\| y(t) \| \leqslant \| y(t) - x(t) \| + \| x(t) \| \quad \text{and} \quad \| x(t) \| \leqslant \varepsilon ,$$

then we obtain

$$\| y(t) - x(t) \| \leqslant \int_{t_0}^{t} \left[M\varepsilon + (M + L) \| y(t) - x(t) \| \right] dt .$$

Inequality (4.13) now immediately follows from lemma 1.1 of Chapter 1. Alongside system (4.4) consider now the system

$$\frac{dX}{d\tau} = Y ,$$

$$\frac{dY}{d\tau} = R + \rho \varphi_1(X, Y) ,$$

$$\frac{dR}{d\tau} = -|X| + \rho F_1(X, Y, R, \tau) . \tag{4.14}$$

In the region $|X| < \infty$, $|Y| < \infty$, $R > 0$, $\tau \geqslant 0$, assume that the functions $\varphi_1(X, Y)$ and $F_1(X, Y, R, \tau)$ satisfy the conditions

$$\left. \begin{array}{l} |\varphi_1(X, Y)| \leqslant L_1(|X| + |Y|) , \\ |F_1(X, Y, R)| \leqslant L_2(|X| + |Y| + R) , \end{array} \right\} \tag{4.15}$$

where L_1, L_2 are positive constants.

Lemma 4.5. *Every solution of system* (4.14) *determined by the initial point* $M_0(X_0, Y_0, R_0)$ *lying in the region* $|X| < \delta, |Y| < \delta, 0 < R < \delta$, *satisfies the inequalities*

$$|X| < 5\delta + A_1\rho\delta, \quad |Y| < 4\delta + A_2\rho\delta, \quad R < \delta + A_3\rho\delta,$$

in the half-space R, *where* A_1, A_2, A_3 *are constants which depend on* L_1 *and* L_2.

The validity of lemma 4.5 follows immediately from the preceding lemma. Indeed, from the proof of lemma 4.3, it follows that a point $M(\tau)$ moving along the trajectory of system (4.4) will be found outside the region $|X| < \delta, |Y| < \delta, R > 0$ for not more than three units of time; however, this point does not pass outside the limits of the region

$$|X| < 5\delta, \quad |Y| < 4\delta, \quad 0 < R < \delta.$$

From this it follows that the norm of the vector $P(0, \rho\varphi_1, \rho F_1)$ characterising the error of systems (4.4) and (4.14) may, with account of (4.15), be estimated in the following way:

$$\|P\| \leqslant N_1 \rho \|F\|,$$

where F denotes the vector with projections X, Y, R. In addition, from lemma 4.3 we have $\|F\| < N_2\delta$. Thus, setting $M = N_1\rho$ and $\varepsilon = N_2\delta$, we can apply the estimate given in lemma 4.4 and obtain an estimate for the error of the solutions of systems (4.4) and (4.14). The result we are seeking follows from this estimate.

Note 4.1. We note now that it is easy to formulate results similar to those given in lemmas 4.1, 4.2, 4.3 and 4.5 for the system

$$\frac{dX}{d\tau} = Y, \quad \frac{dY}{d\tau} = R, \quad \frac{dR}{d\tau} = |X|, \tag{4.16}$$

which is equivalent to system (4.3) in the region $R < 0$.

Thus, for example, considerations of the symmetry of disposition of the trajectories of systems (4.4) and (4.6) lead to the conclusion that if the initial point does not lie on the straight line $X = -Y = R$, the solution of (4.16) possesses the property $\lim_{\tau \to \infty} X(\tau) = \lim_{\tau \to \infty} Y(\tau) = \lim_{\tau \to \infty} R(\tau) = \infty$. The remaining lemmas can be re-phrased in a similar way.

Theorem 4.1. *Assume $A > 0$, $B > 0$ and let conditions* (3.5) *be fulfilled. It is possible to find a positive number K_0 such that for $K > K_0$ the zero solution of system* (3.2) *will be asymptotically stable for any initial perturbations.*

For the sake of definiteness assume that the initial point M_0 lies in the region $R > 0$ (if point M_0 lies in the region $R < 0$ then everywhere in the discussion that follows account should be taken of note 4.1). From lemma 4.1 it follows that point $M(\tau)$, moving along a trajectory of system (4.3), either strikes the surface $R = 0$ in the course of a finite interval of time or will approach asymptotically the coordinate origin along the straight line (4.5).

Let us now surround the straight line (4.5) by a sufficiently narrow tube. If the image point $M(\tau)$ lies outside this tube then, for a given bounded region of the initial conditions of the phase space, the time that lapses before it strikes the plane $R = 0$ will be limited. Therefore, according to theorem 1.1 of Chapter 1, one can find a value of ρ that is so small that the deviation of the trajectories of systems (4.2) and (4.3) during the stated time interval will be smaller than the previously specified positive number. Thus we arrive at the conclusion that all points not lying inside the tube which are moving along the trajectories of system (4.2) fall onto the plane $R = 0$.

If the initial point lies inside the tube, then in the course of its motion it may either come out of the tube and never again fall into it or it will fall into the tube after arbitrarily along large intervals of time. In the first case the arguments that have just been given are applicable. In the second case we arrive at the conclusion that the image point is bound to strike the plane $R = 0$ or, what amounts to the same thing, the plane $s = 0$.

Having fallen onto the plane $s = 0$, the image point will move in accordance with system (3.10) which describes the sliding mode. Conditions $A > 0$, $B > 0$ ensure that the point moves along the plane S towards the coordinate origin.

To complete the proof of this theorem it remains now to show that Lyapunov stability holds. Thus, it is necessary to prove that for any given $\varepsilon > 0$ there exists a number δ such that from the inequalities $|X_0| < \delta$, $|Y_0| < \delta$, $|R_0| < \delta$ for the solutions of (4.2) there follow the inequalities

$$|X(\tau)| < \varepsilon, \quad |Y(\tau)| < \varepsilon, \quad |R(\tau)| < \varepsilon \quad \text{for} \quad \tau > 0.$$

However the number δ may be chosen in accordance with lemma 4.5.

Points lying on the plane $R = 0$ introduce a complication because lemma 4.5 says nothing about these points; however, since they slide along the plane $R = 0$ by virtue of the fact that system (3.10) is asymptotically stable the required property must hold for them also.

We should now note the following. The characteristic equation (3.10) describing the sliding process has the form

$$\lambda^2 + B\lambda + A = 0 \,. \tag{4.17}$$

Taking into account the first of the conditions (3.5) for the existence of sliding, the roots of this equation are given by the formula $\lambda_{1,2} = -\frac{1}{2}B \pm (-\frac{3}{4}B^2 + aB - b)^{\frac{1}{2}}$. It can be seen from this that to ensure a high sliding velocity the value of B must be chosen to be as large as the second of the conditions (3.5) allows. The roots of the characteristic equation (4.17) may become complex and the sliding mode will take the form of a damped oscillatory process.

If, for some reason or other, the sliding process turns out to be non-oscillatory then (because of the increase in B) condition $A = B^2 - aB + b$ has to be violated in order for the roots of the characteristic equation (4.17) to be real. It can be shown that stability does not vanish in this case [34]. These questions will be considered in more detail in section 7 where the non-linear case is discussed.

5. Stabilization of an *n*-th Order System

Consider the equation

$$x^{(n)} + a_1 x^{(n-1)} + \ldots + a_n x = -\alpha K x \,, \tag{5.1}$$

where α is defined by the equation

$$\alpha = \operatorname{sign}(c_{n-1} x_1 + \ldots + c_0 x_n) x_1 \,, \tag{5.2}$$

where $c_0, \ldots, c_{n-1}$ are constants.

Equation (5.1) is obviously equivalent to the system

$$\left.\begin{aligned} \dot{x}_i &= x_{i+1} \,, \\ \dot{x}_n &= -a_n x_1 - a_{n-1} x_2 - \ldots - a_1 x_n - \alpha K x_1 \,. \end{aligned}\right\} \tag{5.3}$$

Consider now the hyperplane

$$s = c_{n-1} x_1 + \ldots c_0 x_n = 0 \,, \tag{5.4}$$

where $c_0 = 1$.

Theorem 5.1 (Emel'yanov and Taran [50]). *For the hyperplane $s=0$ to be a hyperplane of sliding it is necessary and sufficient that the following conditions be fulfilled*

$$c_{i+1} = rc_i + a_{i+1}, \qquad i=0, 1, ..., n-2, \qquad (5.5)$$

$$|a_n + rc_{n-1}| \leqslant K, \qquad (5.6)$$

where r is a real parameter.

Let us prove the necessity of these conditions. In place of the coordinates x_n, we introduce the new coordinate $s = c_{n-1}x_1 + ... + c_0x_n$. System (5.3) can be written in the following form:

$$
\left.
\begin{aligned}
&\dot{x}_i = x_{i+1}, \qquad i=1, ..., n-2, \\
&\dot{x}_{n-1} = -\sum_{i=1}^{n-1} c_{n-1}x_i + s, \\
&\dot{s} = -[(a_n+rc_{n-1})+\alpha K]x_1 + (c_{n-1}-a_{n-1}+rc_{n-2})x_2 + \\
&\qquad + ... + (c_2-a_2+rc_1)x_{n-1} + rs,
\end{aligned}
\right\} \quad (5.7)
$$

For the derivative $\dot{s}$ to change sign on the hyperplane $s=0$ only when x_1 changes sign, as is required if the conditions of sliding (see section 1)

$$x_1\dot{s}|_{\alpha=1} \leqslant 0, \qquad x_1\dot{s}|_{\alpha=-1} \geqslant 0, \qquad (5.8)$$

are to be fulfilled, it is necessary that all the coefficients of $x_2, ..., x_{n-1}$ in the last equation of (5.7) should vanish. Thus we obtain conditions (5.5). In addition, for conditions (5.8) to be satisfied, it is clearly necessary to consider inequality (5.6) to be fulfilled since, when conditions (5.5) are fulfilled, the last equation of (5.7) becomes

$$\dot{s} = -[a_n+rc_{n-1}+\alpha K]x_1.$$

The sufficiency of the conditions can be demonstrated in a similar way. Consider now the function

$$f(r) = r^n + a_1 r^{n-1} + ... + a_n.$$

From conditions (5.5) it follows that

$$f(r) = a_n + rc_{n-1}. \qquad (5.9)$$

Thus inequality (5.6) may be written in the form

$$|f(r)| \leqslant K.$$

Let us now turn to the question of the stability of this system.
The same arguments that we gave in section 3 when deducing system
(3.10) lead us now to the conclusion that the sliding process is described
in the present case by the system

$$\dot{x}_i = x_{i+1}, \qquad i = 1, \ldots, n-2, \\ \dot{x}_{n-1} = -\sum_{i=1}^{n-1} c_{n-i} x_i . \qquad \left. \right\} \tag{5.10}$$

System (5.10) can obviously be obtained from (5.7) by removing the first
$n-1$ equations and setting $s = 0$.
If the conditions for the existence of sliding (5.5) and (5.6) are fulfilled,
system (5.7) has the form

$$\dot{x}_i = x_{i+1}, \qquad i = 1, \ldots, n-2, \\ \dot{x}_{n-1} = -\sum_{i=1}^{n-1} c_{n-i} x_i + s, \\ \dot{s} = -[f(r) + \alpha K] x_1 + rs . \qquad \left. \right\} \tag{5.11}$$

Consider now the conditions that will ensure the asymptotic stability
of the zero solution of system (5.10) which describes the sliding process.

Theorem 5.2 (Gerashchenko [37]). *Assume conditions* (5.5) *and* (5.6) *are
fulfilled for a given fixed value of r. Then for the zero solution of system*
(5.10) *to be asymptotically stable it is necessary and sufficient that the roots
of the equation*

$$\lambda^n + a_1 \lambda^{n-1} + \ldots + a_n = f(r), \tag{5.12}$$

*apart from the trivial root $\lambda = r$, shall lie in the left-hand half-plane of the
complex variable.*

It is not difficult to see that equation (5.12) is the characteristic equation
of the system

$$\dot{x}_i = x_{i+1}, \qquad i = 1, \ldots, n-2 \\ \dot{x}_{n-1} = \sum_{i=1}^{n-1} c_{n-i} x_i + s, \\ \dot{s} = rs . \qquad \left. \right\} \tag{5.13}$$

In fact, when $\alpha = -1$, the characteristic equation of system (5.11), which is equivalent to (5.1), has the form $\lambda^n + a_1 \lambda^{n-1} + \ldots + a_n = K$. On the other hand (5.13) can be obtained from (5.11) by setting $\alpha = -1$ and $f(r) = K$ in the latter system.

Since all the roots of equation (5.12), apart from the trivial root $\lambda = r$, lie in the left-hand half-plane, and since these roots are also roots of the characteristic equation of system (5.10), the truth of the theorem is established. In particular, if the equation $\lambda^{n-1} + a_1 \lambda^{n-2} + \ldots + a_{n-1} = 0$ possesses roots with negative real parts only then, for $r=0$ (or even for $|r| < \varepsilon$, where ε is a sufficiently small quantity), the conditions of theorem (5.2) are fulfilled and the zero solution of system (5.10) will be asymptotically stable.

Let us turn now to the formulation and derivation of the stability conditions of the zero solution of the basic system (5.11).

Theorem (5.3) (Gerashchenko [39]). *If the conditions of sliding* (5.5) *and* (5.6) *are fulfilled and all the roots of equation* (5.12) *have negative real parts, then the zero solution of system* (5.11) *will be asymptotically stable for any initial perturbation.*

Proof. The asymptotic stability of the zero solution of system (5.10) follows from the conditions of the theorem. In addition, in the present case, the trivial root $\lambda = r$ of equation (5.12) must be negative.

By virtue of theorem 9.1 of Chapter 1 there exists a positive definite quadratic form $v(x_1, \ldots, x_n)$ such that its derivative taken according to system (5.10) will be equal to the function $w = -x_1^2 - \ldots - x_{n-1}^2$. Consider the function $v = v_1(x_1, \ldots, x_{n-1}) + \frac{1}{2}As^2$, where $A > 0$. The time derivative of this function taken according to system (5.11) will have the form

$$\dot{v} = w + \frac{\partial v_1}{\partial x_{n-1}} s + Ars^2 - A[f(r) + \alpha K] x_1 s . \tag{5.14}$$

It is clear that by virtue of conditions (5.2) and (5.6) the expression $A[f(r) + \alpha K] x_1 s$ will always be positive since

$$A[f(r) + \alpha K] x_1 s = A|x_1 s| \left[\frac{f(r)}{\alpha} + K \right]$$

and the expression between the square brackets is positive. On the other hand it follows from the Silvester criterion that, for sufficiently large A, the quadratic form $w + (\partial v_1 s / \partial x_{n-1}) + A r s^2$ will be a negative definite form of the variables $x_1, ..., x_{n-1}, s$. Thus the asymptotic stability on the whole of the zero solution of (5.11) follows from theorem 12.1 of Chapter 1. We have already seen that the requirement that all the roots of equation (5.12) should have negative real parts is equivalent to the requirement of asymptotic stability of the zero solution of (5.10) for $r < 0$. Thus theorem 5.3 may be formulated in the following way.

Let the condition $r < 0$ be fulfilled. The zero solution of system (5.11) will be asymptotically stable on the whole if the same property is possessed also by the zero solution of system (5.10).

6. Stability of a System Incorporating a Limiter in the Critical Case of a Single Zero Root

1. Consider the equation

$$x^{(n)} + a_1 x^{(n-1)} + ... + a_{n-1} \dot{x} = -\alpha \varphi(x), \tag{6.1}$$

where

$$\varphi(x) \neq 0 \quad \text{for} \quad x \neq 0, \quad |\alpha| \leqslant 1.$$

Suppose that the equation

$$\lambda^{n-1} + a_1 \lambda^{n-2} + ... + a_{n-1} = 0 \tag{6.2}$$

has only roots with negative real parts. Equation (6.1) is equivalent to the system

$$\left.\begin{array}{l} \dot{x}_i = x_{i+1}, \quad i=1, ..., n-1, \quad x_1 = x \\ \dot{x}_n = -a_{n-1} x_2 - ... - a_1 x_n - \alpha \varphi(x_1). \end{array}\right\} \tag{6.3}$$

Consider the system

$$\left.\begin{array}{l} \dot{x}_i = x_{i+1}, \quad i=2, ..., n-1, \\ \dot{x}_n = -a_{n-1} x_2 - ... - a_1 x_n. \end{array}\right\} \tag{6.4}$$

By virtue of theorem 9.1 of Chapter 1 there exists a positive definite quadratic form $v_1(x_2, ..., x_n)$ whose derivative taken according to system (6.4) is equal to $w = -x_2^2 - ... - x_n^2$.

Consider the function

$$v(x_1, ..., x_n) = v_1(x_2, ..., x_n) + \tfrac{1}{2}y^2 ,$$

where

$$y = a_{n-1}x_1 + a_{n-2}x_2 + ... + a_1 x_{n-1} + x_n .$$

Computing the derivative of function v according to system (6.3), we obtain

$$\dot{v} = w - \left(\frac{\partial v_1}{\partial x_n} + y \right) \alpha\varphi(x_1) , \qquad (6.5)$$

since the derivative of y, taken according to (6.3), is identically equal to $-\alpha\varphi(x_1)$.

We see that by setting

$$\operatorname{sign} \alpha = \operatorname{sign} \left(\frac{\partial v_1}{\partial x_n} + y \right) \varphi(x) , \qquad (6.6)$$

all the conditions of theorem 12.1 of Chapter 1 are fulfilled. These conditions ensure the asymptotic stability on the whole of the zero solution of system (6.3).

If we seek α starting out from the requirement of maximum rate of decrease of v along the trajectory of system (6.3) [66, 67], we obtain

$$\alpha = \operatorname{sign} \left(\frac{\partial v_1}{\partial x_n} + y \right) \varphi(x) . \qquad (6.7)$$

The most typical case is when the function $\varphi(x)$ satisfies the condition $\varphi(x)x > 0$ for $x \neq 0$; formula (6.7) may then be written in the form

$$\alpha = \operatorname{sign} \left(\frac{\partial v_1}{\partial x_n} + y \right) x .$$

The last condition ensures stability for any initial perturbations for any function $\varphi(x)$ which, with $x \neq 0$, satisfies the inequality $\varphi(x)x > 0$. This type of stability is usually called absolute stability.

Let us now specify the function $\varphi(x)$ in the following way:

$$\varphi(x) = Kx \quad \text{for} \quad |Kx| \leqslant H ,$$
$$\varphi(x) = H \operatorname{sign} x \quad \text{for} \quad |Kx| > H ,$$

where K and H are positive constants. In this case equation (6.1) describes a control system in which a limiter is incorporated at the input of the object being controlled. With $K = \infty$, we have a pure relay system;

with $H = \infty$ and K finite we have the class of systems investigated in the preceding paragraph.

It is important to note that the law governing the choice of α given here ensures asymptotic stability for any positive value of K whereas, before, the requirement was that K should be sufficiently large.

2. Let us investigate now the above problem from a more general point of view.

Let the control system be described by a system of differential equations with constant coefficients

$$\dot{x}_i = a_{i1}x_1 + \ldots + a_{in}x_n, \qquad i = 1, \ldots, n . \qquad (6.8)$$

We shall suppose that the characteristic equation of system (6.8) has one zero root and $n-1$ roots with negative real parts.

We set ourselves the problem of describing the possible methods of correcting the control system which will ensure its asymptotic stability for any initial disturbances. This problem is of special interest because in practical applications one often comes across systems for which the transfer function of the object of control has zero as a simple pole. From a mathematical point of view our method of reasoning will be similar to that used when investigating stability problems in the critical case of a single zero root [1].

We shall in future suppose, for the sake of definiteness, that amongst the non-zero minors of the $n-1$ th order of the matrix A composed of the coefficients of the system there is at least one composed of coefficients which enter into the first $n-1$ equations of system (6.8).

In conjunction with (6.8), consider the system

$$\dot{x}_i = a_{i1}x_1 + \ldots + a_{in}x_n - \alpha(x_1, \ldots, x_n)\varphi_i(x_i, \ldots, x_n), \qquad i = 1, \ldots, n, \qquad (6.9)$$

where the functions $\varphi_i(x_1, \ldots, x_n)$ are given and the function $\alpha(x_1, \ldots, x_n)$ is to be determined.

There exists a non-singular linear transformation

$$y = b_1 x_1 + \ldots + b_n x_n ,$$
$$y_i = b_i x_1 + \ldots + b_{in} x_n, \qquad i = 1, \ldots, n-1, \quad b_n \neq 0 ,$$

that transforms (6.8) into the system of differential equations

$$\dot{y} = 0 ,$$
$$\dot{y}_i = p_{i1} y_1 + \ldots + p_{i,n-1} y_{n-1}, \qquad i = 1, \ldots, n-1 . \qquad (6.10)$$

The same transformation translates (6.9) into the system

$$\dot{y} = -\alpha(b_1\varphi_1 + \ldots + b_n\varphi_n),$$

$$\dot{y}_i = p_{i1}y_1 + \ldots + p_{i,n-1}y_{n-1} - \alpha(b_{i1}\varphi_1 + \ldots + b_{in}\varphi_n),$$

$$i = 1, \ldots, n-1. \qquad (6.11)$$

Since the roots of the characteristic equation of the matrix P made up of the coefficients $p_{i,k}$, $i = 1, \ldots, n-1$, $k = 1, \ldots, n-1$ have negative real parts then, by theorem 9.1 of Chapter 1, for any negative definite quadratic form $w(y_1, \ldots, y_{n-1})$ of the variables $y_1, \ldots, y_{n-1}$, there exists a positive definite quadratic form $v_1(y_1, \ldots, y_{n-1})$ of these same variables such that, by virtue of the first equations of system (6.10) we obtain

$$\frac{dv_1}{dt} = \sum_{i=1}^{n-1} \frac{\partial v_1}{\partial y_i}(p_{i1}y_1 + \ldots + p_{i,n-1}y_{n-1}) = w(y_1, \ldots, y_{n-1}).$$

Consider the quadratic form

$$v(y_1, \ldots, y_{n-1}, y) = v_1(y_1, \ldots, y_{n-1}) + \tfrac{1}{2}y^2$$

and let us find its derivative according to system (6.11)

$$\frac{dv}{dt} = w(y_1, \ldots, y_{n-1}) - \alpha \sum_{k=1}^{n} \left(\sum_{i=1}^{n-1} \frac{\partial v_1}{\partial y_i} b_{ik} + b_k y \right) \varphi_k.$$

We now impose an additional restriction on the function φ_k, namely we require that for $y_1 = y_2 = \ldots = y_{n-1} = 0$, $y \neq 0$ the inequality $b_1\varphi_1 + \ldots + b_n\varphi_n \neq 0$ be fulfilled. In this case the condition

$$\text{sign } \alpha = \text{sign} \sum_{k=1}^{n} \left(\sum_{i=1}^{n-1} \frac{\partial v_1}{\partial y_i} b_{ik} + b_k y \right) \varphi_k$$

is clearly a sufficient condition of asymptotic stability on the whole of the zero solution of (6.9). Since, inside the brackets on the right-hand side, we have a linear form of the variables $y_1, \ldots, y_{n-1}, y$, by reverting to the old variables we can re-write this condition in the form

$$\text{sign } \alpha = \text{sign} \sum_{k=1}^{n} (c_{k1}x_1 + \ldots + c_{kn}x_n)\varphi_k.$$

It is interesting to consider the case when the function $\alpha(x_1, \ldots, x_n)$, which is the equation of the control system, belongs to the class of functions given earlier.

Assume, for example, that the function α satisfies the condition $\|\alpha\| \leqslant 1$

and, in addition, assume $\varphi_1 = \varphi_2 = \ldots \varphi_{n-1} = 0$, $\varphi_n = \varphi$. If we seek a function α that will ensure the most rapid decrease of the Lyapunov function v along the trajectory of system (6.9), we obtain

$$\alpha = \text{sign}\,(c_1 x_1 + \ldots + c_n x_n)\,\varphi(x_1, \ldots, x_n)\,.$$

Thus, α will be a step-function and, for $\varphi = 1$, we obtain a pure relay system.

If we set $\varphi = K x_n$ with $|K x_n| \leqslant H$, $\varphi = H$ sign x_n with $|Kx| > H$, where K and H are positive constants then, for $\alpha = \text{sign}\,(c_1 x_1 + \ldots + c_n x_n) x_n$, we have a stable system with a limiter at the input.

3. Following Lyapunov [1], we will now give a method of constructing a linear transformation that will translate system (6.8) into system (6.10). We define first the quantity $y = b_1 x_1 + \ldots + b_n x_n$ $(b_n = 1)$ such that by virtue of system (6.8) the following equality holds

$$\dot{y} = \sum_{i=1}^{n} \sum_{k=1}^{n} b_i a_{ik} x_k = 0\,. \tag{6.12}$$

Condition (6.12) leads to the system of equations

$$a_{1k} b_1 + \ldots + a_{nk} b_n = 0, \qquad k = 1, \ldots, n\,, \tag{6.13}$$

which clearly possesses the required solution since the rank of the matrix A is equal to $n-1$. Assume further that $y_i = x_i - d_i y$, $i = 1, \ldots, n-1$ and let us find coefficients d_i using the condition that $\dot{y}_i$ is independent of y. Some simple manipulations lead us to the system

$$\dot{y}_i = \sum_{k=1}^{n-1} (a_{ik} - a_{in} b_k) y_k + \left[\sum_{k=1}^{n-1} (a_{ik} - a_{in} b_k) d_k + a_{in} \right] y\,,$$
$$i = 1, \ldots, n-1\,.$$

Equating the coefficients of y to zero, we obtain the following system for d_k

$$\sum_{k=1}^{n-1} (a_{ik} - a_{in} b_k) d_k + a_{in} = 0, \qquad i = 1, \ldots, n\,, \tag{6.14}$$

which has a solution since its determinant is non-zero. Indeed, transferring from the coordinates $x_1, \ldots, x_n$ to the coordinates $y_1, \ldots, y_{n-1}, y$ does not alter the rank of the matrix made up of the coefficients of the system. The rank of the matrix made up of the coefficients of the equation $\dot{y} = 0$ and system (6.13) is equal to $(n-1)$, and $\det(a_{ik} - a_{in}b_k) \neq 0$ since, in the opposite case, the characteristic equation of this system would have at least one more zero root.

Thus, the transformation we are seeking has the form

$$y = b_1 x_1 + \dots + b_n x_n \,,$$
$$y_i = x_i - d_i(b_1 x_1 + \dots + b_n x_n) \,,$$

where d_i and b_k are found from (6.13) and (6.14).

7. Non-Linear Systems with Variable Structure. Control of the Coordinate x

1. Here and in the following section we shall be considering the problem of the stability of a non-linear system of the third order. In a sense, theorem 7.1 presented below, can be regarded as a generalisation of the results of Barbashin, Tabueva and Eidinov [34] who considered the linear case. The principal results for the non-linear case have been given in papers published elsewhere [35, 36]. The characteristic feature of these papers is that they do not insist on the conditions of sliding being fulfilled. In this case a pole of sewability is obtained on the switching plane although this pole may be made as narrow as one pleases by increasing the gain K. Consider the differential equation

$$\dddot{x} + F(x, \dot{x}, \ddot{x}, t) + Kx \, \text{sign} \left[x(\ddot{x} - \varphi(x, \dot{x})) \right] = 0 \,, \tag{7.1}$$

where K is a positive constant, the function $F(x, \dot{x}, \ddot{x}, t)$ is continuous with respect to all its arguments in the region $|x| < \infty$, $|\dot{x}| < \infty$, $|\ddot{x}| < \infty$, $0 \leqslant t < \infty$; it is bounded with respect to t for fixed values of $x, \dot{x}, \ddot{x}$ and it possesses continuous partial derivatives of the first order with respect to the arguments $x, \dot{x}, \ddot{x}, t$. The function $\varphi(x, \dot{x})$ is continuous and has piecewise continuous partial derivatives of the first and second orders in $x, \dot{x}$ in the region $|x| < \infty$, $|\dot{x}| < \infty$.

Equation (7.1) is equivalent to the system of differential equations

$$\dot{x} = y, \quad \dot{y} = z \,,$$
$$\dot{z} = -F(x, y, z, t) - Kx \, \text{sign} \left[x(z - \varphi(x, y)) \right] \,. \tag{7.2}$$

Let us impose the following restrictions on the function (x, y) and $F(x, y, z, t)$:

(a) $|\rho^2 F(x, \rho^{-1}y, \rho^{-2}z, \rho t| < A(x, y, z)$

and

$|\rho\varphi(x, \rho^{-1}y)| < B(x, y)$

for sufficiently small values of the parameter ρ. Here, $A(x, y, z)$ and $B(x, y)$ are assumed to be continuous functions of their arguments for all values x, y, z;

(b) $\varphi(0, 0) = 0,$ $\varphi(x, 0)x < 0$ for $x \neq 0$

$[\varphi(x, y) - \varphi(x, 0)]y < 0$ for $y \neq 0$

$\int_{\mp\infty}^{0} (x, 0)\,dx = \infty$.

We note that condition (a) is satisfied in the case when the function $F(x, y, z, t)$ is linear in x, y, z and bounded with respect to t for $0 \leqslant t < \infty$. Any linear function $\varphi(x, y) = cx + dy$, where c and d are constants, also satisfies condition (a); moreover, such a function will also satisfy condition (b) if one sets $c < 0$ and $d < 0$.

In general, equation (7.1) describes a control system for a non-linear object which processes an input signal of arbitrary form.

Certain problems concerned with finding the optimum control for a system reduce to systems of the type (7.2). Indeed, let us consider the system of differential equations

$\dot{x} = y,$ $\dot{y} = z,$ $\dot{z} = -F(x, y, z, t) - Ku(t)x$,

and try to find a function $u(t)$ such that, for $|u(t)| \leqslant 1$ some function $v(x, y, z)$, according to this system, has the greatest rate of decrease. It is not difficult to see that in this case the function $u(t)$ should have the form $u(t) = $ sign $x(\partial y/\partial z)$. This leads to (7.2) when certain additional assumptions are made about the structure of the function v.

Theorem 7.1.   *Let conditions (a) and (b) be fulfilled and let a positive number ε be specified. Then, for a given bounded region of phase space G, it is possible to find a positive number K_0 such that for $K \geqslant K_0$ any solution of system (7.2) determined by the initial conditions of region G will, after a certain instant of time, satisfy the conditions $|x(t)| < \varepsilon, |y(t)| < \varepsilon, |z(t)| < \varepsilon$.*

2. *Proof.*   We shall first show that any point of region G, i.e. the region of possible initial positions, which is moving in accordance with the equa-

tions of (7.2) will, at some instant, strike the surface S given by the equation $s = z - \varphi(x, y) = 0$. For this purpose, in system (7.2), we make the change of variables

$$t = \rho\tau, \quad X = x, \quad Y = \rho y, \quad Z = \rho^2 z .$$ (7.3)

The new system is written in the form

$$\left.\begin{aligned}
\frac{dX}{d\tau} &= Y , \\[2mm]
\frac{dY}{d\tau} &= Z . \\[2mm]
\frac{dZ}{d\tau} &= -\alpha X - \rho^3 F(X, \rho^{-1} Y, \rho^{-2} Z, \rho\tau) ,
\end{aligned}\right\}$$ (7.4)

where

$$\alpha = \operatorname{sign}\left[X(Z - \rho^2 \varphi(X, \rho^{-1} Y)) \right] .$$

In conjunction with the system (7.4), which is equivalent to the system (7.2), let us consider the simplified system

$$\left.\begin{aligned}
\frac{dX}{d\tau} &= Y , \\[2mm]
\frac{dY}{d\tau} &= Z , \\[2mm]
\frac{dZ}{d\tau} &= -|X| \operatorname{sign} R ,
\end{aligned}\right\}$$ (7.5)

where

$$R = Z - \rho^2 \varphi(X, \rho^{-1} Y) .$$

Let $R > 0$ at the initial instant of time. System (7.4) then has the form

$$\left.\begin{aligned}
\frac{dX}{d\tau} &= Y , \\[2mm]
\frac{dY}{d\tau} &= Z , \\[2mm]
\frac{dZ}{d\tau} &= -|X| .
\end{aligned}\right\}$$ (7.6)

From lemma 4.1 it follows that the solution of (7.5) possesses the property $X \to -\infty$, $Y \to -\infty$, $Z \to -\infty$ if the initial point lies on the straight line $X = -Y = Z$. From condition (b) it follows that for $X < 0$ we have $\varphi(X, 0) > 0$. Since

$$Y\varphi(X, Y) < Y\varphi(X, 0),$$

then, for $X < 0$, $Y < 0$, we have $\varphi(X, Y) > 0$, whence we obtain

$$R = Z - \rho^2 \varphi(X, \rho^{-1} Y) < Z.$$

Since $Z \to -\infty$, the quantity R must become negative, with the result that any point M of phase space must fall out of the region $R > 0$ onto the surface $R = 0$. We can make a similar deduction for the points of the region $R < 0$.

Thus, we have proved that a point $M(\tau)$ lying inside region G and moving in accordance with the equations of the simplified system (7.5) either falls onto the surface S at a finite instant of time τ, or, when point $M(0)$ belongs to the straight line $X = -Y = Z$, it will asymptotically approach the coordinate origin.

By virtue of the theorem about the continuity of solutions as a function of a parameter, we can make a similar deduction for system (7.4), and so also for system (7.2) which we are studying. In other words, we have proved that with a sufficiently large value of K, a point $M(t)$ lying inside the region G of possible initial conditions and moving in accordance with the equations of system (7.2) will fall onto the switching surface S as time increases.

3. We will now go on to the second part of the proof of the theorem. We will investigate the behaviour of an image point $M(t)$ which has fallen onto the switching surface S under the action of the equations of system (7.2). For this purpose we shall transfer to a new system of coordinates in which x and y remain as before and the coordinate $s = z - \varphi(x, y)$ is introduced. System (7.2) then transforms to an equivalent system of differential equations

$$\dot{x} = y, \quad \dot{y} = s + \varphi(x, y),$$

$$\dot{s} = -\varphi'_y(x, y)s - F(x, y, s + \varphi(x, y), t) +$$
$$+ \varphi'_x(x, y)y - \varphi'_y(x, y)\varphi(x, y) - \alpha Kx, \quad (\alpha = \text{sign } xs). \quad (7.7)$$

Under this transformation of coordinates, the switching surface $z =$

$\varphi(x, y)$ goes over to the switching plane $s=0$. Thus, having investigated what happens to an image point that has fallen onto the plane $s=0$ under the action of equations (7.7), we are in a position to make corresponding deductions about the behaviour of the image point of system (7.2) on the surface S.

On the plane $s=0$ the quantity $\dot{s}$ is written in the form

$$\dot{s} = -\alpha K x - \Phi(x, y, t), \tag{7.8}$$

where we have introduced the notation

$$\Phi(x, y, t) = F(x, y, \varphi(x, y), t) + \varphi'_x(x, y) + \varphi'_y(x, y)\varphi(x, y).$$

Let us denote by D the region of the plane $s=0$ generated by the ends of the arcs of trajectories passing out of the region G. From the preceding part of the proof it follows that for $K \to \infty$ the region D is a uniformly bounded region. In fact, the transformation (7.3) translates the region G into the region G_ρ, it being easy to see that for $\rho_1 > \rho_2$ we will have $G_{\rho_1} \supset G_{\rho_2}$. As they move along the trajectories of system (7.5), points in regions G_{ρ_1} and G_{ρ_2} go over to points in the regions D_{ρ_1} and D_{ρ_2} lying on the plane $s=0$, where $D_{\rho_1} \supset D_{\rho_2}$. Taking into account the theorem about the continuous dependence of solutions on a parameter, we come to a conclusion about the boundedness of the points of surface S that have arrived from region G_ρ along the trajectories of system (7.4). Returning now to the standard coordinates we find that the region D is bounded for $\rho \to 0$.

By virtue of the assumptions we made above about the functions $F(x, y, z, t)$ and $\varphi(x, y)$, the following relation holds in region D.

$$|\Phi(x, y, t)| < m. \tag{7.9}$$

From equality (7.8) it is easy to see that on the plane $s=0$ the straight lines $x = \Delta x$ and $-\Delta x$, where $\Delta x = m/k$, separate out a pole $|x| \leq \Delta x$ outside which the sign of the derivative $\dot{s}$ for system (7.7) is given by the relation sign $\dot{s} = -\alpha$ sign x. An analysis of this formula shows that the points of the plane $s=0$ situated outside this pole are sliding points for system (7.7). The motion of the image point $M(t)$ from this part of the plane $s=0$ (outside the pole $|x| \leq \Delta x$) is determined by the limiting differential equation $\ddot{x} = \varphi(x, \dot{x})$, which is equivalent to the system of differential equations

$$\dot{x} = y, \quad \dot{y} = \varphi(x, y). \tag{7.10}$$

Inside the pole $|x| \leqslant \Delta x$ of the plane $s=0$ the sign of the derivative $\dot{s}$ is indefinite. The pole contains regions of "sewing" bounded by the curves

$$\Phi(x, y, t) + \alpha Kx = 0 , \tag{7.11}$$

where, with increasing time, the trajectories of system (7.7) intersect the plane $s=0$.

Thus, after it has fallen on the plane $s=0$, the image point $M(t)$ of system (7.7) moves along this plane in accordance with the equations (7.10) until at some instant $t=t_0 > 0$ it falls onto the boundary of the region of sewing, i.e. onto one of the curves (7.11) at a certain point $M_0(x_0, y_0)$. The very fact that it falls there is due to the stability on the whole of the zero solution of system (7.10). This stability is a consequence of the fact that conditions (b) are fulfilled for the function $\varphi(x, y)$ (see example 4 in section 14 of Chapter 1). Thereafter, with increasing t, the image point $M(t)$ falls off the plane $s=0$ and starts to move under the action of the equations of system (7.7) either in the half-space $s>0$ (with $\alpha=-1$) or in the half-space $s<0$ (with $\alpha=1$). We shall show that for a sufficiently large value of

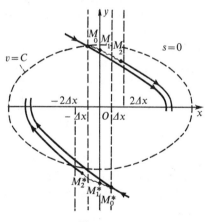

Fig. 13.

K the point $M(t)$ of system (7.7), after it has spent a short time outside the plane $s=0$, returns to it again at a point situated sufficiently close to the Oy-axis.

For definiteness, assume that the point M is located in the second quadrant of the plane $s=0$, i.e. for the coordinates of this point, let the relationships $-\Delta x = x_0 < 0$, $y_0 > 0$ be fulfilled (Fig. 13). In addition, let us suppose that the relation

$$y_0 \gg \Delta x \tag{7.12}$$

is also fulfilled. Using the equations

$$y \frac{dy}{dx} = s + \varphi(x, y),$$

$$\left.\begin{array}{l} \\ y \frac{ds}{dx} = -\varphi'_y s - F(x, y, s + \varphi(x, y), t) - \alpha K x - \varphi'_x y - \varphi'_y \varphi, \end{array}\right\} \tag{7.13}$$

obtained from the differential equations of system (7.7), we will find an approximate solution $y(x)$ and $s(x)$ of system (7.13) corresponding to the trajectory of the image point $M(t)$ with the initial point $M_0(x_0, y_0) = M(t_0)$. Since for the point M we have, according to our assumption, $y_0 > 0$ then, with increasing time $t > t_0$, the image point falls off the plane $s = 0$ and moves in the direction of increasing x, i.e. along the direction which takes it to the plane $x = 0$. On the other hand, since $|x_0| \leqslant \Delta x$, and since the quantity $\Delta x = m/K$ can be made as small as one pleases by increasing K, we shall consider the solution we are seeking in the interval $[x_0, 0]$. Thus, to find the appropriate solution, we shall confine ourselves to the first approximation.

$$y(x) = y_0 + \frac{\varphi(x_0, y_0)}{y_0}(x - x_0),$$

$$s(x) = \alpha K x_0 - \frac{\Phi(x_0, y_0, t_0)}{y_0}(x - x_0).$$

The formulae we have obtained permit us to find the approximate values of the coordinates of the point $M_1(x_1, y_1, s_1)$, i.e. the points at which the trajectory intersects the plane $x = 0$ at a certain value of $t = t_1 > t_0$, namely we find that the equalities

$$x_1 = 0, \quad y_1 = y_0 - \frac{\varphi(x_0, y_0)}{y_0} x_0 \approx y_0, \quad s_1 \approx 0,$$

are valid for values of K sufficiently large to be able to neglect terms of the first order of smallness in Δx.

As time increases $t > t_1$ the point $M(t)$ moves away from M_1 and moves in the half-space $x > 0$ for as long as the ordinate of the point remains positive. Since, as a consequence of the fulfilment of relation (7.12), the point M_1

is positive once more, with increasing time the image point $M(t)$ moves away from the point M_1, the direction again being that of increasing $x(t)$ at least for values of x that are positive, sufficiently small and comparable in magnitude with Δx. Let us find the solution $s(x)$ of system (7.13) corresponding to a trajectory emerging from point M_1. We shall seek this solution in the form of a power series in x, neglecting powers of x from x^3 onwards. Taking into account the boundedness of the functions $F(x, y, z, t)$, $\varphi(x, y)$ and their derivatives, and treating K as a sufficiently large number, we obtain

$$s(x) = -\frac{\Phi(0, y_0, t_1)}{y_0} x - \alpha K \frac{x^2}{2y_0}, \qquad (7.14)$$

whence we find the value of x for which the function $s(x)$ vanishes. In this way we find the value of the abscissa of the point $M_2 = M(t_2)$ i.e. the point where for $t = t_2 > t_1$, the image point returns to the plane $s = 0$. It is clear that for the abscissa of point M we have $x_2 = -2\Phi(0, y_0, t_1)/\alpha K$. Taking condition (7.9) into account, we obtain the relation $|x_2| \leqslant 2\Delta x$. In addition, for the trajectory we are considering, it is obvious that $x_2 > 0$, since the difference between the ordinate of M_2 and that of the initial point M_0 is a quantity of the first order of smallness with magnitude Δx, i.e., in our case, in the interval $[-\Delta x, 2\Delta x]$ the sign of the ordinate of the point remains positive.

Thus, we have shown that for a sufficiently large value of K the image point $M(t)$ of system (7.7) first falls off the plane $s = 0$ at the point $M_0(x_0, y_0)$ whose coordinates satisfy the relationships $|x_0| \leqslant \Delta x$, $y_0 \gg \Delta x$, and then returns again onto the plane $s = 0$ at the point $M_2(x_2, y_2)$ whose ordinate is, as before, positive and comparable in magnitude to y_0, and whose abscissa does not exceed the number $2\Delta x$ (see Fig. 13). Since the abscissa of the points M_0 and M_2 do not differ by more than $3\Delta x$, the transfer time of the image point from M_0 to M_2 for sufficiently small K will be small. Similar arguments apply to the trajectory of system (7.7), which falls off the plane $s = 0$ at a point $M_0^*(x_0^*, y_0^*)$, where $y_0^* < 0$ and $0 < x_0^* \leqslant x$, only if the relation $|y_0^*| \gg \Delta x$ is fulfilled. That is, in this case also, it can be shown that the image point $M(t)$, having left the plane $s = 0$ at the point M_0^*, intersects the plane $x = 0$ after which, having spent a short time outside that plane, it returns to it again in the sliding region at the point $M_2^*(x_2^*, y_2^*)$. For the coordinates of this point the relations $x_2^* < 0$, $|x_2^*| \leqslant 2\Delta x$ hold.

Thus, the presence of the pole $|x| \leqslant \Delta x$ which contains within itself the sewing region of system (7.7) causes the trajectories of the system to deviate from the plane $s = 0$. This deviation occurs at the pole which does not emerge from the pole $|x| \leqslant 2\Delta x$. Since $\Delta x = m/K$ where, from (7.9), m is a constant, one can always choose K to be so large that Δx can be made as small as one pleases. Simultaneously with Δx, both the maximum deviation of the function $s(x)$ from zero, and the time the image point of the trajectories spends outside the plane $s = 0$, become as small as one pleases.

4. In the first part of the proof of the theorem we showed that with increasing time the image point of system (7.2) falls onto the surface $s = 0$ regardless of the point of phase space it came from. The future behaviour of the image point depends on its motion on the surface S and on the deviation from this surface, as determined by the existence of sewing regions for the system.

On the plane $s = 0$, consider now, in addition to system (7.10), the system

$$\dot{x} = y, \quad \dot{y} = \varphi(x, y) + s(t), \tag{7.15}$$

formed by the first two equations of system (7.7). Here $s(t)$ denotes the value of s while point $M(t)$ is in the process of moving in the manner discussed above. Therefore $s(t) = 0$, if $M(t)$ slides along the plane $s = 0$, and $s(t) \neq 0$ if point $M(t)$ falls off this plane. Consequently, system (7.15) describes the motion of the projection of the point $M(t)$ on the plane $s = 0$. It was shown above that for sufficiently large K the absolute magnitude of the function $s(t)$ can be made as small as one pleases. Moreover, as a consequence of the fulfilment of condition (b), the zero equilibrium position for system (7.10) is asymptotically stable for any initial disturbances. Let us consider now the function $v = y^2 - 2\int_0^x \varphi(x, 0)dx$. The derivative of this function taken according to system (7.15) has the form

$$\dot{v} = 2y[\varphi(x, y) - \varphi(x, 0)] - 2s(t)y =$$
$$= 2y\varphi(0, y) + 2y[\varphi(x, y) - \varphi(0, y)] - 2y\varphi(x, 0) - 2ys(t).$$

However, from (7.14), it immediately follows that $|ys(t)| < m^2/2K$, where m is a positive constant. On the other hand, if y_0 is an arbitrarily small positive number, then taking account of the fact that the inequality $y\varphi(0, y) < 0$ follows from condition (b) and that there is a limit to the magnitude of the y-ordinate of a point lying in the region D, we have, for $|y| > y_0$, the strict inequality $y\varphi(0, y) < -r_0$, where r_0 is a positive constant.

Furthermore, by choosing a sufficiently large value for K, and by virtue of the continuity of the function $\varphi(x, y)$ for points of the pole $|x| \leqslant 2\Delta x$ (within the bounds of region D), it is possible to fulfill the inequalities $|y[\varphi(x, y) - \varphi(0, y)]| < \frac{1}{4}r_0^2$ and $|y\varphi(x, 0)| < \frac{1}{4}r_0$. Finally, for $K > 2m^2/r_0$, we also have the relation $|ys(t)| < \frac{1}{4}r_0$. Thus, at the pole $|x| \leqslant 2\Delta x$ and for $|y| > y_0$ we will have $\dot{v} < -\frac{1}{2}r_0 < 0$ for the derivative $\dot{v}$.

In addition, $\dot{v} \leqslant 0$ everywhere within the region D outside the pole $|x| \leqslant 2\Delta x$. Whence it follows that by choosing a sufficiently large value of K the derivative $\dot{v}$ can be made negative everywhere inside the region D with the exception of the neighbourhood of the coordinate origin, which can be made as small as one pleases, and the points of the straight line $y = 0$. Since there are no entire trajectories of system (7.10) on the straight line $y = 0$, we arrive at the conclusion that any trajectory of system (7.15) falls into the ε-neighbourhood of the coordinate origin if K is sufficiently large.

8. Non-Linear Systems with Variable Structure. Control with Respect to the x-coordinate and Its Derivatives

1. As in the preceding paragraph we shall be considering here non-linear systems of the third order. As before, the points of phase space are first translated onto a surface and then slide along this surface to the coordinate origin. However, in contrast to the method of forming the control considered previously, the introduction of additional variable control parameters enables one to guarantee that, for any motion, the system will spend the whole time in the sliding mode after a certain initial instant of time. This circumstance permits us to obtain asymptotic stability of the zero solution of the system.

Consider the differential equation

$$\dddot{x} + F(x, \dot{x}, \ddot{x}, t) + (K|x| + K_1|\dot{x}|) \operatorname{sign}(\ddot{x} - \varphi(x, \dot{x})) = 0. \tag{8.1}$$

Here K, K_1 are positive parameters, $F(x, \dot{x}, \ddot{x}, t)$, $\varphi(x, \dot{x})$ are continuous functions of their arguments for all values x, $\dot{x}$, $\ddot{x}$, and $t \geqslant 0$.

Equation (8.1) is equivalent to the system

$$\dot{x} = y,$$

$$\dot{y} = z,$$

$$\dot{z} = -F(x, y, z, t) - [K|x| + K_1|y|] \operatorname{sign}(z - \varphi(x, y)). \tag{8.2}$$

Let us suppose that the following conditions are fulfilled:

(a) $F(x, y, z, t) \leqslant a|x| + b|y| + c|z|$ for any values of $x, y, z, t \geqslant 0$. Here a, b, c are non-negative constants.

(b) The function $\varphi(x, y)$ is everywhere well-defined and differentiable with respect to x and y, and there exist positive numbers M and N such that the relations $|\varphi'_x| \leqslant M$, $|\varphi'_y| \leqslant N$ are fulfilled for all x and y.

(c) $x\varphi(x, 0) < 0$ for $x \neq 0$, $y[\varphi(x, y) - \varphi(x, 0)] < 0$ for $y \neq 0$, $\int_{\mp\infty}^{0} \varphi(x, 0) \, dx = \infty$.

We note that condition (a) ensures the continuability of motion of system (8.2) at least up to the instant of time when the point falls onto the surface S specified by the equation $z = \varphi(x, y)$. If all the points of a certain region G of phase space fall onto the surface S and after a further lapse of time t they move along S towards the coordinate in accordance with the system

$$\dot{x} = y, \quad \dot{y} = \varphi(x, y), \tag{8.3}$$

we obtain the required property of asymptotic stability of the zero solution.

Theorem 8.1. *Assume that the functions $F(x, y, z, t)$ and $\varphi(x, y)$ satisfy the conditions (a), (b), (c), let the parameter K_1 be fixed and chosen in accordance with the inequality*

$$K_1 \geqslant b + M + cN + N^2 \tag{8.4}$$

and let a bounded region G of phase space be specified. One can find a positive number K_0 such that for $K > K_0$ the zero solution of system (8.2) will be asymptotically stable and the region G will lie inside the region of attraction of the coordinate origin.

We shall show first that by increasing K sliding conditions will obtain over the whole of surface S. In fact, by taking the derivative of the function $s(x, y, z) = z - \varphi(x, y)$ according to system (8.2), we obtain

$$\frac{ds}{dt} = \Phi(x, y, s, t) - (K|x| + K_1|y|) \operatorname{sign} s, \tag{8.5}$$

where $\Phi(x, y, s, t) = -F(x, y, s + \varphi(x, y), t) - \varphi'_x y - \varphi'_y(s + \varphi(x, y))$. Since relations (a) and (b) are fulfilled for functions $F(x, y, z, t)$ and $\varphi(x, y)$, the function $\Phi(x, y, s, t)$ must also satisfy an inequality similar to (a):

$$|\Phi(x, y, s, t)| \leqslant A|x| + B|y| + C|s|, \tag{8.6}$$

where $A = a + cM + NM$, $B = b + M + cN + N^2$, $C = c + N$.
Let us calculate the limiting values of the derivative $\dot{s}$ as the image point
of (8.2) approaches the surface S:

$$\lim_{s \to -0} \dot{s} = \Phi(x, y, 0, t) + K|x| + K_1|y| > (K - A)|x| + (K_1 - B)|y|$$

and

$$\lim_{s \to +0} \dot{s} = \Phi(x, y, 0, t) - K|x| - K_1|y| < (A - K)|x| + (B - K_1)|y|$$

for all values of x and y.
To ensure that sliding obtains over the whole of the surface $z = \varphi(x, y)$,
it is clearly sufficient that the inequalities $K \geqslant A$ and $K_1 \geqslant B$ be fulfilled.
We shall show now that for any bounded region G of phase space one
can chose such a value of K_0 that with $K > K_0$ any point $M(t)$ which, as t
increases, moves along a trajectory of system (8.2) must fall onto the surface S. As before, we make the change of variables in (8.2) $t = \rho\tau$, $X = x$,
$Y = \rho y$, $Z = \rho^2 z$, $\rho = K^{-\frac{1}{3}}$. The new system will have the form

$$\frac{dX}{d\tau} = Y, \quad \frac{dY}{d\tau} = Z \quad (R = Z - \rho^2\varphi(X, \rho^{-1}Y)),$$

$$\frac{dZ}{d\tau} = -|X| \operatorname{sign} R - \rho^2 K_1|Y| \operatorname{sign} R - \rho^3 F(X, \rho^{-1}Y, \rho^{-2}Z, \rho\tau).$$

$$(8.7)$$

With K large, ρ can be considered a small parameter and so we can write
down a simplified system with $\rho = 0$ in the form

$$\frac{dX}{d\tau} = Y, \quad \frac{dY}{d\tau} = Z, \quad \frac{dZ}{d\tau} = -|X| \operatorname{sign} R. \quad (8.8)$$

We investigated system (8.8) before when we were proving theorem (7.1).
Any point of phase space moving along a trajectory of system (8.8) falls
onto the surface S after a finite interval of time. The only exceptions are
those points of phase space lying on the integral straight line $X = -Y = Z$;
these points approach the coordinate origin asymptotically.
It follows from condition (a) that the quantity $\rho^2 F(X, \rho^{-1}Y, \rho^{-2}Z, \rho\tau)$
is bounded in region G for small values of ρ. By choosing ρ to be sufficiently
small, and using well-known arguments based on the continuity of solutions with respect to a parameter, we arrive at the conclusion that all the
points of region G, with the exception of a sufficiently narrow tube cir-

cumscribing the straight line $X = -Y = Z$, which are moving in accordance with (8.7) fall onto the surface S after a finite interval of time. The points of the tube, however, either leave it after a while and fall onto S, or they remain inside it with the result that eventually they too, after a finite or infinite time, fall onto S.

Having fallen onto the surface S, the image point moves along it in accordance with system (8.3). From example 4, section 14 of Chapter 1, it follows that conditions (c) ensure the asymptotic stability of the zero solution of this system. Thus, we have demonstrated that any point of region G will approach the coordinate origin.

To complete the proof of the theorem we have only to establish the fact of Lyapunov stability by referring to lemma 4.5. It is obvious that arguments completely analogous to those used in proving theorem 4.1 readily lead us to the conclusion we are seeking.

Note 8.1.   Let $x_0 > 0$, $y_0 \geqslant 0$, $z_0 \geqslant \varphi(x_0, y_0)$. Using the results of lemmas 4.1, 4.2, and 4.3, it is not difficult to make an estimate for system (8.2) of the time T required for the point $M(x_0, y_0, z_0)$ to fall onto the sliding surface S. This estimate has the form

$$T \leqslant \frac{z_0 - \varphi(x_0, y_0)}{Kx_0} \left(1 + O(\rho)\right),$$

where $O(\rho)$ is a quantity of the order of smallness of ρ. If x_0, y_0, z_0 are numbers with an arbitrary sign, the overall time the image point stays inside region $|x| > \delta$, $z \neq \varphi(x, y)$ cannot be greater than

$$T_1 = 3 \frac{|z_0 - \varphi(x_0, y_0)|}{K\delta} \left(1 + O(\rho)\right).$$

2.   Consider the differential equation

$$\ddot{x} + F(x, \dot{x}, \ddot{x}) + (K|x| + K_1|\dot{x}| + K_2|\ddot{x}|)\,\text{sign}\,(\ddot{x} - \varphi(x, \dot{x})) = 0 , \qquad (8.9)$$

where the functions $F(x, \dot{x}, \ddot{x})$, $\varphi(x, \dot{x})$ again satisfy conditions (a), (b) and (c). In contrast with the preceding case, let us assume that the function $F(x, \dot{x}, \ddot{x})$ is explicitly independent of t.

Equation (8.9) is equivalent to the system

$$\dot{x} = y,$$

$$\dot{y} = z,$$

$$\dot{z} = -F(x, y, z) - (K|x| + K_1|y| + K_2|z|) \operatorname{sign}(z - \varphi(x, y)). \quad (8.10)$$

Theorem 8.2. *If the functions $F(x, y, z)$ and $\varphi(x, y)$ satisfy conditions (a), (b) and (c) and the parameters K, K_1, K_2 are chosen in accordance with the inequalities*

$$K \geqslant a, \quad K_1 \geqslant b + 1 + M, \quad K_2 \geqslant c + N, \quad (8.11)$$

then the zero solution of system (8.10) will be asymptotically stable on the whole.

Proof. Consider the new coordinate $s = z - \varphi(x, y)$ and re-write system (8.10) in the new coordinates x, y, s:

$$\left.\begin{aligned} \dot{x} &= y, \\ \dot{y} &= s + \varphi(x, y), \\ \dot{s} &= -F(x, y, s + \varphi(x, y)) - \varphi'_x y - \varphi'_y(s + \varphi(x, y,)) - \\ &\quad - (K|x| + K_1|y| + K_2|s + \varphi(x, y)|) \operatorname{sign} s. \end{aligned}\right\} \quad (8.12)$$

Consider now the Lyapunov function

$$v = s^2 + y^2 - 2 \int_0^x \varphi(x, 0) dx. \quad (8.13)$$

From condition (c) it follows that v is positive definite and infinitely large. Having computed v in accordance with system (8.12), we obtain

$$\dot{v} = 2y[\varphi(x, y) - \varphi(x, 0)] - 2|s|[K|x| + K_1|y| + \\ + K_2|s + \varphi(x, y)|] + 2s[-F(x, y, s + \varphi(x, y)) - \\ - \varphi'_x y - \varphi'_y(s + \varphi(x, y)) + y].$$

Taking conditions (a) and (b) into account, we obtain

$$\dot{v} \leqslant 2y[\varphi(x, y) - \varphi(x, 0)] - 2|s|[(K - a)|x| + \\ + (K_1 - b - M - 1)|y| + (K_2 - c - N)|s + \varphi(x, y)|].$$

Since, according to the stipulations of the theorem, relations (c) and (8.11) are fulfilled, it follows from the last inequality that the derivative of v, taken according to (8.12), will be a function of negative signs which vanishes on the Ox-axis. It is clear that with the exception of the singular point $O(0, 0, 0)$ there are no entire trajectories of system (8.2) on the Ox-axis; furthermore, v is infinitely large. Thus, we can now apply theorem (12.2) of Chapter 1, and the theorem is proved.

With regard to the qualitative disposition of the trajectories of system (8.9), it is easy to see that the surface $Z = \varphi(x, y)$ is a sliding surface at every point in it. This is verified by calculations similar to those made in proving theorem (8.1). Consequently, as $t \to \infty$, the image point of system (8.9) either immediately makes an asymptotic approach to the coordinate origin, or it falls first on the sliding surface for a finite time and then, after moving along it, also asymptotically approaches the coordinate origin.

9. Investigation of a Third Order System with a Discontinuous Switching Surface

Consider the third order equation

$$\dddot{x} + a\ddot{x} + b\dot{x} + cx = -\alpha Kx , \tag{9.1}$$

equivalent to the system

$$\dot{x} = y, \quad \dot{y} = z, \quad \dot{z} = -cx - by - az - \alpha Kx . \tag{9.2}$$

We shall suppose that the parameters a, b, c, K are arbitrary constants and that the coefficient K is positive. Let us consider first the problem of finding the law of variation of α which, for $|\alpha| \leqslant 1$, will ensure that the system operates at maximum speed, i.e. we seek a law that will ensure that the points of phase space will fall into a sufficiently small region in the neighbourhood of the coordinate origin in the shortest possible time. Investigation of this problem shows that one must introduce a complex law of switching for α. The law must necessarily be non-linear since one of the switching surfaces must necessarily be non-linear, although part of this surface contains plane manifolds. In view of the fact that a non-linear law of switching is difficult to realise, we can seek the solution by constructing a linear switching surface in sections in such a manner that, as a point of phase space moves along it, a change of sliding conditions occurs with the idea of speeding up the action of the system.

A detailed analysis of optimal problems suggests that one should construct switching surfaces out of two planes. In contrast to the surface we
considered before, such a surface (Fig. 14) has a discontinuity at the plane
$x = 0$. In effect, it represents a first approximation to the optimal problem
considered above.

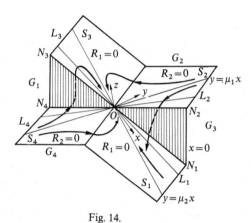

Fig. 14.

Here, however, we shall consider the problem of stabilising the system (9.2)
rather than the problem of optimising it. This means that in simplifying
the structure of the switching surface we have made the transient response
given by (9.2) differ from the optimum response. We also want to find a
law of switching that will not only stabilise the system (the system, in
general, being unstable) but which will at the same time ensure that the
control of the system is of high quality. With this idea in mind we shall
define the law of variation of α in the following manner

$$R_1(x, y, z) = Ax + By + z = 0 ,$$
$$R_2(x, y, z) = Ax + By + z - \theta(x + Ty) = 0 , \tag{9.3}$$

where A, B, θ, T are positive constants. In addition, we shall divide the
three-dimensional phase space into four regions. Region G_1 will be defined as the region in which $x > 0$ and one of the pairs of inequalities
(a) $R_1 > 0$, $R_2 > 0$; (b) $R_1 > 0$, $R_2 \leqslant 0$; (c) $R_1 \leqslant 0$, $R_2 > 0$ is fulfilled. We
will define region G_2 by the inequalities $x < 0$, $R_1 > 0$, $R_2 > 0$. G_3 is the
region in which $x < 0$ and one of the pairs of inequalities (a) $R_1 < 0$, $R_2 < 0$;
(b) $R_1 \geqslant 0$, $R_2 < 0$; (c) $R_1 < 0$, $R_2 \geqslant 0$ is fulfilled. Finally, G_4 is the region

where $x > 0$, $R_2 < 0$. In Fig. 14, regions G_1 and G_2 are located above the switching surface and regions G_3 and G_4 below it. Let us assume that $\alpha = -1$ in regions G_2 and G_4, and $\alpha = 1$ in a region which we shall call G. Region G consists of regions G_1 and G_3 together with the part of the plane $x = 0$ for which $R_1 R_2 < 0$. It is clear that for $x \neq 0$ the law of variation of α can be expressed by the formula

$$\alpha = \text{sign} \left[(R_1 + R_2) \, \text{sign} \, x + |R_1 - R_2| \right] . \tag{9.4}$$

Thus the system we are considering is a double switching system.

If $R_1 R_2 > 0$, α undergoes a change of sign as one passes through the plane $x = 0$ but maintains its sign if $R_1 R_2 < 0$. The switching surface illustrated in Fig. 14, which we shall call S, consists of sections S_1 and S_3 of the plane $R_1 = 0$, and S_2, S_4 of the plane $R_2 = 0$.
On the surface S, near the lines $N_1 N_3$, $N_2 N_4$, we distinguish sectors $L_i O N_i$, $i = 1, 2, 3, 4$ in which the trajectories of system (9.2) "sew" the surface S. It easy to show that by choosing a sufficiently large value of K the angles of the sectors may be made as small as one pleases. At all other points, surface S is a sliding surface. The plane $x = 0$, as follows from the first equation of system (9.2), is the plane that is "sewn".
Let A and B be chosen to fulfill the conditions

$$0 < A < B^2/4 . \tag{9.5}$$

The quantities θ and T occurring in (9.3) will be defined by the inequalities

$$A < \theta < \mu_2 B , \quad \mu_1 \leqslant -T^{-1} \leqslant \mu_2 , \tag{9.6}$$

where μ_1, μ_2 are roots of the equation

$$\mu^2 + B\mu + A = 0 . \tag{9.7}$$

It will be shown below that inequality (9.6) can always be satisfied.

Theorem 9.1. *If conditions* (9.5) *and* (9.6) *are fulfilled one can choose a number* $K_0 > 0$ *such that for* $K > K_0$, *and provided the law of switching* (9.4) *is obeyed, any solution of system* (9.2) *will have the property*

$$\lim_{t \to \infty} x(t) = \lim_{t \to \infty} y(t) = \lim_{t \to \infty} z(t) = 0 .$$

The proof of this theorem involves the following steps. It is shown first that any point M of phase space falls onto the surface S. The future behaviour of this point depends upon the section of the surface it hits, i.e. on whether it hits the plane $R_1 = 0$ or the plane $R_2 = 0$. If the point M falls onto plane $R_1 = 0$ (onto sections S_1 or S_3 of surface S; see Fig. 14) into the sliding region, then its future motion is given by the system

$$\dot{x} = y, \quad \dot{y} = -Ax - By, \tag{9.8}$$

by virtue of which the point will approach the coordinate origin along the straight line $y = \mu_2 x$, $R_1(x, y, z) = 0$. If point M falls onto the plane $R_2 = 0$ (S_2 or S_4), then it will move along it in accordance with the system

$$\dot{x} = y, \quad \dot{y} = -Ax - By + \theta(x + Ty), \tag{9.9}$$

whereupon, either it will arrive at the coordinate origin along the separatrix, or it will reach the line $R_1 = 0$, $x + Ty = 0$ along a hyperbolic type of curve and transfer to the plane $R_1 = 0$, or it will reach the sewing sector $N_2 O L_2$ or $N_4 O L_4$. In the last case M will come off the surface S but will return to strike it in sections S_1 or S_3 of the plane $R_1 = 0$ in just that region where sliding exists. Thus, point M will move towards the coordinate origin. The proof of all these statements is given below.

1. We shall first show that it is possible to choose such values of A, B, θ, T that inequalities (9.5) and (9.6) are fulfilled. Let us take an arbitrary pair of positive numbers A and B satisfying inequality (9.5). We then have

$$(B/2 - A/B)^2 > B^2/4 - A > 0.$$

whence

$$|B/2 - A/B| > (B^2/4 - A)^{\frac{1}{2}}. \tag{9.10}$$

However, $B/2 - A/B > A/B > 0$, so that relation (9.10) can be re-written in the form

$$B/2 - A/B > (B^2/4 - A)^{\frac{1}{2}} \text{ from which } A < -\mu_2 B.$$

This means that we can choose θ so that

$$A < \theta < -\mu_2 B, \tag{9.11}$$

but, since $\mu_1 < \mu_2 < 0$, the inequality

$$\mu_1 \leqslant -T^{-1} \leqslant \mu_2 \tag{9.12}$$

is fulfilled as well, where $T > 0$.

Since inequalities (9.5) and (9.6) are admissible we shall consider them to be everywhere fulfilled.

2. We shall prove now that the image point of system (9.2) falls onto one of the sections S_i $(i=1, 2, 3, 4)$ of the switching surface.
The notation S_1 and S_3 are applied to those sections of the plane $R_1 = 0$ belonging to the switching surface S and situated in the half-spaces $x > 0$ and $x < 0$, respectively.
The sections of the plane $R_2 = 0$ belonging to the switching surface S and lying in the half-spaces $x < 0$ and $x > 0$ are labelled S_2 and S_4, respectively.
Each of the two regions G_1 and G_3 is divided into two parts by the plane made up of the integral curves of system (9.2) with $\alpha = 1$.
The equation of this integral curve has the form

$$(\alpha^2 + \beta^2)x - 2\alpha y + z = 0, \tag{9.13}$$

where α and β are the real and imaginary parts of the complex roots of the characteristic equation:

$$\lambda^3 + a\lambda^2 + b\lambda + c + K = 0. \tag{9.14}$$

The presence, when K is sufficiently large, of a pair of complex roots $\alpha \pm i\beta$ $(\alpha > 0, \beta > 0)$ and of a real negative root $-\lambda(\lambda > 0)$ for equation (9.14) follows from Cardan's formulae. The same formulae show that as K tends to infinity, α, β and λ also tend to infinity.
The regions G_2 and G_4 are dissected by the integral plane of (9.2) for $\alpha = -1$. The equation of this plane has the form

$$(\gamma^2 + \delta^2)x - 2\gamma y + z = 0, \tag{9.15}$$

where γ and δ are the real and imaginary parts of the roots of the equation

$$\lambda^3 + a\lambda^2 + b\lambda + c - K = 0. \tag{9.16}$$

The presence, for sufficiently large K, of a pair of complex roots $\gamma \pm i\delta$ $(\gamma < 0, \delta > 0)$ and of a real positive root μ for equation (9.16) also follows from the Cardan formulae. It is obvious that if K tends to infinity, γ, δ and μ also tend to infinity.
Consider a point $M_0(x_0, y_0, z_0)$ in region G_2 located above the integral plane (9.15). The solution appropriate to the initial point has the following form

$$x = c_1 e^{\mu t} + \varphi_1(t), \quad y = c_1 \mu e^{\mu t} + \varphi_2(t), \quad z = c_1 \mu^2 e^{\mu t} + \varphi_3(t), \qquad (9.17)$$

where

$$c_1 = [(\gamma^2 + \delta^2) x_0 - 2\gamma y_0 + z_0]((\mu - \gamma)^2 + \delta^2)^{-1},$$

$$x_0 = x(0), \quad y_0 = y(0), \quad z_0 = z(0),$$

$\varphi_i(t) \to 0$ as $t \to \infty$, $i = 1, 2, 3$.

Since $c_1 > 0$ for the point M_0, then as $t \to \infty$ we have $x(t) \to \infty$. Thus, as time increases, the point $M(t)$ moves along the trajectory and either falls onto section S_2 of the switching surface or it moves onto the plane $x = 0$ in that part of it where $y \geqslant 0$.

If the point $M_0(x_0, y_0, z_0)$ lies in region G_2 below the integral plane (9.15), we have $c_1 < 0$ for this point. In this case the image point cannot leave region G_2 through the plane $x = 0$.

In fact, the point $M(t)$ can move out of the region G_2 through the plane $x = 0$ only in that section of it which is included between the traces of the planes $R_1 = 0$ and (9.15); the equations of these straight lines are written in the form $z + By = 0$ and $z = 2\gamma y$, where $B < -2\gamma$ for sufficiently large values of K.

It is easy to see that in the indicated section of the $x = 0$ plane we have $\dot{x} = y < 0$, and consequently x cannot transfer from the region $x < 0$ to the region $x > 0$.

We will calculate now the variation of the function $R_1(x, y, z) = Ax + By + z$ along the trajectory of the point. According to formulae (9.17) we can write

$$R_1(t) = c_2 e^{\mu t} (A + B\mu + \mu^2) \varphi(t),$$

where $\varphi(t) \to 0$ as $t \to \infty$. Since $c_2 < 0$, $\mu > 0$ $A + B\mu + \mu^2 > 0$, then, as t increases, the value of $R_1(t)$ moves out of the region of positive values $(R_1(0) > 0)$ into the region of negative values. This means that $M(t)$ falls at some finite time t either onto section S_2 of plane $R_2 = 0$ or onto section S_3 of plane $R_1 = 0$ without leaving region G_2.

Finally, if the initial point $M_0(x_0, t_0, z_0)$ belongs to the integral plane (9.15), then the image point $M(t)$ moves in a spiral on the plane (9.15) and at some finite value of t it falls onto section S_2 of the switching surface. Thus, for initial points M_0 lying in the region G_2 below the integral plane (9.15) the image point $M(t)$ at some finite value of t falls onto one of the sections S_2 or S_3 of the switching surface without leaving region G_2.

For initial points M_0 lying in the region G_2 on the integral plane (9.15), the image point $M(t)$ falls onto section S_2 of the switching surface at same finite value t.

If the initial point M_0 lies in the region G_2 above the integral plane (9.15) then with increasing t the image point $M(t)$ either falls onto section S_2 or moves onto the $x=0$ plane at that part where $y \geqslant 0$.

3. Suppose now that the initial point $M_0(x_0, y_0, z_0)$ belongs to region G_1. If the image point $M(t)$ does not leave region G_1 as t increases, the solution corresponding to this image point may be written in the form

$$x(t) = a_1 e^{-\lambda t} + e^{\alpha t}(a_2 \cos \beta t + a_3 \sin \beta t). \tag{9.18}$$

It is easy to see that when $a_2 \neq 0$, i.e. when the point M_0 does not belong to the integral straight line $x = -y/\lambda = z/\lambda^2$ of the system acting in region G_1, the points of this straight line tend to the coordinate origin as $t \to \infty$; the image point $M(t)$ falls onto the plane $x=0$ at a certain time t provided that up to this instant of time it has not fallen onto one of the sections S_1 and S_4 of the switching surface.

All that remains now is to discuss those points M_0 for which the image point $M(t)$ with increasing t can leave the region G_1 intersecting the plane $x=0$.

Let us assume that the point $M(t)$ leaves the region G_1 intersecting the $x=0$ plane between the straight lines $z + (B - \theta T)y = 0$ and $z + By = 0$, i.e. it falls into the region G_3. In that case, after a finite interval of time, it falls onto section S_3 of the switching surface.

In fact, let the point $M(t)$ fall into region G_3 above the integral plane (9.13). Then, in accordance with formula (9.18), point $M(t)$ must leave region G_3 after a finite interval of time. As it leaves G_3, point $M(t)$ can neither intersect the plane $x=0$ nor the integral plane (9.13), so that it must necessarily after a finite time t cross the S_3 section of the switching surface.

As we showed earlier, when $M(t)$ leaves G_1 and crosses the plane $x=0$ between the straight lines $z + By = 0$ and $z - 2\gamma y = 0$ it falls onto one of the sections S_2 or S_3 of surface S without leaving region G_2.

If, when it leaves region G_1, the image point $M(t)$ falls onto the plane $x=0$ between the line $z - 2\gamma y = 0$ and the z-axis, it can return to region G_1, crossing the plane $x=0$ for $y \geqslant 0$. Therefore, let us consider further the motion of the z-axis along the trajectory of system (9.2), operating in region G_1, for the case $\alpha = 1$. Since this system is linear, at any instant t, the image of the z-axis is a straight line. If this straight line falls onto neither section S_1 nor S_4 of the switching surface then, at some time t, it must again find itself in the $x = 0$ plane and will take up the position $z = ky$, where $k < 0$.

We shall show that for sufficiently large K the inequality $k > 2\gamma$ holds, i.e. for $y < 0$ the half-line $z = ky$ lies below the half-line $z = 2\gamma y$. Whence it follows that any point of the plane $x = 0$ having $y \geqslant 0$ which, with increasing t, crosses over from the plane $x = 0$ to the region G_1, either falls onto one of the sections S_1 or S_4 of the switching surface or leaves region G_1 and crosses the plane $x = 0$ between the straight lines $z + (B - \theta T)y = 0$ and $z - 2\gamma y = 0$. After that, in accordance with the arguments given above, it falls onto either S_2 or S_3 of the switching surface after a finite time.

To evaluate k we must find the values of the arbitrary constants a_1, a_2, a_3 in expression (9.18) assuming the initial conditions $x(0) = 0$, $y(0) = 0$, $z(0) = z_0$. Clearly, we obtain

$$a_1 = \frac{z_0}{\Delta}, \quad a_2 = -\frac{z_0}{\Delta}, \quad a_3 = \frac{\alpha + \lambda}{\beta \Delta} z_0, \tag{9.19}$$

where $\Delta = (\alpha + \lambda^2) + \beta^2$. The value of T, the time at which the image of the z-axis meets the plane $x = 0$, is a root of the equation

$$e^{-(\alpha + \lambda)T} - \cos \beta T + \frac{a + \lambda}{\beta} \sin \beta T = 0. \tag{9.20}$$

Making use of the equality (9.19) we find the values $y = \dot{x}$ and $z = \ddot{x}$ as functions of time

$$y(t) = \frac{z_0}{\Delta} \left[-\lambda e^{-\lambda t} + e^{\alpha t} \left(\lambda \cos \beta t + \frac{\alpha^2 + a\lambda + \beta^2}{\beta} \sin \beta t \right) \right],$$

$$z(t) = \frac{z_0}{\Delta} \left\{ \lambda^2 e^{-\lambda t} + e^{\alpha t} \left[(\alpha^2 + 2\alpha\lambda + \beta^2) \cos \beta t + \right. \right.$$
$$\left. \left. + \frac{\alpha^2(\alpha + \lambda) + \beta^2(\alpha - \lambda)}{\beta} \sin \beta t \right] \right\}.$$

Using equation (9.20), we obtain $y(T) = (z_0/\beta) e^{\alpha T} \sin \beta T$ and

$$z(T) = \frac{z_0}{\beta} e^{\alpha T} [\beta \cos \beta T + (\alpha - \lambda) \sin \beta T],$$

whence it follows that

$$k = \frac{z(T)}{y(T)} = \beta \cot \beta T + \alpha - \lambda. \qquad (9.21)$$

We introduce the notation $\beta T = r$, $\sigma = (\alpha + \lambda)/\beta$ and investigate the function $F(r) = f_1(r) - f_2(r)$, where $f_1(r) = e^{-\sigma r}$ and $f_2(r) = \cos r - \sigma \sin r$. The zero of the function $F(r)$ corresponds to the value of r for the point of intersection of the graphs of the functions $f_1(r)$ and $f_2(r)$. Clearly, we have $f_1(0) = f_2(0) = 1$. The values of the derivatives of these functions for $r = 0$ coincide, i.e. the graphs of the functions $f_1(r)$ and $f_2(r)$ have a common tangent at this point. Moreover, since everywhere $f_1''(r) = \sigma^2 e^{-\sigma r} > 0$, the graph of $f_1(r)$ is concave and for all r it lies above the tangent to the graph at the point where $r = 0$. On the other hand, we have sign $f_2''(r) = -$ sign $f_2(r)$ for all r.

Consequently, for values of r taken from the interval $(0, r_1)$, where r_1 is the zero of function $f_2(r)$, the graph of $f_2(r)$ is concave and lies below the tangent. It is easy to verify that the next zero of function $f_2(r)$, $r = r_2$ satisfies the inequality $r_2 > \pi$, i.e. in the interval (r_1, r_2) this function assumes negative values and its graphs lie below the r-axis. Therefore, in the interval $(0, r_2)$ at least, we have $f_1(r) > f_2(r)$. The graphs of these functions will only intersect in the interval $(r_2, \frac{3}{2}\pi)$ since $f_2(\frac{3}{2}\pi) > f_1(\frac{3}{2}\pi)$. Thus, the first positive zero of the function $F(r)$ lies in the interval $(\pi, \frac{3}{2}, \pi)$, which means that the smaller positive root of equation (9.20) is in the interval $\pi/\beta < T < 3\pi/2\beta$. However, from (9.21), it immediately follows that $k = \beta \cot \beta T + \alpha - \lambda > \alpha - \lambda$. By virtue of the Cardan formulae, we obtain

$$\alpha - \lambda = \frac{u_1 + v_1}{2} - \tfrac{2}{3}a, \qquad 2\gamma = -u_2 - v_2 - \tfrac{2}{3}a,$$

where

$$u_1 = \left(-q_1 + \sqrt{q_1^2 + p_1^3}\right)^{\frac{1}{3}}, \qquad v_1 = \left(-q_1 - \sqrt{q_1^2 + p_1^3}\right)^{\frac{1}{3}},$$

$$u_2 = \left(-q_2 + \sqrt{q_2^2 + p_2^3}\right)^{\frac{1}{3}}, \qquad v_2 = \left(-q_2 - \sqrt{q_2^2 + p_2^3}\right)^{\frac{1}{3}},$$

$$q_1 = \tfrac{1}{2}\left[\frac{2a^3}{27} - \frac{ab}{3} + c + K\right], \qquad q_2 = \tfrac{1}{2}\left[\frac{2a^3}{27} - \frac{ab}{3} + c - K\right].$$

It is clear that for $K \to \infty$, we have $u_1 \to 0$, $v_1 \to -\infty$, $u_2 \to \infty$, $v_2 \to 0$, where u_2 and v_2 have identical rates of increase. From this it follows that for sufficiently large K the following inequality will be fulfilled,

$$\frac{u_1 + v_1}{2} + u_2 + v_2 > 0 \, ,$$

which gives us the relation we require: $k > 2\gamma$.

We note now that if the initial point $M_0(x_0, y_0, z_0)$ is situated in region G_1 below the integral plane (9.13) then after a finite time its image point will fall onto the section S_1 of the switching surface without leaving region G_1. In fact, according to formula (9.18), the point $M(t)$ must leave region G_1. However, on leaving region G_1 it can cross neither the plane $x = 0$ (because the moment it falls onto the plane $x = 0$ we have $\dot{x} = y > 0$ for this point), nor onto the integral plane (9.13) (because of the uniqueness theorem). Therefore, if it does leave region G_1, the point $M(t)$ can do so only at section S_1 of the surface S.

It can be shown that sectors of sewability exist on sections S_i $(i = 1, 2, 3, 4)$ of the switching surface. If the point $M(t)$ falls into a sector of sewability belonging to section S_3, it will sew the switching surface S and appear in region G_2 below the integral plane (9.15). Consequently, after a finite time, it will fall onto either S_2 or S_3. If it falls onto section S_3 the point will be in a sliding region.

4.   By investigating the sign of the total derivative of the function $R_1(x, y, z)$ taken according to each of the systems (9.2), we can convince ourselves that if $A - B^2 + aB - b \neq 0$ (if this expression is equal to zero the plane R_1 is a sliding surface of system (9.2)), then there are sectors of sewability on sections S_1 and S_3 of the switching surface included between the plane $x = 0$ and one of the planes

$$(AB - aA + c \pm K)x = (A - B^2 - aB - b)y \, . \tag{9.22}$$

Treating the function $R_2(x, y, z)$ in a similar way, we can convince ourselves that if $A - \theta - (B - \theta T)^2 + (B - \theta T)a - b \neq 0$ (i.e. if the sliding condition is not fulfilled for the plane $R_2 \neq 0$; see Section 3) there are sectors of sewability on sections S_2 and S_4 of the switching surface included between the plane $x = 0$ and one of the planes

$$[(A - \theta)(B - \theta T) - a(A - \theta) + c \pm K]x =$$
$$= [A - \theta - (B - \theta T)^2 + (B - \theta T)a - b]y \, . \tag{9.23}$$

The choice of sign for K in the equation for the planes described by (9.22) and (9.23) depends on the signs of the coefficients of y in these equations.

By choosing a sufficiently high gain, the angles of the sectors of sewability can be made as small as one pleases.

After it has fallen onto section S_1 or S_3 of the switching surface into the sliding region, the image point moves over the switching surface S in accordance with the equation

$$\ddot{x} + B\dot{x} + Ax = 0 \tag{9.24}$$

until it falls into the sector of sewability. The behaviour of the integral curves of equations (9.24) on the phase plane is determined by the roots μ_1 and μ_2 of the characteristic equation (9.7). By virtue of the inequalities $\mu_1 < 0$, $\mu_2 < 0$, the coordinate origin for equation (9.24) is a singular point of the assembly. By virtue of the same inequalities, as $t \to \infty$ any point of the phase plane moves along its trajectory in a manner which takes it to the coordinate origin. All the trajectories, with the exception of the integral straight line $y = \mu_1 x$, are tangential to the straight line $y = \mu_2 x$ at the coordinate origin.

After it has fallen onto either of the sections S_2 or S_4 of the switching surface into the sliding region, the image point moves over the switching surface S in accordance with the equation

$$\ddot{x} + (B - \theta T)\dot{x} + (A - \theta)x = 0, \tag{9.25}$$

until it falls into the sector of sewability. The behaviour of the integral curves of equation (9.25) on the phase plane is determined by the roots of the characteristic equation

$$\lambda^2 + (B - \theta T)\lambda + A - \theta = 0. \tag{9.26}$$

By virtue of conditions (9.5) and (9.6), we have

$$\lambda_1 = -\frac{B - \theta T}{2} - \left(\frac{(B - \theta T)^2}{4} + \theta - A \right)^{\frac{1}{2}} < 0, \tag{9.27}$$

$$\lambda_2 = -\frac{B - \theta T}{2} + \left(\frac{(B - \theta T)^2}{4} + \theta - A \right)^{\frac{1}{2}} > 0. \tag{9.28}$$

Consequently, the coordinate origin for equation (9.25) is a singular point of the saddle type.

If the point $M(t)$ moves along the integral straight line $y = \lambda_1 x$ then as $t \to \infty$ it must approach the coordinate origin. If $M(t)$ moves along the integral straight line $y = \lambda_2 x$ then as $t \to \infty$ it moves off to infinity.

From conditions (9.5) and (9.6) it follows that

$$-T^{-1} \geqslant \lambda_1 , \tag{9.29}$$

the sign of the equality in relation (9.29) being attained if, and only if, it is attained from the right or from the left in the system of inequalities

$$\mu_1 \leqslant -T^{-1} \leqslant \mu_2 . \tag{9.30}$$

Let us describe the motion of a point which has fallen into the sliding mode on the switching surface.

From the equalities (9.28) and (9.29) it follows that the integral straight line $y = \lambda_2 x$ of equation (9.25) does not belong to the switching surface. From inequalities (9.30) it follows that either the integral straight line $y = \mu_1 x$ of equation (9.24) does not belong to the switching surface, or it coincides with the straight line $x + Ty = 0$ belonging to this surface.

From inequality (9.30) it also follows that the integral straight line $y = \mu_2 x$ of equation (9.24) belongs to the switching surface and can coincide with the straight line $x + Ty = 0$ belonging to this surface.

If the point $M(t)$ falls onto either of the sections S_2 or S_4 of the switching surface into the sliding mode between the straight lines $x = 0$ and $y = \lambda_1 x$ then, after a finite interval of time, it will fall into the sector of sewability. If it should fall onto either of the sections S_2 or S_4 between the straight lines $y = \lambda_1 x$ and $Ty + x = 0$ (with $-T^{-1} > \lambda_1$) then, after a finite interval of time, it will fall onto the straight line $Ty + x = 0$, will sew it and, continuing its motion over sections S_3 or S_1, will approach the coordinate origin as $t \to \infty$.

When it falls into the sliding mode onto section S_1 or S_3 of the switching surface the point $M(t)$ does not move off this section but moves over S, approaching the coordinate origin as $t \to \infty$.

5. To investigate the behaviour of a point $M(t)$ which has fallen onto the the sector of sewability of sections S_2 or S_4 of the switching surface, we shall change the variables in system (9.2)

$$t = \rho\tau, \quad X = x, \quad Y = \rho y, \quad Z = \rho^2 z , \tag{9.31}$$

where $\rho = K^{-\frac{1}{3}}$. We thereupon obtain the system

$$\frac{dX}{d\tau} = Y, \quad \frac{dY}{d\tau} = Z, \quad \frac{dZ}{d\tau} = -\alpha X + \rho(-aZ - \rho bY - \rho^2 cX); \tag{9.32}$$

here ρ plays the role of a small parameter provided K is sufficiently large. With the same change of variables, the planes $R_1 = 0$ and $R_2 = 0$ transform respectively to the planes

$$r_1 = A\rho^2 X + B\rho Y + Z = 0$$

and

$$r_2 = -(\theta - A)\rho^2 X + (B - \theta T)\rho Y + Z = 0.$$

At the same time G and G_i transform respectively into regions Q and Q_i $(i = 1, 2, 3, 4)$, the quantities X, r_1 and r_2 in the new regions satisfying the same inequalities as were satisfied by x, R_1 and R_2 in the old regions. Let the initial point $M_0(x_0, y_0, z_0)$ belong to the sector of sewability of system (9.2) situated in section S_2 of the switching surface. With the change of variables (9.31) the point M_0 transforms to the point $L_0(X_0, Y_0, Z_0)$, with $X_0 < 0$, $Y_0 > 0$ and

$$Z_0 = (A - \theta)\rho^2 X_0 - (B - \theta T)\rho Y_0 < 0. \tag{9.33}$$

In the new coordinate system equation (9.23) has the form

$$[(A - \theta)(B - \theta T)\rho^3 - a(A - \theta)\rho^3 + c\rho^3 \pm 1] X =$$
$$= \rho^2 [A - \theta - (B - \theta T)^2 + (B - \theta T)a - b] Y. \tag{9.34}$$

It can be seen from formula (9.34) that X_0/Y_0 is a small quantity of the order of ρ^2. From relation (9.33) it follows that Z_0/Y_0 is a small quantity of the order of ρ.

For the initial point L, we have

$$qX(\tau) = r\,e^{-v\tau} + e^{\sigma\tau}\{[(v^2 + 2\sigma v)X_0 + 2\sigma Y_0 - Z_0]\cos\psi\tau +$$
$$+ \psi^{-1}[v(\psi^2 - \sigma v - \sigma^2)X_0 + (\psi^2 - v^2 - \sigma^2)Y_0 +$$
$$+ (v + \sigma)Z_0]\sin\psi\tau\},$$

$$qY(\tau) = -vr\,e^{-v\tau} + e^{\sigma\tau}\{[v(\sigma^2 + \psi^2)X_0 +$$
$$+ (\sigma^2 + \psi^2 + v^2)Y_0 + vZ_0]\cos\psi\tau + \psi^{-1}[-v(\sigma + v)(\sigma^2 +$$
$$+ \psi^2)X_0 + \sigma(-\psi^2 + v^2 - \sigma^2)Y_0 + (\sigma^2 + \psi^2 + \sigma v)Z_0]\sin\psi\tau\},$$

$$qZ(\tau) = v^2 r\,e^{-v\tau} + e^{\sigma\tau}\{[-v^2(\sigma^2 + \psi^2)X_0 + 2\sigma v^2 Y_0 +$$
$$+ (\sigma^2 + \psi^2 + 2\sigma v)Z_0]\cos\psi\tau + \psi^{-1}[-v(\sigma^2 + \psi^2)(\sigma^2 + \psi^2 +$$
$$+ \sigma v)X_0 + [-(\sigma^2 + \psi^2)^2 + v(\sigma^2 - \psi^2)]Y_0 +$$
$$+ [(\sigma^2 - \psi^2)v + v(v^2 + \psi^2)]Z_0]\sin\psi\tau\}.$$

Here $q = (\sigma + v)^2 + \psi^2$, $r = (\sigma^2 + \psi^2)X_0 - 2\sigma Y_0 + Z_0$ and, as $\rho \to 0$, we have $v \to 1$, $\sigma \to 0.5$, $\varphi \to \sqrt{\tfrac{3}{2}}$.

In the new coordinates equation (9.22) has the form

$$\rho^2 mY - (1 + \eta\rho^3)X = 0 ,$$

where $m > 0$ and the η are constants. We introduce the auxiliary function

$$p(\tau) = \rho^2 mY(\tau) - (1 + \eta\rho^3)X(\tau) .$$

The equations

$$X(\tau) = 0 ,$$

$$r_1(\tau) = r_1(X(\tau), \quad Y(\tau), \quad Z(\tau)) = 0 ,$$

$$r_2(\tau) = r_2(X(\tau), \quad Z(\tau)) = 0 ,$$

$$p(\tau) = 0 ,$$

will now be put in the form, respectively,

$$e^{-(v+\sigma)\tau} = p_0 \cos(\psi\tau - \varphi_0) , \tag{9.35}$$

$$e^{-(v+\sigma)\tau} = p_1 \cos(\psi\tau + \varphi_1) , \tag{9.36}$$

$$e^{-(v+\sigma)\tau} = p_2 \cos(\psi\tau + \varphi_2) , \tag{9.37}$$

$$e^{-(v+\sigma)\tau} = p_3 \cos(\psi\tau - \varphi_3) . \tag{9.38}$$

Here $p_i \to 2$, and $\varphi_i \to \pi/3$ as $\rho \to 0$ ($i = 0, 1, 2, 3$).

Let $\tau_0, \tau_1, \tau_2, \tau_3$ denote, respectively, the smallest positive zeros of the equations (9.35)–(9.38).

It is easy to verify that $1 - p_0 \cos \varphi_0 > 0$ and $1 - p_3 \cos \varphi_3 > 0$ are small quantities of the order of ρ^2, and $1 - p_1 \cos \varphi_1 < 0$ is a small quantity of the order of ρ. Whence it follows that the quantities τ_i ($i = 0, 1, 2, 3$) satisfy the inqualities

$$0 < \tau_0 < \tau_3 < \tau_1 < \tau_2 . \tag{9.39}$$

Returning now to the old variables, we conclude from inequalities (9.39) that the trajectory of the point M_0 belonging to the sector of sewability on section S_2 of the switching surface, for $x_0 < 0$, falls into the sliding region on section S_1 of surface S at a certain finite instant of time t without leaving region G.

If now $X_0 = 0$, then $p(\tau)$ vanishes earlier than $r_1(\tau)$, and $r_1(\tau)$ vanishes earlier than $X(\tau)$ and $r_2(\tau)$. Consequently, in the case when $x_0 = 0$ after a finite interval of time, the trajectory of M_0 intersects section S_1 of the switching surface in the sliding region without moving out of region G.

From this it follows that the trajectories of the initial points M_0 of region G_2 which leave region G_2 and enter region G_1 below the integral plane (9.13) will, after a finite interval of time t, fall onto section S_1 of surface S in the sliding region without coming out of region G_1.

Thus it is proved that for any initial point M_0 belonging to the closed regions G_1 and G_2, an image point $M(t)$ moving in accordance with the the equations of system (9.2), will approach the coordinate origin as $t \to \infty$.

One can provide similar arguments for regions G_3 and G_4; consequently, for any initial point M_0 taken in a three-dimensional space, an image point $M(t)$ that is moving in accordance with the equations of system (9.2) will approach the coordinate origin as $t \to 0$. The theorem is therefore proved.

This problem was tested on a type MN-14 computer. It was shown that with $c = 0$ and with positive values of b the value of θ had only a very slight effect upon the quality of the transient response. It was therefore thought necessary to seek other ways of improving the dynamical properties of systems of the kind we have been discussing. One such way is to employ forced sliding modes in variable structure systems.

10. A System Operating under Forced Sliding Conditions

One can speed up the transient response of a variable structure system in part by reducing the dimensionality of its phase space. We can see that this must be so by noting that the transition to a sliding mode of motion corresponds to a transition from motion of a point in phase space to motion on a sliding surface, which has a lower dimensionality.

This suggests the idea of speeding up the sliding process by establishing new sliding conditions over a surface of even lower dimensionality. In this way, by successively reducing the dimensionality of the sliding surface, we should be able after a finite number of steps to produce a motion along a uni-dimensional line. A consideration of optimal systems will lead to the same reasoning since a characteristic feature of the passage of an optimal process is a successive reduction in the dimensionality of the manifolds according to which a point of phase space moves.

It is clear that the sliding process is described by a system of differential equations with discontinuous right-hand sides. Since, after making the usual transformation from coordinates to derivatives, the equation for the sliding surface transforms to a differential equation describing the sliding process, it follows that for sliding of higher orders to be present the principal $(n-1)$-dimensional sliding surface must be discontinuous.

We see therefore that it is not possible to organise a pure (ideal) sliding of higher order; it is possible only to obtain a non-ideal sliding characterised by rapid motion of the points of phase space in the neighbourhood of a surface of discontinuity. Neglecting these rapid oscillations and focussing attention on the slow motion of a point of phase space, one can reduce the problem from one of considering non-ideal sliding to one of considering an ideal sliding process described by an equation of lower order.

Thus, we shall treat all non-ideal sliding modes as ideal sliding modes up to the accuracy of such rapid motions. From this point of view the basic system of differential equations will be treated as a system describing non-ideal sliding. Neglecting rapid motions, we obtain a system describing sliding of the first order. Separating the rapid from the slow motions in the new system, we obtain a system of the $(n-2)$th order describing sliding of the second order, and so on.

It is possible to separate fast and slow motions by introducing a small parameter.

If the servo-system works satisfactorily after first order sliding has been introduced there is no need to introduce second order sliding. However, if the transient response of the system is too slow, then one should introduce second order sliding. In this way, by introducing sliding into the control system up to a sufficiently high order (possibly up to the $(n-1)$th order, inclusive), one can improve the dynamic properties of the system to the extent required.

1.   Let us now define m-th order sliding.

Consider the system of differential equations

$$\left.\begin{array}{l} \dot{x}_i = x_{i+1}, \qquad i=1, \ldots, n-1, \\[2mm] \dot{x}_n = -\sum_{k=1}^{n} c_{0k} x_k, \end{array}\right\} \tag{10.1}$$

where the coefficients c_{0k} are arbitrary constants with $k=2, ..., n$ and the quantity c_{01} is defined by the relations

$$
\left.
\begin{aligned}
&c_{01} = b_0(K)\operatorname{sign} x_1\sigma_1, \quad \sigma_1 = \sum_{k=1}^{n} c_{1k}x_k, \\
&\quad\quad\quad \cdots\cdots\cdots\cdots\cdots\cdots\cdots\cdots\cdots \\
&c_{m1} = b_m(K)\operatorname{sign} x_1\sigma_{m+1}, \quad \sigma_{m+1} = \sum_{k=1}^{n-m} c_{m+1,k}x_k, \quad m=1, ..., n-1, \\
&c_{n1} = 1, \quad\quad\quad\quad\quad\quad \sigma_n = x_1.
\end{aligned}
\right\} \quad (10.2)
$$

Here K is a sufficiently large positive constant, $b_0(K), ..., b_{n-1}(K)$ are positive functions of K, and

$$
\lim_{k \to \infty} \frac{b_{i+1}(K)}{b_i(K)} = 0, \quad b_i(K) \to \infty, \quad i=0, 1, ..., n-1,
$$

as $K \to \infty$. When $k \neq 1$, the coefficients c_{ik} are assumed to be constants and $c_{k,n-k+1} = 1$ for $k=1, ..., n$. In certain cases the law of variation of c_{01} can be simplified and the chain of relations (10.2) shortened. This can be done by fulfilling the requirement $\sigma_r = x_1$ for certain values of r, $1 \leqslant r < n$. In this case we assume $c_{r1} = b_r(K) = 1$ and $c_{mk} = 0$ for $m=r+1, ..., n$. Changing the time variable in system (10.1), $t = \mu\tau$, where $\mu = [b_0(K)]^{-1}$ plays the role of a small parameter, we obtain a new system in the form

$$
\left.
\begin{aligned}
&\frac{dx_i}{d\tau} = \mu x_{i+1}, \quad i=1, ..., n-1, \\
&\frac{dx_n}{d\tau} = -|x_1|\operatorname{sign} \sigma_1 - \mu \sum_{k=2}^{n} c_{0k}x_k.
\end{aligned}
\right\} \quad (10.3)
$$

With $\mu=0$, we obtain the equation

$$
\frac{dx_n}{d\tau} = -|x_1|\operatorname{sign} \sigma_1, \quad (10.4)
$$

which describes the fast motion of the system. This equation, taken in conjunction with the conditions

$$
x_i = x_i^0 = \text{const}, \quad i=1, ..., n-1 \quad (10.5)
$$

enables one to extract the coordinate x_n, which has a faster variation than the remaining coordinates. Let us suppose at first that $x_1^0 \neq 0$. By virtue of equation (10.4), a point of phase space executes a fast motion along the straight line (10.5) towards the point determined by the equation $\sigma_1 = 0$ or, what amounts to the same thing, by the equation

$$x_n = -c_{11}x_1^0 - \ldots - c_{1,n-1}x_{n-1}^0 \, . \tag{10.6}$$

We note that the quantity c_{11}, which depends on $x_1^0, \ldots, x_{n-1}^0$, is a constant so that for given initial values equation (10.6) exactly determines the limiting magnitude of the variable x_n.

One can, without carrying out a complete analysis of the motion of the image point governed by (10.1), deduce that for this system a point of phase space executes its slow motion either on, or close to, the surface (10.6). Whence it follows that equation

$$x_1^{(n-1)} + c_{1,n-1}x_1^{(n-2)} + \ldots + c_{11}x_1 = 0 \, , \tag{10.7}$$

which is equivalent to the system

$$\left.\begin{aligned} \dot{x}_i &= x_{i+1}, \qquad i = 1, \ldots, n-2 \, , \\ \dot{x}_{n-1} &= -\sum_{k=1}^{n-1} c_{1k}x_k \, , \end{aligned}\right\} \tag{10.8}$$

describes approximately the slow motion of the system, (10.1).

Thus, for K sufficiently large, system (10.8) may be considered as the system describing first order sliding.

We now regard (10.8) as the initial system and apply similar arguments to it. In particular, by changing the time $t = \mu_1\tau$, where $\mu_1^{-1} = b\,(K)$, we obtain a system similar to (10.8):

$$\left.\begin{aligned} \dot{x}_i &= x_{i+1}, \qquad i = 1, \ldots, n-3 \, , \\ \dot{x}_{n-2} &= -\sum_{k=1}^{n-2} c_{2k}x_k \, , \end{aligned}\right\} \tag{10.9}$$

which describes second order sliding.

Sliding of the m-th order is described by the system

$$\left.\begin{aligned} \dot{x}_i &= x_{i+1}, \qquad i = 1, \ldots, n-m-1 \, , \\ \dot{x}_{n-m} &= -\sum_{k=1}^{n-m} c_{m,k}x_k \, . \end{aligned}\right\} \tag{10.10}$$

In particular, sliding of the $(n-1)$th order is given by the equation

$$\dot{x}_1 = -x_1 . \tag{10.11}$$

We note again that the transition from a system of the $(n-m+1)$th order to a system of the $(n-m)$th order describing m-th order sliding was achieved as a result of a certain idealisation of the motion which consisted in considering it only up to the accuracy of its rapidly varying component.

2. If the preceding arguments are to represent anything more than a formal discussion of the problem it will be necessary to examine two points in more detail: we must show that the sliding mode exists, and that after a certain instant of time has been reached the system enters the sliding mode. Consider first the question of the existence of the sliding mode.
For the surface $\sigma_1 = 0$ (at points where $\sigma_2 \neq 0$) to be a sliding surface of system (10.1) it is necessary for the following relations to be fulfilled at the points of this surface

$$\lim_{\sigma_1 \to +0} \dot{\sigma}_1 < 0, \quad \lim_{\sigma_1 \to -0} \dot{\sigma}_1 > 0 . \tag{10.12}$$

From equations (10.1) and (10.2) we obtain

$$\dot{\sigma}_1 = -c_{01}x_1 + (c_{11} - c_{02})x_2 + \ldots + (c_{1,n-1} - c_{0n})x_n .$$

For conditions (10.12) to be fulfilled it is sufficient to require that the inequality

$$b_0(K)|x_1| > |(c_{11} - c_{02})x_2 + \ldots + (c_{1,n-1} - c_{0n}) x_n|$$

be fulfilled. Thus, sliding is absent in the part of the surface $\sigma_1 = 0$ where the following inequality is fulfilled.

$$b_0(K)|x_1| < |(c_{11} - c_{02})x_2 + \ldots + (c_{1,n-1} - c_{0n})x_n| .$$

For sufficiently large K, this will be a narrow sector containing the manifold $\sigma_1 = 0$, $x_1 = 0$. We shall call this sector the sector of sewability When it has reached the boundary of the sector of sewability a point of phase space leaves the surface $\sigma_1 = 0$ only to make a rapid return to it. We therefore have a fast motion here and, applying the procedure given above, we duly neglect it. When it has reached the surface $\sigma_1 = 0$ a point of phase space again begins to execute a fast motion from one part of the surface $\sigma_1 = 0$ (for which $c_{11} > 0$) to the other (for which $c_{11} < 0$). This motion constitutes second order sliding and we consider it in detail below.

The discussion we gave for the existence of the sliding mode in the case of system (10.1) is clearly valid also for system (10.10). Thus, it is proved that for system (10.1) sliding of all orders from the first to the $(n-1)$th, inclusive, exists.

3. The task of proving that a point of phase space falls onto the surface $\sigma_i = 0$ is complicated by the fact that the coefficients entering into the equations for these surfaces are liable to be non-positive. Moreover, the coefficients c_{i1} with $i = 1, ..., n-2$ have alternating sign.

From equation (10.4) it follows that if $x_1^0 \neq 0$ and $\sigma_1 > 0$, then x_n decreases until σ_1 becomes equal to zero. If $\sigma_1 < 0$, then x_n will increase again until we have $\sigma_1 = 0$. Since the image point falls onto the surface $\sigma_1 = 0$ in a finite interval of time, a similar deduction can also be made for the complete system (10.3) if the inequality $|x_1^0| > \varepsilon$ holds during the course of its motion. If the inequality $|x_1^0| < \varepsilon$ is fulfilled, where ε is a sufficiently small number, we shall consider the purpose of the control system to have been achieved. Similar arguments can be given for any of the systems (10.10).

A more detailed discussion of the problem of the incidence of an image point upon a switching surface will be given in the next paragraph for a third order system.

4. Let us consider now in more detail the motions of system (10.1) which accompany first order sliding. We showed above that these motions can be described by equation (10.4) in conjunction with the conditions $x_i = x_i^0 = \text{const}$, for $i = 1, ..., n-1$. On the axis of the variable x_n, consider the points

$$\sigma_1^+ = x_n + b_1(K)x_1^0 + c_{12}x_2^0 + ... + c_{1,n-1}x_{n-1}^0 = 0 ,$$
$$\sigma_1^- = x_n - b_1(K)x_1^0 + c_{12}x_2^0 + ... + c_{1,n-1}x_{n-1}^0 = 0 .$$

It is obvious that for sufficiently large K the points $\sigma_1^+ = 0$ and $\sigma_1 = 0$ are on different sides of the point $x_n = 0$.

The quantity $\sigma_2(x_1^0, ..., x_{n-1}^0)$ is a constant so long as we are considering fast motions. For the sake of definiteness we shall assume that $x_1^0 > 0$ and $\sigma_2(x_1^0, ..., x_{n-1}^0) > 0$. At points of the x_n-axis where the inequality $\sigma_1^- > 0$ is fulfilled we also have $\sigma_1^+ > 0$ and therefore $\sigma_1 > 0$. In the region $\sigma_1^+ < 0$

we correspondingly obtain $\sigma_1 < 0$. If the inequalities $\sigma_1^+ < 0$ and $\sigma_1^- < 0$ are fulfilled simultaneously then, assuming $\sigma_2 > 0$, we obtain from relation (10.2) the result $\sigma_1 = \sigma_1^+$ and, consequently, $\sigma_1 > 0$ in this region. Thus, in region $\sigma_1^+ > 0$, the equation

$$\frac{dx_n}{d\tau} = -x_1^0,$$

is operative, and in the region $\sigma_1^+ < 0$, the equation

$$\frac{dx_n}{d\tau} = x_1^0.$$

is operative. From any position on the straight line Ox_n the motion of point M is governed by equation (10.4) up to the position $\sigma_1^+ = 0$ which, in this case, is the equilibrium position.

If the inequality $\sigma_2(x_1^0, \ldots, x_{n-1}^0) < 0$ is fulfilled, the equilibrium position will be the point $\sigma_1^- = 0$. If $x_1^0 < 0$, the points σ_1^- and σ_1^+ will interchange their positions relative to the coordinate origin and the situation will be the same as before.

Since $x_1^0, \ldots, x_{n-1}^0$ are in fact slowly varying quantities, the equilibrium position also moves slowly but, at the instant when $\sigma_2(x_1^0, \ldots, x_{n-1}^0)$ or x_1^0 change their sign, the equilibrium position instantaneously changes its coordinate, i.e. it transfers from point $\sigma_1^+ = 0$ to point $\sigma_1^- = 0$, or *vice versa*. At the same time the image point changes its direction of motion away from the former equilibrium towards the new one. Thus, in the concluding stages of the motion, the image point executes oscillations between the positions $\sigma_1^+ = 0$ and $\sigma_1^- = 0$. We note that the amplitude of these oscillations diminishes.

Indeed, the coordinate x_n of the equilibrium position is linearly dependent upon the remaining slowly varying coordinates $x_1^0, \ldots, x_{n-1}^0$. The variation of these coordinates is described approximately by system (10.8). If system (10.8) is stable, then even the points $\sigma_1^+ = 0$, $\sigma_1^- = 0$ will execute a slow motion towards the zero point. Thus, from the stability of system (10.8), there follows the stability of system (10.1).

All the arguments given here are valid for any system of the same form as (10.10). Since the process described by equation (10.11) is stable, then, by considering systems of successively increasing order, we can convince ourselves that system (10.1) is stable also.

5. We have defined second order sliding as the motion described by system (10.9). System (10.9) was obtained by ignoring the rapid motions of system (10.8) which describes first order sliding. Instead of examining second order sliding indirectly, it is interesting to examine it directly in the phase space of system (10.1), taking rapid motions into account. For this purpose we change the coordinates of (10.1): $y_i = x_i$, $(i = 1, ..., n-1)$, $y_n = vx_n$, $t = v\tau$, $v^{-2} = b_0(K)$. The new system assumes the form

$$
\left.
\begin{aligned}
\frac{dy_i}{d\tau} &= vy_{i+1}, \qquad i = 1, ..., n-2, \\[2mm]
\frac{dy_{n-1}}{d\tau} &= y_n, \\[2mm]
\frac{dy_n}{d\tau} &= -vc_{0n}y_n - v^2 \sum_{k=2}^{n-2} c_{0k}y_k - |y_1| \operatorname{sign} \sigma_1 .
\end{aligned}
\right\} \tag{10.13}
$$

Let us suppose that $\lim_{k \to \infty} b_1^2(K) b_0^{-1}(K) = 0$. For $v = 0$, we obtain the second order system:

$$
\left.
\begin{aligned}
\frac{dy_{n-1}}{d\tau} &= y_n, \\[2mm]
\frac{dy_n}{d\tau} &= -|y_1^0| \operatorname{sign} \sigma_1, \quad y_i = y_i^0 = \text{const for } i = 1, ..., n-2 .
\end{aligned}
\right\} \tag{10.14}
$$

which describes the rapid motions. The surface $\sigma_1 = 0$ is represented on the plane (y_{n-1}, y_n) by a line made up of the half-lines:

$$
\left.
\begin{aligned}
\sigma_1^+ &= y_n + vc_{1,n}y_{n-1} + v\left(\sum_{k=2}^{n-2} c_{1k}y_k^0 + b_1(K)y_1^0 \right) = 0, \\[2mm]
\sigma_1^- &= y_n + vc_{1,n}y_{n-1} + v\left(\sum_{k=2}^{n-2} c_{1k}y_k^0 - b_1(K)y_1^0 \right) = 0.
\end{aligned}
\right\} \tag{10.15}
$$

If K is sufficiently large, the straight lines $\sigma_1^+ = 0$ and $\sigma_1^- = 0$ lie on opposite sides of the coordinate origin. The line corresponding to the surface $\sigma_2 = 0$ will be made up of segments of the straight lines

$$
\left.
\begin{aligned}
\sigma_2^+ &= y_{n-1} + b_2(K)y_1^0 + \sum_{k=2}^{n-2} c_{2k}y_k^0 = 0, \\[2mm]
\sigma_2^- &= y_{n-1} - b_2(K)y_1^0 + \sum_{k=2}^{n-2} c_{2k}y_k^0 = 0.
\end{aligned}
\right\} \tag{10.16}
$$

It is clear that for K sufficiently large the lines $\sigma_2^+ = 0$ and $\sigma_2^- = 0$ lie on opposite sides of the coordinate origin.

For the sake of definiteness, let $y_1^0 > 0$. The quantity $\sigma_3(y_1^0, ..., y_{n-2}^0)$ is constant and therefore it either has a definite sign or it is equal to zero. Let $\sigma_3(y_1^0, ..., y_{n-2}^0) > 0$. From relation (10.2) it follows that $\sigma_2(y_1^0, ..., y_{n-1}) = \sigma_2^+ (y_1^0, ..., y_{n-1})$ in this case. Thus, we have $\sigma_1 > 0$ in region $\sigma_1^- > 0$ and in the region $\sigma_2^+ > 0$, $\sigma_1^+ > 0$. Consequently, in these regions the following system will be operative

$$\frac{dy_{n-1}}{d\tau} = y_n, \qquad \frac{dy_n}{d\tau} = -y_1^0. \tag{10.17}$$

In region $\sigma_1^+ < 0$ and in region $\sigma_1^- < 0$, $\sigma_2^+ < 0$ the system

$$\frac{dy_{n-1}}{d\tau} = y_n, \qquad \frac{dy_n}{d\tau} = y_1^0$$

will be operative. Thus, the switching line of system (10.4) will be the broken line $ABCEF$ (Fig. 15). If $\sigma_3(y_1^0, ..., y_{n-2}^0) < 0$, the switching line

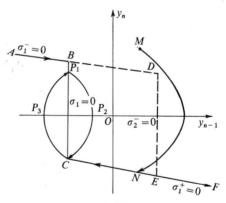

Fig. 15.

will be the broken line $ABDEF$. Fig. 15 shows the form of the integral curve of system (10.14) in the case when $\sigma_3 > 0$, $y_1^0 > 0$, $c_{12}y_2^0 + ... + c_{1,n-2}\,y_{n-2}^0 < 0$.

The point M moves along a parabola under the action of system (10.16), falls onto the straight line CF, and slides along it to the point C. From point C the motion again follows a parabola in accordance with system

(10.17) to the point P_1 which lies on the straight line $\sigma_2^+ = 0$. At point P_1 switching occurs whereupon the motion continues along the limiting cycle $P_1 P_2 C P_3$.

We have now described the rapid motion of the system. The diameter of the limit cycle is obviously of the same order of smallness as v. Moreover, with the (slow) decrease of $y_1^0, \ldots, y_{n-2}^0$ along the trajectory, the diameter of the limit cycle also decreases. From this it follows that if system (10.9) describing second order sliding is stable then system (10.1) also will be stable.

11. An Example of Third Order Focussing under Forced Sliding

1. Consider the third order equation

$$\dddot{x} + a\ddot{x} + b\dot{x} + cx = -\alpha K x .\tag{11.1}$$

equivalent to the system

$$\dot{x} = y, \quad \dot{y} = z, \quad \dot{z} = -cx - by - az - \alpha K x .\tag{11.2}$$

Let the parameters a, b, c and K be arbitrary constants, with K positive. We shall find α using the formula

$$\alpha = \text{sign}\,[xA\,\text{sign}\,x(y + Dx) + By + z]x ,\tag{11.3}$$

where A, B, D are positive constants.

Thus, α can change sign on one of the planes:

$$x = 0, \quad T(x, y) = y + Dx = 0$$

$$R_1(x, y, z) = \quad Ax + By + z = 0 ,\tag{11.4}$$

$$R_2(x, y, z) = -Ax + By + z = 0 .$$

The switching surface is made up of the plane $x = 0$, the surface S consisting of sections S_1 and S_3 of the plane $R_1 = 0$, sections S_2 and S_4 of the plane $R_2 = 0$, and sections T_1 and T_2 of the plane $T(x, y) = y + Dx = 0$ (Fig. 16). The points of the surface S for which $y + Dx \neq 0$ clearly satisfy the equation

$$R(x, y, z) = Ax\,\text{sign}\,x(y + Dx) + By + z = 0 .\tag{11.5}$$

The surface S and the plane $x=0$ divide the phase space into four regions G_1, G_2, G_3, G_4 defined, respectively, by the inequalities:

region G_1: $x>0$, $R>0$
region G_2: $x<0$, $R>0$
region G_3: $x<0$, $R<0$
region G_4: $x>0$, $R<0$.

Clearly, $\alpha=1$ in regions G_1 and G_3 and $\alpha=-1$ in regions G_2 and G_4.

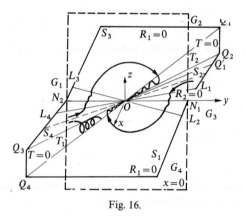

Fig. 16.

On the surface S, near the straight line N_1ON_2 along which the planes $R_1=0$, $R_2=0$ and $x=0$ intersect, there are two sectors L_1OL_2 and L_3OL_4 inside which the trajectories of system (11.2) sew the surface S. It can be shown that by choosing K large enough the angles of these sectors can be made as small as one pleases. At all other points surface S is a sliding surface. The plane $x=0$ is a "sewable" plane.

2. Theorem 11.1. *If parameters A, B, D are positive and* $K \geqslant K_0$, *where* K_0 *is a sufficiently large number, all solutions of system* (11.2) *possess the property*

$$\lim_{t\to\infty} x(t) = \lim_{t\to\infty} y(t) = \lim_{t\to\infty} z(t) = 0 .$$

Of particular interest is the behaviour of the trajectories when the inequalities

$$B^2-4A<0 , \quad D<0.5(B+\sqrt{B^2+4A}) \tag{11.6}$$

are fulfilled. Since this case is more difficult, we shall consider it in detail later on. The typical behaviour of a trajectory when the inequalities (11.6) are fulfilled can be described as follows. An arbitrary point of phase space either falls onto the surface S after a finite interval of time or it falls directly into the coordinate origin during the course of an infinite interval of time. If the point M falls onto sections S_1 or S_3 of surface S, it will thereafter move in accordance with the system

$$\dot{x} = y, \quad \dot{y} = -Ax - By \qquad (11.7)$$

along a spiral curve until it arrives at the plane $T = 0$. Passing through the plane $T = 0$, point M should, for example, fall from section S_3 onto S_2 and from section S_1 onto S_4. On sections S_2 and S_4 of the plane $R_2 = 0$ the motion is governed by the system

$$\dot{x} = y, \quad \dot{y} = Ax - By, \qquad (11.8)$$

and, if K is large enough, M moves along a hyperbolic type of curve towards the plane $T = 0$ again. However, in passing through this plane, the point again falls into the region of attraction of the plane $R_1 = 0$. Thus, having gone from one side of the plane $T = 0$ to the other, and having oscillated between the planes $R_1 = 0$ and $R_2 = 0$, point M arrives at the coordinate origin, i.e. we obtain ideal sliding conditions for the motion of M over the surface S. The straight line

$$y + Dx = 0, \quad z + Dy = 0, \qquad (11.9)$$

exists in the plane $T = 0$ and this line, in a sense, directs the motion of the image point towards the coordinate origin.

In certain cases when inequalities (11.6) are fulfilled the final stages of the motion of the image point may be different. Having moved over the surface S_3 as far as the plane $T = 0$, the point M leaves it, but it is unable to reach section S_2 and turn around the line (11.9) back to S_3. In this case point M spirals rapidly about the line (11.9), and asymptotically approaches the coordinate origin.

We give below in detail the basis for the assertions made above.

3. Let us first prove the theorem. Suppose, for the sake of definiteness, that at zero time the point M lies in region G_1. We shall show first that with increasing t point M falls onto the surface S.

From the proof of theorem (9.1) of the present chapter, it follows that as time increases M either falls onto the plane $R_1 = 0$, and, consequently, onto section S_1 or S_4 of surface S, or it falls onto the plane $x = 0$. In the last case M moves to region G_2. Region G_2 is divided into two parts by the integral plane of system (11.2) when $\alpha = -1$. The equation of this plane has the form

$$(\gamma^2 + \delta^2)x - 2\gamma y + z = 0,$$ (11.10)

where γ and δ are the real and imaginary parts of the roots of the equation

$$\lambda^3 + a\lambda^2 + b\lambda + c - K = 0.$$ (11.11)

For K sufficiently large, equation (11.11) has a pair of complex roots $\gamma \pm i\delta$ ($\gamma < 0$, $\delta > 0$), and a real positive root μ. It is clear that as K increases the quantities $|\gamma|$, δ, μ increase without limit. If point M lies above the integral plane (10.10) then, with increasing t, it moves onto the plane $x = 0$ (for $y < 0$), or falls onto the plane $R_2 = 0$, i.e. onto sections S_2 or S_4 of surface S.

If the point $M(x_0, y_0, z_0)$ lies below the plane (11.10), it is not difficult to show that M cannot leave region G_2 *via* the plane $x = 0$. The truth of these assertions follows from the proof of theorem 9.1.

On the other hand, it is easy to see that along the trajectory of point M we have

$$R_2(x, y, z) = c_0 e^{\mu t}(\mu^2 + B\mu - A) + \varphi(t),$$ (11.12)

where $\varphi(t) \to 0$ for $t \to \infty$ and

$$c_0 = [(\gamma^2 + \delta^2)x_0 - 2\gamma y_0 + z_0][(\mu - \gamma)^2 + \delta^2]^{-1}.$$

Since, for sufficiently large K, the quantity $\mu^2 + B\mu - A$ is positive, then $R_2(x, y, z)$ must necessarily move from the region of positive values $(R_2(x_0, y_0, z_0) > 0)$ to the region of negative values. Thus, point M either falls onto sections S_2 or S_3 of surface S or it moves onto the plane $x = 0$, with $y \geqslant 0$. However, in the last case of Section 9, it was proved that, having fallen into region G_1, M must necessarily fall onto the plane $R_1 = 0$, i.e. either onto sections S_1, S_4 of surface S or onto section T_1 of the plane $T = 0$.

Thus, any point of phase space necessarily falls onto the surface S.

4.   Let us consider further the motion of point M along the surface S assuming that inequalities (11.6) are fulfilled.

Since $B^2 - 4A < 0$, point O is a singular point of the "focus" type for system (11.7), and a singular point of the "saddle" type for system (11.8).

From the second inequality of (11.6) it follows that one of the separatrices of system (11.8) lies on sections S_2 and S_4 of surface S. Thus it is easy to establish the character of the motion of the point along the surface S up to the time when it has reached the plane $T = y + Dx = 0$, or as far as the sectors of sewability L_1OL_2, L_3OL_4. In the last case M moves off surface S but it falls onto it again on the other side of the sector. With increasing K the magnitude of the deviation of the point from S can be made as small as one pleases (see Section 7 of this Chapter).

It remains now to consider the behaviour of points which have fallen onto the plane $T = 0$, i.e. those that have fallen onto one of the lines OQ_i ($i = 1, 2, 3, 4$; Fig. 16).

Let us assume for definiteness that M lies on the line OQ_1. It is not difficult to see that when conditions (11.6) are fulfilled the line of intersection of the plane $z + Dy = 0$ with the plane $T = 0$ lies in the sector formed by the line of intersection of the planes $R_1 = 0$ and $R_2 = 0$. Therefore, the quantity $\dot{T}$ changes sign along the trajectory of point M and the motion is substantially curvilinear.

Taking the small parameter method as a basis one can show by means of the arguments given in Section 10 that in its final stages the motion of the image point takes it along a spiral curve which twists around the straight line (11.9); this motion will also constitute second order sliding. Thus, second order sliding is complicated by rapid motions around the straight line (11.9). Disregarding the rapid motions leads to an idealisation of second order sliding, and we obtain the equation $\dot{x} + Dx = 0$ which describes ideal sliding of the second order.

5.   Let us describe briefly the remaining cases when one of the inequalities (11.6) is not fulfilled. If the equality

$$B^2 - 4A \geqslant 0 . \tag{11.13}$$

is fulfilled, then the coordinate origin for system (11.7) will be a singular point of the "knot" type. If, in addition to (11.7), the inequality

$$D < 0.5\left(B + \sqrt{B^2 + 4A}\right) , \tag{11.14}$$

is fulfilled, then some of the points S_1 and S_3 will enter the coordinate origin along the straight line

$$y = -0.5(B - \sqrt{B^2 - 4A})x, \qquad R_1 = 0, \tag{11.15}$$

the remaining points will again fall onto the plane $y + Dx = 0$ and thereafter execute a sliding motion towards point O. This motion will be of exactly the same kind as that considered earlier.

If, in addition to (11.13), the condition

$$D \geqslant 0.5(B + \sqrt{B^2 + 4A}), \tag{11.16}$$

is fulfilled, then all the points of surface S will complete their motion towards the coordinate origin along the straight line (11.15).

If, in addition to (11.16), the inequality $B^2 - 4A < 0$ is fulfilled, then "second sliding" will not occur. In this case the image point having fallen, for example, onto section S_3 goes as far as the line OQ_1. If K is sufficiently large, the line OQ_1 crosses over as a whole into the line OQ'_1, which lies arbitrarily close to the line OQ_2. In fact, the line of intersection of the plane $Dy + z = 0$ with the plane $T = 0$ in this case lies outside the sector formed by the lines of intersection of the planes $R_1 = 0$, $R_2 = 0$. In the region $T_1 \geqslant 0$, $R_2 > 0$, $x < 0$ an unstable system is in operation, since $\alpha = -1$. The quantity $\dot{T}$ does not change sign along the trajectory of the motion. Consequently, for K sufficiently large, it can be assumed that point M crosses over from line OQ_1 to line OQ'_1 along a straight line.

Having fallen onto the line OQ'_1, the image point M will slide along section S_2 untill it reaches the sector of sewability L_1OL_2. Having fallen onto the line OL_1 the image point moves off the surface S and, after a short interval of time (compare Section 7), it again falls not onto the surface S but this time onto S_1.

We note that if the projection of point M on the plane (x, y) moves in accordance with system (11.7) then, during time Δt, it will fall onto the line $D_1 x + y = 0$ (with an accuracy up to the small quantities $\partial(K^{-1})$). This fact suggests the following interpretation of the motion along the surface S: the surface $R = 0$ is continuous, $R = R_1(x, y, z)$, and A changes its sign on the plane $T' = D_1 x + y = 0$ and not on the plane $T = 0$.

If in this case we neglect an error of the same order as K^{-2}, the motion of the point along the surface S can be described by the system

$$\dot{x} = y, \quad \dot{y} = -By - \alpha_1 Ax, \quad \alpha_1 = \text{sign } x(y + D_1 x). \tag{11.17}$$

The time derivative of the function $v = Ax + y$ taken in accordance with system (11.17) has the form

$$\dot{v} = -2By^2 + 2A(1-\alpha_1)xy =$$

$$= \begin{cases} -2By^2 & \text{for} \quad (D_1x+y)x \geqslant 0, \\ -2By^2 - 4A|xy| & \text{for} \quad (D_1x+y)x < 0. \end{cases}$$

Consequently, the function $v(x, y)$ satisfies the conditions of theorem 12.2 of Chapter 1, and from that there follows the asymptotic stability on the whole of the zero solution of (11.17). In the given case, though, the truth of our theorem follows from a direct qualitative study of the behaviour of the trajectories on the surface S. We note that in this case the image point moves towards point O along a spiral curve inclined insignificantly from S in the sectors L_1OL_2, L_3OL_4.

Finally, we note that the theorem we have proved could be interpreted as a theorem about the asymptotic stability of the zero equilibrium position. For the sake of mathematical rigour one could in this case show that for any $\varepsilon > 0$ it is possible to find a number δ such that from $x_0^2 + y_0^2 + z_0^2 < \delta^2$ there would follow, for $t > 0$, $x^2(t) + y^2(t) + z^2(t) \leqslant \varepsilon^2$, where $x(t)$, $y(t)$, $z(t)$ is the solution of system (11.2) determined by the initial conditions $x(0) = x_0$, $y(0) = y_0$, $z(0) = z_0$.

We shall, however, omit the proof of this statement; we shall simply note that a proof could be given along exactly the same lines as that given in section 8 of this Chapter.

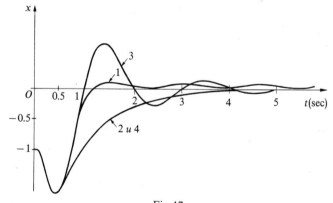

Fig. 17.

Fig. 17 presents some transient response graphs obtained on an MN-14 computer with the following parameters: $a=0$, $b=0$, $c=1$, $K=100$. Curve (1) corresponds to the parameters $A=12$, $B=2$, $D=2, 3, 4$. Clearly, both the inequalities (11.6) are fulfilled in this case. Curve (2) corresponds to the case when the inequalities (11.13) and (11.14) are fulfilled; here we have taken $A = 10$, $B = 10$, $D = 5$. Curve (4) coincides with curve (2) since it was obtained with the values $A = 10$, $B = 10$, $D = 20$. In this case changing D ensured that the inequalities (11.13) and (11.16) were fulfilled without affecting the course of the transient response. This is completely in accord with the conclusions reached above since in both the cases considered the motion is completed along the straight line (11.15).

Finally, curve (3) corresponds to the values $A = 10$, $B = 2$, $D = 10$. In this case the inequalities $B^2 - 4A < 0$ and (11.16) are fulfilled and therefore second order sliding is absent.

Thus, only the transient response represented by (1) corresponds to a process where second order sliding is present. From a comparison of these curves one can conclude that variable structure systems operating under forced sliding conditions possess a number of significant advantages.

Chapter 3

STABILITY OF THE SOLUTIONS OF DIFFERENTIAL EQUATIONS IN BANACH SPACE

1. Banach Space

1. Consider a set E and let us introduce the two mathematical operations: addition of the elements and multiplication by a number. Let these operations satisfy the following conditions:

(1) $x + y = y + x$ (commutativity of addition),
(2) $(x + y) + z = x + (y + z)$ (associativity of addition),
(3) $\lambda(x + y) = \lambda x + \lambda y$ (distributivity of multiplication with respect
(4) $(\lambda + \mu)x = \lambda x + \mu x$ to addition),
(5) $\lambda(\mu x) = (\lambda \mu)x$ (associativity of multiplication),
(6) there exists in E a (zero) element 0 such that $0x = 0$,
(7) $1 \cdot x = x$.

Let us further suppose that for each element x of E there exists a well-defined non-negative number $\|x\|$ called the norm of element x. Let the norm of x satisfy the following conditions:

(a) $\|x\| = 0$ is equivalent to $x = 0$,
(b) $\|\lambda x\| = |\lambda| \, \|x\|$ (uniformity of the norm)
(c) $\|x + y\| \leqslant \|x\| + \|y\|$ (triangle inequality).

If the operations of addition and multiplication by a number that are introduced into set E satisfy conditions 1–7 and if, in addition, the concept of a norm is defined in accordance with conditions (a), (b) and (c), then the set E is called a linear normalised space.

The simplest example of a linear normalised space is a finite-dimensional vector space. Examples in which the norm was introduced into this space were given in Section 1 of Chapter 1.

A normalised linear space E is said to be complete if, from $\|x_n - x_m\| \to 0$, $(m, n \to \infty)$, it follows that the sequence $\{x_n\}$ along the norm converges to an element x_0 of this space. A complete linear normalised space will be called a Banach space, or simple a B-space.

Consider two linear normalised spaces E_1 and E_2. In a certain sub-set X of the space E_1 let a function $F(x)$ be defined having values in the space E_2.

In other words, a mapping $F(x)$ of set X into the space E_2 is specified. The mapping $F(x)$ will henceforth be designated an operator. As a special case the spaces E_1 and E_2 may coincide. The operator mapping E_1 onto the number axis is called a functional.

The operator $F(x)$ is said to be linear if it is additive and homogeneous, i.e. if the relation

$$F(\alpha x_1 + \beta x_2) = \alpha F(x_1) + \beta F(x_2)$$

is fulfilled, where α, β are scalar quantities.

The operator $F(x)$ is said to be continuous if it translates every converging (with respect to the norm in E_1) sequence of elements into a converging (with respect to the norm in E_2) sequence of elements. The operator $F(x)$ is said to be bounded if it translates every bounded (with respect to the norm) set into a bounded set.

A linear operator is continuous if and only if it is bounded ([71]). For a linear continuous operator F, a positive number K can be found such that for all elements $x \subset E_1$ on which the operator F is defined the following inequality holds.

$$\|F(x)\| \leqslant K\|x\| . \tag{1.1}$$

The smallest of the numbers K for which inequality (1.1) is fulfilled is called the norm of operator F and is denoted by $\|F\|$. We shall in future often use the notation $F(x) = Fx$ for the linear operator.

It is easy to see that the norm of a linear bounded operator may be defined by the relation

$$\|F\| = \sup_{\|x\| \leqslant 1} \|Fx\| . \tag{1.2}$$

2. A linear operator acting in a finite-dimensional space E_n can be specified by a matrix. Thus, relation (1.2) can be regarded as the definition of the norm of the matrix, this norm being consistent with the specified way of introducing the norm in the space E_n. Let us consider examples of the definition of the norm of a matrix A which transforms the vector space E_n into its part.

Example 1. Let the norm of a vector in the n-dimensional space E_n be defined by the formula

$$\|x\| = \left(\sum_{i=1}^{n} x_i^2 \right)^{\frac{1}{2}} . \tag{1.3}$$

and let A be a square $n \times n$ matrix with elements a_{ik}.
It is easy to see that

$$\|A\|^2 = \sup_{\|x\| \leqslant 1} \|Ax\|^2 = \sup_{\|x\| \leqslant 1} \sum_{i=1}^{n} \left(\sum_{k=1}^{n} a_{ik} x_k \right)^2 = \sup_{\|x\| \leqslant 1} (A^* Ax, x) .$$

By virtue of inequality (10.3) of Chapter 1, the quantity $\|A\|^2$ is in this case equal to the largest eigenvalue of the quadratic form $(A^* Ax, x)$. We note also that in this case the following simple estimate is valid for the norm of matrix A

$$\|A\| \leqslant \left(\sum_{i,k=1}^{n} a_{ik}^2 \right)^{\frac{1}{2}} . \tag{1.4}$$

Example 2. Let the norm of a vector be specified by the formula

$$\|x\| = \max_i |x_i| . \tag{1.5}$$

Clearly, we have

$$\|Ax\| = \sup_i \left| \sum_{k=1}^{n} a_{ik} x_k \right| \leqslant \|x\| \sup_i \sum_{k=1}^{n} |a_{ik}| = L \|x\| .$$

Thus

$$\|A\| \leqslant \sup_i \sum_{k=1}^{n} |a_{ik}| = L .$$

We shall show now that $\|A\| \geqslant L$. Consider a value of i_0 for which $\Sigma_{k=1}^{n} |a_{i_0 k}| = L$, and consider the vector $x^0 (x_1^0, \ldots, x_n^0)$, where $x_k^0 = \operatorname{sign} a_{i_0 k}$. It is easy to see that $\|x^0\| = 1$ and $\|A\| \geqslant \|Ax^0\| = \Sigma_{k=1}^{n} |a_{i_0 k}| = L$. Thus, in this case, we have

$$\|A\| = \sup_i \sum_{k=1}^{n} |a_{ik}| . \tag{1.6}$$

Example 3. Let the norm of a vector be specified by the formula

$$\|x\| = \sum_{i=1}^{n} |x_i| . \tag{1.7}$$

We shall show that for the norm of matrix A the following relation is valid:

$$\|A\| = \sup_k \sum_{i=1}^n |a_{ik}| . \tag{1.8}$$

Indeed, it is easy to see that

$$\|Ax\| = \sum_{i=1}^n \left| \sum_{k=1}^n a_{ik} x_k \right| \leqslant \|x\| \sup_k \sum_{i=1}^n |a_{ik}| .$$

Thus,

$$\|A\| \leqslant \sup_k \sum_{i=1}^n |a_{ik}| = M .$$

Let k_0 be the value of the index for which $M = \sum_{i=1}^n |a_{ik_0}|$. Consider the vector $\bar{x}$ with projections $x_i = 0$ with $i \neq k_0$ and $x_{k_0} = 1$. It is clear that $\|\bar{x}\| = 1$ and, in addition

$$\|A\| \geqslant \|A\bar{x}\| = \sum_{i=1}^n |a_{ik_0}| = M .$$

3.   Consider now the case when E is a linear normalised space and B is a Banach space. We shall consider the aggregate of all linear operators which translate the space E into the space B, and we shall denote this aggregate by the symbol $[E \rightarrow B]$. Let F_1 and F_2 be operators belonging to $[E \rightarrow B]$. According to definition, $F = F_1 + F_2$ if for any $x \subset E$ we have $Fx = F_1 x + F_2 x$. Linear operators may also act simply as multipliers. Let E_1, E_2, E_3 be linear normalised spaces and let $F \in [E_1 \rightarrow E_2]$ and $\Phi \in [E_2 \rightarrow E_3]$. The product of F and Φ will be understood to mean the operator ΦF which translates E_1 into E_3 according to the rule $\Phi F(x) = \Phi(F(x))$, where $x \in E_1$.

It is easy to see the validity of the inequality

$$\|\Phi F\| \leqslant \|\Phi\| \, \|F\| .$$

If in the space $[E \rightarrow B]$ the norm is introduced according to (1.2), then it can be shown that the space $[E \rightarrow B]$ will be a complete linear normalised space, i.e. a Banach space.

In what follows we shall need the following theorems.

Theorem 1.1 (Banach–Steinhaus) ([71]). *If a sequence of bounded linear operations $\{F_n\}$ which translates the Banach space E_1 into a linear normalised* space E_2, is bounded at every point, i.e. if

$$\sup_n \|F_n x\| < \infty,$$

then the norms of these operations are bounded in the aggregate $\|F_n\| \leqslant M < \infty$ $(n = 1, 2, ...)$.

Theorem 1.2 (the principle of condensed mappings [72]. *Let the operator F translate the sphere T of a Banach space into itself and let the condition*

$$\|F(x_1) - F(x_2)\| \leqslant \alpha \|x_1 - x_2\|,$$

be fulfilled, where $0 < \alpha < 1$.
The equation $F(x) = x$ *has a unique solution* x *in sphere* T *which may be found by the method of successive approximations.*

4.   Let the function $x(t)$ with values in the Banach space E be specified on the number axis.
Following the usual rules, one can define the derivative and the integral of function $x(t)$. Thus, for example, the derivative (according to Fresh) of function $x(t)$ at point t_0 can be defined according to the rule

$$\dot{x}(t_0) = \lim_{t \to t_0} \frac{x(t) - x(t_0)}{t - t_0},$$

provided a limit (in the sense of convergence along the norm) exists. We shall define the definite integral (according to Bochner) of the function $x(t)$ as the limit of an integral sum of the form

$$S_n = \sum_{k=0}^{n-1} x(\tau_k)(t_{k+1} - t_k),$$

where $\alpha = t_0 < t_1 < t_2 < ... < t_n = \beta$, $t_k \leqslant \tau_k \leqslant t_{k+1}$, $k = 0, 1, ..., n-1$, with the condition that $n \to \infty$ and $\sup_k |t_{k+1} - t_k| \to 0$. If the limit exists and if it is independent of the method of partitioning of the interval $[\alpha, \beta]$ into partial intervals and independent of the choice of the points τ_k within the partial intervals, then we shall say that the integral of function $x(t)$ with respect to the interval $[\alpha, \beta]$ exists, and we shall denote this integral by the symbol $\int_\alpha^\beta x(t) dt$.
We shall discuss now the idea of a complete variation of an abstract function $g(t)$ which assumes values in E.
Consider again the interval $[\alpha, \beta]$ of the t-axis and all possible partitions of this interval $\alpha = t_0 < t_1 < ... < t_n = \beta$ into a finite number of partial

intervals. According to definition, the quantity

$$\sup \sum_{k=0}^{n-1} \|g(t_{k+1}) - g(t_k)\| = \bigvee_{\alpha}^{\beta} g(t),$$

where the upper limit is taken in accordance with this division of the interval $[\alpha, \beta]$ into all possible partitions, is called the complete variation of the function $g(t)$ on the interval $[\alpha, \beta]$. With this definition it is, of course, possible to suppose that $\beta = \infty$. In this case we will assume that the function $g(t)$ has a bounded variation on the set $\alpha \leqslant t < \infty$ if $g(t)$ has a bounded variation in any finite part $[\alpha, t]$, and if the complete variations $\bigvee_{\alpha}^{t} g(t)$ are bounded in their aggregate. In this case we suppose that

$$\bigvee_{\alpha}^{\infty} g(t) = \sup_{t \geqslant \alpha} \bigvee_{\alpha}^{t} g(s).$$

If E is a Banach space, then a function $g(t)$ with a bounded variation can have at most a denumerable number of points of discontinuity and its one-sided limits exist at any point of the interval $[\alpha, \beta]$ (Reference [73], p. 73).

We will now give a definition of the Stieltjes integral. Let $U(t)$ be a linear operator which is continuous with respect to t and which translates the elements of E into E, and let $g(t)$ be a function with a bounded variation over the interval $[\alpha, \beta]$.

Let us compose an integral sum of the form

$$S_n = \sum_{k=0}^{n-1} U(\tau_k)(g(t_{k+1}) - g(t_k)), \qquad t_k \leqslant \tau_k \leqslant t_{k+1},$$

where the points t_k $(t_0 = \alpha, t_n = \beta)$ partition the interval $[\alpha, \beta]$. If a limit S_n exists for $n \to \infty$, $\sup_k |t_{k+1} - t_k| \to 0$, which is independent of the way in which the interval $[\alpha, \beta]$ is sub-divided into partial intervals, then we shall say that this limit is a generalised Stieltjes integral of the operator $U(t)$ with respect to the function $g(t)$. We shall write this integral:

$$\int_{\alpha}^{\beta} U(t) \, dg.$$

It is not difficult to verify that the following inequality holds

$$\left\| \int_{\alpha}^{\beta} U(t) \, dg \right\| \leqslant M \bigvee_{\alpha}^{\beta} g(t), \tag{1.9}$$

where $M = \sup_{\alpha \leqslant t \leqslant \beta} \|U(t)\|$.

Consider the scalar function $v(t) = \overset{t}{\underset{\alpha}{\vee}}\, g(t)$. It is easy to see that

$$\left\| \int_\alpha^\beta U(t)\,dg \right\| \leqslant \int_\alpha^\beta \| U(t)\|\,dv\,, \tag{1.10}$$

where the integral on the right-hand side is an ordinary Stieltjes integral with the integrating function $v(t)$.

2. Differential Equations in Banach Space

1. Suppose that in correspondence with each real value of t an operator $X(x, t)$ is formed which translates the space E into itself. In that case one can consider the differential equation

$$\dot{x} = X(x, t)\,, \tag{2.1}$$

where $\dot{x}$ denotes, as usual, the derivative of the abstract function $x(t)$ with respect to t.

It is clear that the solution of equation (2.1), which satisfies the initial condition $x(t_0) = x$, must also be a solution of the integral equation

$$x(t) = x_0 + \int_{t_0}^t X(x(t), t)\,dt\,. \tag{2.2}$$

Let D denote the region $\|x - x_0\| \leqslant r$, $|t - t_0| \leqslant T$, and let us suppose that in this region the operator function $X(x, t)$ is continuous and satisfies the Lipschitz condition

$$\| X(x, t) - X(y, t)\| \leqslant L\|x - y\|\,. \tag{2.3}$$

By virtue of the continuity of $X(x, t)$, the function $\| X(x_0, t)\|$ will be bounded over the interval $|t - t_0| \leqslant T$. Let $M_0 = \sup \| X(x_0, t)\|$ over this interval. From the Lipschitz condition we have

$$\| X(x, t)\| \leqslant \| X(x_0, t)\| + L\|x - x_0\| \leqslant M_0 + rL\,.$$

Thus, assuming $M = M_0 + rL$, in region D we obtain

$$\| X(x, t)\| \leqslant M\,. \tag{2.4}$$

We shall now give the simplest version of the theorem for the existence and uniqueness of the solution of equation (2.1) based on the principle of condensed mappings.

Theorem 2.1.   *Assuming the conditions given above, equation* (2.1) *has a unique solution* $x(t)$ *which satisfies the condition* $x(t_0) = x_0$ *and this solution is well-defined over the interval* $|t - t_0| < rM^{-1}$.

To prove this theorem consider the operator

$$A(x(t)) = x_0 + \int_{t_0}^{t} X(x(t), t)\, dt\,,$$

which translates the continuous function $x(t)$ into another continuous function. The space C of continuous functions with the norm

$$\|x(t)\|_C = \sup_{|t-t_0| \leqslant T} \|x(t)\|_E$$

will clearly be a Banach space.
From condition (2.3) it follows that

$$\|A(x(t)) - A(y(t))\|_C \leqslant L|t - t_0|\, \|x(t) - y(t)\|_C\,,$$

and from the inequality (2.4) we obtain

$$\|A(x(t)) - x_0\|_C \leqslant M(t - t_0)\,.$$

If we set $|t - t_0| < rM^{-1}$, then we obtain $\|A(x(t) - x_0\|_C \leqslant r$ and, in addition,

$$\|A(x(t)) - A(y(t))\|_C \leqslant \alpha \|x(t) - y(t)\|_C\,,$$

where $\alpha = rLM^{-1} = rL(M_0 + rL)^{-1} < 1$. Thus, the operator A translates a sphere $\|x(t) - x_0\| \leqslant r$ of Banach space into itself and satisfies the conditions of theorem (1.2).

The theorem we have proved asserts that a solution exists in the interval $|t - t_0| < d$ only, when $d = rM^{-1}$. Taking the end of this interval for the starting point we can continue the solution further, but there is no guarantee that this continuation is possible over the whole of an infinite interval of time. It is clear that where the solution cannot be continued, for bounded values of the time t the trajectory moves outside the limits of an arbitrary bounded region of space E.
Let us make the last statement more precise. For $t \geqslant t_0$, suppose that the solution $x(t)$ does not move out of the region G_1 given by the inequality $\|x - x_0\| < r_1$, where $r_1 < r$. Suppose that in region G specified by the

inequality $\|x - x_0\| < r$, condition (2.3) is fulfilled for $t \geq t_0$ and, also the condition

$$\| X(x_0, t)\| \leq N < \infty .$$ (2.5)

From conditions (2.3) and (2.5) it follows that $\|X(x, t)\| \leq M$ for $t \geq t_0$, where $M = N + rL$.

It is clear that at any instant of time during which the trajectory is in region G_1 it can be continued further for an interval of time $d = rM^{-1}$ which is independent of the particular instant at which the continuation is made. Thus, in this case, the solution can be continued into the time interval $t_0 \leq t < \infty$. We have therefore just proved the following assertion:

Theorem 2.2. *If conditions (2.3) and (2.5) are fulfilled in the region $\|x - x_0\| \leq r < \infty$, then any trajectory which does not pass out of a subregion $\|x - x_0\| \leq r_1 < r$ is continuable into the infinite time interval $t_0 \leq t < \infty$.*

We give also some other tests of continuability for the solutions.

Theorem 2.3. *For $\|x\| < \infty$, $t \geq t_0$ let the condition*

$$\|X(x, t)\| \leq L(\|x\|) ,$$ (2.6)

be fulfilled, where $L(r)$ is a continuous function possessing the property

$$\int_{r_0}^{r} \frac{dr}{L(r)} \to \infty \quad for \quad r \to \infty .$$ (2.7)

Every solution of the equation (2.1) may be continued into the infinite time interval $t_0 \leq t < \infty$.

Indeed, since

$$\left\| \frac{x(t_2) - x(t_1)}{t_2 - t_1} \right\| \geq \left| \frac{\|x(t_2)\| - \|x(t_1)\|}{t_2 - t_1} \right| ,$$

we have $\|dx/dt\| \geq |(d\|x\|)/dt|$. Whence it follows that $|(d\|x\|)/dt| \leq L(\|x\|)$. Taking the integral along the curve $x = x(t)$ from the point $x_0 = x(t_0)$ to the point x in the sense of increasing t, we obtain,

$$t - t_0 \geq \int_{\|x_0\|}^{\|x\|} \frac{dr}{L(r)} .$$ (2.8)

Thus, if $\|x\| \to \infty$ then $t \to \infty$ also, which means that the solution is continuable. If $\|x\|$ remains bounded, the solution will be continuable by virtue of theorem 2.2.

Theorem 2.4 (Krasnosel'skii and Krein [74]). *Suppose a functional $\Phi(x)$ exists which possesses the property*

$$\lim_{\|x\| \to \infty} \Phi(x) = \infty , \quad \frac{d\Phi}{dt} \leqslant L(\Phi(x))$$

for $t \geqslant t_0$, where $d\Phi/dt$ is the derivative of $\Phi(x)$ along the trajectories of equations (2.1) and the function $L(r)$ satisfies condition (2.7). Then every solution of equation (2.1) will be continuable in the interval $t_0 \leqslant t < \infty$.

In fact, from condition (2.7) we get (2.8) again. If $\|x\| \to \infty$, then $\Phi(x) \to \infty$ also, so that we have $t \to \infty$, which demonstrates the continuability of the unbounded solution.

In particular, from theorem 2.3 it follows that if in E conditions (2.3) and (2.5) are fulfilled for $t \geqslant t_0$, then every solution of equation (2.1) is continuable over a semi-infinite time interval. It is clear that for theorem 2.3 to be applicable in this case one should set $L(r) = Lr + N$.

In conclusion, we will state a theorem which considerably extends the conditions of existence given in theorem 2.1.

Theorem 2.5 (Krasnosel'skii and Krein [74]). *Let $X(x, t) = X_1(x, t) + X_2(x, t)$, where the operator $X_1(x, t)$ is completely continuous, i.e. it translates every bounded set from D into a compact set of the space E, and the operator $X_2(x, t)$ is continuous in D and satisfies the condition*

$$\|X_2(x, t) - X_2(y, t)\| \leqslant K(t)\|x - y\| .$$

Let $d > 0$ so that $\displaystyle\int_{t_0 - d}^{t_0 + d} K(t)\, dt < 1$ *and*

$$d \left[\sup_D \|X_1(x, t)\| + \sup_D \|X_2(x, t)\| \right] \leqslant r .$$

Then there exists a solution $x(t)$ of equation (2.1) which is well-defined over the interval $t_0 - d \leqslant t \leqslant t_0 + d$ and such that $x(t_0) = x_0$.

From now on we shall not specifically state the conditions that ensure the existence of the solutions of the differential equations under consideration; we shall always assume that such conditions are fulfilled.

2. The following lemma considerably generalises lemma 1.1 of Chapter 1.

Lemma 2.1. *Let $u(t)$ and $f(t)$ be scalar non-negative functions integrable over the interval $t_0 \leqslant t \leqslant t_0 + T$ of the function. In addition, assume that the scalar non-negative function $K(t, s)$ is bounded for $t_0 \leqslant s \leqslant t \leqslant t_0 + T$. If the inequality*

$$u(t) \leqslant f(t) + \int_{t_0}^{t} K(t, s) u(s) ds, \tag{2.9}$$

is valid then the inequality $u(t) \leqslant \psi(t)$ is also valid for $t_0 \leqslant t \leqslant t_0 + T$, where $\psi(t)$ is the solution of the integral equation.

$$\psi(t) = f(t) + \int_{t_0}^{t} K(t, s) \psi(s) ds. \tag{2.10}$$

In our proof of lemma 2.1 we shall follow Krein [75] (p. 64) who considered the case of continuous functions $u(t), f(t)$ and $K(t, s)$. Using the notation

$$Ku = \int_{t_0}^{t} K(t, s) u(s) ds,$$

we obtain from (2.9)

$$u \leqslant f + Kf + \ldots + K^{n-1}f + K^n u. \tag{2.11}$$

Let $|K(t, s)| \leqslant M$ for $t_0 \leqslant s \leqslant t \leqslant t_0 + T$. It is easy to prove ([74], p. 23) that

$$|K^n u| \leqslant \frac{M^n T^{n-1}}{(n-1)!} \int_{t_0}^{t_0 + T} |u(s)| ds.$$

Consequently, $|K^n u| \to 0$ as $n \to \infty$ and the series $\Gamma f = f + Kf + \ldots + K^{n-1}f + \ldots$ converges to the solution of the integral equation (2.10). Thus, from (2.11), we have $u(t) \leqslant \psi(t)$.

Lemma 2.2 (Repin [77]). *Let $u(t), f(t)$ be non-negative functions integrable over the interval $t_0 \leqslant t \leqslant t_0 + T$ of the function; let L be a positive constant. If the inequality*

$$u(t) \leqslant f(t) + L \int_{t_0}^{t} u(s)\,ds, \qquad t_0 \leqslant t \leqslant t_0 + T, \tag{2.12}$$

is fulfilled then the following inequality holds

$$u(t) \leqslant f(t) + L \int_{t_0}^{t} e^{L(t-s)} f(s)\,ds. \tag{2.13}$$

The validity of this lemma follows immediately from lemma (2.1). It is easy to convince oneself by a direct check that the function

$$\psi(t) = f(t) + L \int_{t_0}^{t} e^{L(t-s)} f(s)\,ds$$

satisfies the integral equation

$$\psi(t) = f(t) + L \int_{t_0}^{t} \psi(s)\,ds.$$

Lemma 2.3. *Assume that the conditions of the preceding lemma are fulfilled. Let $f(t)$ be a function of bounded variation over the interval $t_0 \leqslant t \leqslant t_0 + T$, then it follows from inequality (2.12) that*

$$u(t) \leqslant f(t_0) e^{L(t-t_0)} + \int_{t_0}^{t} e^{L(t-s)} df(s), \tag{2.14}$$

where the integral on the right-hand side is a Stieltjes integral. If the function $f(t)$ is differentiable, then the following inequality is valid

$$u(t) \leqslant f(t_0) e^{L(t-t_0)} + \int_{t_0}^{t} e^{L(t-s)} f'(s)\,ds. \tag{2.15}$$

Inequality (2.14) follows directly from inequality (2.13) if the formula for integrating by parts is used for the integral on the right-hand side, the conditions of applicability of this formula being fulfilled in the case we are considering.

3.   Consider now the equation

$$\dot{x} = X(x, t) \tag{2.16}$$

together with the equation

$$\dot{y} = X(y, t) + R(y, t) . \tag{2.17}$$

Suppose that in the region $D: \|x\| \leqslant r, t_0 \leqslant t \leqslant t_0 + T$ the following conditions are fulfilled

$$\|X(x, t) - X(y, t)\| \leqslant L\|x - y\| , \tag{2.18}$$

and

$$\|R(x, t)\| \leqslant \eta(t) , \tag{2.19}$$

where $\eta(t)$ is a continuous function over the interval $t_0 \leqslant t \leqslant t_0 + T$.
Suppose that, in addition to conditions (2.18) and (2.19), the conditions ensuring the existence of solutions of equations (2.16) and (2.17) in the above region are fulfilled. By virtue of theorem (2.1) these conditions can be either the continuity of the operators $X(x, t)$, $R(x, t)$ in region D and the fulfilment of the Lipschitz condition for $R(x, t)$ or, by virtue of theorem 2.5, the continuity of $X(x, t)$ and the complete continuity of $R(x, t)$.
Let $x(t)$ be a solution of equation (2.6) satisfying the condition $x(t_0) = x_0$ and let $y(t)$ be a solution of equation (2.17) such that $y(t_0) = y_0$.

Theorem 2.6. *For $t_0 \leqslant t \leqslant t_0 + T$, the estimate*

$$\|x(t) - y(t)\| \leqslant \|x_0 - y_0\| e^{L(t - t_0)} + \int_{t_0}^{t} e^{L(t - s)} \eta(s) ds . \tag{2.20}$$

is true.

In fact, from the integral equations

$$x(t) = x_0 + \int_{t_0}^{t} X(x, t) dt ,$$

$$y(t) = y_0 + \int_{t_0}^{t} [X(y, t) + R(y, t)] dt .$$

Corresponding to the conditions (2.16) and (2.17), we have

$$\|x(t) - y(t)\| \leqslant \|x_0 - y_0\| + \int_{t_0}^{t} \{\|X(x, t) - X(y, t)\| +$$

$$+ \|R(y, t)\|\} dt .$$

Using (2.18) and (2.19), we obtain

$$\|x(t) - y(t)\| \leqslant \|x_0 - y_0\| + \int_{t_0}^{t} \eta(t) dt + L \int_{t_0}^{t} \|x(t) - y(t)\| dt .$$

The inequality we wish to prove now follows from inequality (2.15). Consider the special cases:

(a) If $\eta(t) = 0$, we obtain the estimate

$$\|x(t) - y(t)\| \leqslant \|x_0 - y_0\| \, e^{L(t-t_0)} \, ,$$

from which there follows the continuity of the solution of equation (2.16) with respect to the initial data.

(b) If $x_0 = y_0$ and $\eta(t) \leqslant \eta_0$ for $t_0 \leqslant t \leqslant t_0 + T$, we obtain the estimate

$$\|x(t) - y(t)\| \leqslant \frac{\eta_0}{L} \left(e^{L(t-t_0)} - 1 \right) .$$

(c) If we suppose that

$$\int_{t_0}^{t_0 + T} \eta(t) \, dt = \eta_1 \, ,$$

we obtain, for $x_0 = y_0$,

$$\|x(t) - y(t)\| \leqslant \eta_1 \left(1 - \frac{1}{L^2} + \frac{1}{L^2} \, e^{L(t-t_0)} \right) .$$

(d) Let

$$\left(\int_{t_0}^{t_0 + T} \eta^2(t) \, dt \right)^{\frac{1}{2}} = \eta_2 \, .$$

Using the Schwartz inequality, we obtain

$$\|x(t) - y(t)\| \leqslant \eta_2 \left(\frac{e^{2L(t-t_0)} - 1}{2L} \right)^{\frac{1}{2}} .$$

The estimates we have obtained indicate that the solutions are continuous with respect to variation of the right-hand side of the equation (in the metric of the spaces C, L, L_2, respectively; see section 4 of this Chapter).

4. Consider now the linear equation

$$\dot{x} = A(t)x \, . \tag{2.21}$$

Let us suppose that the operator $A(t)$ is a linear bounded operator for each fixed value of t and that the operator function $A(t)$ is continuous with respect to t for $t \geqslant 0$.

In this case the existence and uniqueness of the solutions of equation (2.1) will follow from theorem 2.1; and from theorem 2.3 there follows the unbounded continuability of all the solutions of this equation over a semi-infinite interval of time.

Let $\bar{E}$ denote the space of linear bounded operators which maps E onto E. E will then also be a Banach space ([71], p. 146).

Consider in $\bar{E}$ the equation

$$\dot{U} = A(t)U, \tag{2.22}$$

where $U(t)$ is an operator function with values in $\bar{E}$. Let $U(t)$ be a solution of equation (2.22) satisfying the condition $U(0) = I$. We shall show that an operator $U^{-1}(t)$ exists.

Let $V(t)$ denote the solution of the equation

$$\dot{V} = -VA(t), \tag{2.23}$$

which also satisfies the condition $V(0) = I$. Assuming $W_1(t) = V(t)U(t)$, we find

$$\dot{W}_1(t) = V(t)\dot{U}(t) + V(t)U(t) = VAU - VAU = 0.$$

Consequently, $W_1(t)$ is a constant operator which is also equal to I. Let $W_2(t) = U(t)V(t)$; we have

$$\dot{W}_2(t) = AUV - UVA = AW_2 - W_2A.$$

Since the solution $W_2 = I$ satisfies the latter equation, then every other solution determined by the condition $W_2(0) = I$ must coincide with this solution by virtue of the uniqueness property. Thus, $W_2(t) = I$ and $UV = VU = I$, which is what we set out to prove.

Let us introduce the notation $W(t, t_0) = U(t)U^{-1}(t_0)$. We shall call the operator function $W(t, t_0)$ a Cauchy operator and note one important property of such an operator, namely:

$$W(t, t_1)W(t_1, t_0) = W(t, t_0). \tag{2.24}$$

A direct check will convince us that a solution of (2.21) satisfying the condition $x(t) = x_0$ can be written in the form

$$x(t) = W(t, t_0)x_0. \tag{2.25}$$

Consider now the homogeneous equation

$$\dot{x} = A(t)x + u(t), \tag{2.26}$$

where $u(t)$ is a function with values in E.

A solution of this equation may be obtained with the help of the Cauchy formula

$$x(t) = W(t, t_0)x_0 + \int_{t_0}^{t} W(t, s)u(s)ds .\tag{2.27}$$

The validity of the Cauchy formula can also be established by a direct check.

We note that in practical applications the function $u(t)$ is, as a rule, a discontinuous or even a generalised function. The Cauchy formula will be valid in these more complicated cases if one gives a wider interpretation to the integral on the right-hand side of formula (2.27).

There is one more important property which we shall use later:

$$\|W(t, t_0)\| \leqslant \exp \int_{t_0}^{t} \|A(s)\| ds .\tag{2.28}$$

The validity of this inequality is established as follows. Since we have $\dot{W}(t, t_0) = A(t) W(t, t_0)$ and since

$$\left| \frac{d}{dt} \|W(t, t_0)\| \right| \leqslant \left\| \frac{d}{dt} W(t, t_0) \right\| ,$$

we obtain

$$\frac{d}{dt} \| W(t, t_0)\| \leqslant \| A(t)\| \, \| W(t, t_0)\| .$$

Solving the last inequality, we obtain (2.28).

Inequality (2.28) demonstrates that the linear operator $W(t, t_0)$ is a bounded operator.

We note that all the arguments given above remain valid if, instead of demanding that the operator function $A(t)$ be continuous with respect to t, we require that $\|A(t)\|$ be integrable over any finite interval.

A complete description of linear operators in the finite-dimensional case is given in the monographs by Erugin [78, 79].

3. Examples of Differential Equations in Banach Spaces

1. *Systems of ordinary differential equations in Euclidean space.*

Suppose the space E is a finite-dimensional vector space. The norm in this space may be introduced, for example, by one of the methods (1.3), (1.5) or

(1.7). In section 1 it was shown how one defines the norm of a matrix in correspondence with the norm introduced for the vector.
In our case, equation (2.26) corresponds to the linear system

$$\dot{x}_i = \sum_{k=1}^{n} a_{ik}(t)x_k + u_i(t), \qquad i = 1, 2, \ldots, n. \tag{3.1}$$

The matrix equation (2.22) defines the fundamental matrix $U(t)$, a knowledge of which permits us to find a solution according to the Cauchy formula (2.27).
It is easy to see that if the coefficients $a_{ik}(t)$ entering into system 3.1 are independent of t, then $U(t-t_0)$ is also a solution of equation (2.22). But since $U(t-t_0)$ and $W(t, t_0) = U(t) U^{-1}(t_0)$ are solutions of equation (2.22) and reduce to a unit matrix when $t = t_0$ then, by virtue of the property of uniqueness, we have $W(t, t_0) = U(t-t_0)$.

2. Denumerable systems of differential equations.

Consider a space l^p whose elements are all number sequences $(x_1, x_2, \ldots x_n, \ldots)$ such that $\Sigma_{k=1}^{\infty} x_k^p$ converges. In l^p one can consider the denumerable system of differential equations

$$\dot{x}_i = \sum_{k=1}^{\infty} a_{ik}(t) x_k(t) + u_i(t), \qquad i = 1, 2, \ldots. \tag{3.2}$$

The solution of (3.2) will be an infinite sequence of functions $(x_1(t), x_2(t), \ldots)$ to whose fundamental Cauchy sequence there corresponds an infinite matrix.
The denumerable system (3.2) may also be considered in the space m with the norm $\|x\| = \sup_k |x_k|$. Persidskii and his students [80, 81] have given numerous examples in which the stability of the solutions of denumerable systems of differential equations, as well as equations specified in Banach space, are investigated.

3. Integro-differential equations.

Consider an integro-differential equation of the form

$$\frac{\partial \varphi(x, t)}{\partial t} = \int_a^b K(x, s, t) \varphi(s, t) ds + \lambda \varphi(x, t) + u(x, t), \tag{3.3}$$

where the functions $K(x, s, t)$ and $u(x, t)$ are assumed to be continuous in the region $D: \{a \leqslant x \leqslant b, a \leqslant s \leqslant b, 0 \leqslant t < \infty\}$. We shall assume that the inequalities $|K(x, s, t)| \leqslant M$ and $|u(x, t)| \leqslant m$ are fulfilled in this region. Several papers have been devoted to the investigation of equations of type (3.3) [82–91]. The most accurate results pertaining to the stability of the solutions of this equation are those given by Barbashin and Bisyarina [85] where extensive use is made of a representation of the solution of equation (3.3) made with the help of the Cauchy formula. These authors showed that any solution $\varphi(x, t)$ of equation (3.3) satisfying the condition $\varphi(x, t_0) = \varphi_0(x)$ may be represented by the formula

$$\varphi(x, t) = e^{\lambda(t-t_0)} \left[\varphi_0(x) + \int_{t_0}^t \int_a^b R(x, s, t, \tau) \varphi_0(s) ds d\tau \right] +$$

$$+ \int_{t_0}^t e^{\lambda(t-\tau)} \left[u(x, \tau) + \right.$$

$$\left. + \int_\tau^t \int_a^b R(x, s, t, \tau_1) u(s, \tau) ds d\tau_1 \right] d\tau , \quad (3.4)$$

where $R(x, s, t, \tau)$ are resolvents of the kernel $K(x, s, t)$, i.e. the function defined by the relation

$$R(x, s, t, \tau) = \sum_{n=0}^\infty K_{n+1}(x, s, t, \tau) ,$$

where

$$K_{n+1}(x, s, t, \tau) = \int_\tau^t \int_a^b K(x, s_1, \tau_1) K_n(s_1, s, \tau_1, \tau) ds_1 d\tau_1 ,$$

$$(n = 1, 2, \ldots), \quad K_1(x, s, t, \tau) = K(x, s, \tau) .$$

It is possible to show that $R(x, s, t, \tau)$ satisfies the equation

$$\frac{\partial R(x, s, t, \tau)}{\partial t} = \int_a^b K(x, s_1, t) R(s_1, s, t, \tau) ds_1 , \quad (3.5)$$

which corresponds to equation (2.22).

It is natural to consider the function $\varphi(x, t)$ for fixed $t = t_0$ as an element of the space C of continuous functions with the metric $\|\varphi(x, t_0)\|_c = \sup_{a \leqslant x \leqslant b} |\varphi(x, t)|$. A trajectory in C will then correspond to the solution $\varphi(x, t)$ of equation (3.3). If we are interested in the effect of an "external perturbation" $u(x, t)$ on this trajectory we should use formula (3.4) to solve the problem. It is not necessary, of course, to consider $u(x, t_0)$ as an element of the space C; such an assumption would considerably diminish the value of the investigation. We can, for example, regard $u(x, t)$ as belonging to the space L_p, $1 \leqslant p \leqslant \infty$. In this case we can consider the effect on the solution $\varphi(x, t)$ of perturbations which are bounded on the average in one sense or the other.

4. Systems with incomplete information.

In the n-dimensional vector space R, consider the differential equation

$$\dot{x} = f(x, t), \tag{3.6}$$

where, for a given value of t and for a fixed vector x, the vector function of $f(x, t)$ is not merely a single vector but an entire set of vectors of R. Thus, the function $f(x, t)$ is assumed to be a many-valued function. We usually arrive at system of the form (3.6) when information about the values of some of the parameters of the system is incomplete; all we know is that these parameters may assume any value taken from a given set. We shall call such systems, systems with incomplete information.

Systems with incomplete information provide a useful means of describing control systems containing components possessing hysteresis and relay characteristics [92, 93].

Let S denote a bounded closed set lying in R. Let γ be a single-valued continuous mapping of the set S onto R. We shall call the image of set S, i.e. $\gamma(S)$, the S-set.

Consider the space $E(R)$ of all continuous mappings γ, defining the norm in the following way

$$\|\gamma\| = \sup_{x \subset S} \|\gamma(x)\|_R.$$

It is easy to see that the space $E(R)$ is a Banach space and that it is isometric to the space of the corresponding S-sets $\gamma(S)$ with the metric $\|\gamma(S)\| = \sup_{x \subset S} \|\gamma(x)\|_R$. For this reason we shall in future identify the element γ of space $E(R)$ with the S-set $\gamma(S)$ lying in R. We must emphasise however that the S-set should not be regarded as a simple sub-set of the space R, while it is necessary to ascribe the corresponding mapping γ to the S-set. It is only in this case that the linear operation enters into the space of S-sets in a natural way. It is clear that one must assume that

$\gamma_1(S) + \gamma_2(S) = \gamma(S)$ if, for any vector $x \subset S$, the relation $\gamma_1(x) + \gamma_2(x) = \gamma(x)$ holds.

Suppose now that R_m is an m-dimensional Euclidean space and that $f(p)$ is a many-valued function defined in this space whose values are S-sets of the space R. We associate the many-valued function $f(p)$ with the single-valued function $F(p)$ whose values lie in $E(R)$ which is defined according to the rule $F(p) = \gamma$ if $\gamma(S) = f(p)$. This approach permits us to apply all the ideas of the descriptive theory of functions to the multi-valued function $f(p)$. Thus, for example, we are able to say that the many-valued function $f(p)$ is continuous if the single-valued function $F(p)$ corresponding to it is continuous. Similarly, it is possible to define a class of many-valued functions whose set of points of continuity is G_δ of the second category. To these functions there correspond point-wise discontinuous functions $F(p)$ which are the limit of the sequence of continuous functions. For example, the relay characteristic $f(x) = \text{sign } x$ with the supplementary condition that $f(0)$ is a set of numbers from the interval $[-1, 1]$ at once proves to be one such function.

Let us turn now to equation (3.6) and require the following condition to be fulfilled.

Let X be an S-set and let

$$f(X, t) = \bigcup_{x \subset X} f(x, t) \;;$$

then, for any t, $f(X, t)$ is also an S-set.

In particular, since every vector x from R is an S-set then, clearly, $f(x, t)$ must also be an S-set.

Alongside equation (3.6) consider the equation

$$X = f(X, t), \tag{3.7}$$

whose solutions are the many-valued functions $X(t)$ of a scalar argument t with values which are S-sets of space R. In contrast with the trajectories of system (3.6), the trajectories (3.7) at zero time are generally defined by certain S-sets of the space R rather than by points; they represent tubes disposed in this space. The trajectories—funnels of equation (3.6)—are included amongst the trajectories of equation (3.7) since the points of space R are obviously S-sets.

If X and $f(X, t)$ are regarded as elements of the space $E(R)$ rather than S-sets of the space R, the differential equation (3.7) will be a differential equation with a single-valued right-hand side in Banach space, and to this equation one may apply all the theoretical results obtained in this Chapter.

5. *Systems with random parameters.*

Consider in finite-dimensional Euclidean space the differential equation

$$\dot{x} = f(x, t, \eta(t)),\tag{3.8}$$

where the right-hand side depends on a random function $\eta(t)$. The solution of (3.8) must clearly also be a random function of time. A random quantity may be defined as a measurable function defined in a sample space Ω (or a space of elementary events). If a norm is defined in some way in a linear space of random quantities, then the differential equation (3.8) is transformed into a differential equation specified in the linear normalised space E whose elements are random vector quantities. When solving the Cauchy problem one should take as initial vectors not only determinate vectors but also any other random vectors from E. The integral and derivative of a random function of a scalar argument t have the meaning given to them in section 1 of this Chapter.

In particular, if for the square of the norm of a random vector one takes the mathematical expectation of the square of the length of the vector, then the derivative and integral of a random quantity have their conventional meanings.

4. Problem of Perturbation Build-Up over a Finite Interval of Time

We showed earlier that the solution of the Cauchy problem

$$\dot{x} = A(t)x + u(t), \qquad x(t_0) = 0\tag{4.1}$$

may be represented by the mathematical formula

$$x(t) = \int_{t_0}^{t} W(t, \tau) u(\tau) d\tau, \qquad t_0 \geqslant 0,\tag{4.2}$$

where $W(t, \tau) = U(t) U^{-1}(\tau)$ is a Cauchy operator.

The function $u(t)$ will be treated as an element of the Banach space B. Let us consider a typical method of specifying the norm in this space. We will use J to denote the set of numbers $0 \leqslant t < \infty$.

1. We define the space C as a space of bounded functions continuous on J with the norm

$$\|u\|_C = \sup_{t \geqslant 0} \|u(t)\| . \tag{4.3}$$

2. The space L_p is a space of functions $u(t)$ (measured according to Bochner [73], p. 85) with the norm

$$\|u\|_p = \left(\int_0^\infty \|u(t)\|^p \, dt \right)^{1/p} < \infty . \tag{4.4}$$

We shall in the first instance be interested in the cases $p = 1$, $p = 2$.

3. We define the space M_p as a space of functions for which the integral $\int_t^{t+1} \|u(\tau)\|^p \, d\tau$ exists and is uniformly bounded for any $t \geqslant 0$. We specify the norm in M_p in the following way

$$\|u\|_{M_p} = \sup_{t \geqslant 0} \left(\int_t^{t+1} \|u(\tau)\|^p \, d\tau \right)^{1/p} . \tag{4.5}$$

The most interesting case is again $p = 1$ and $p = 2$. Massera and Schaffer [94, 95] have stressed the importance of the space $M = M_1$ in investigation of stability problems in Banach space.

4. The space C_0 will be treated as a space of functions from C possessing the property $\lim_{t \to \infty} \|u(t)\| = 0$.

5. Let L_∞ denote a space of functions $u(t)$ (measured according to Bochner) which are essentially bounded on J. We define the norm according to the rule

$$\|u(t)\|_\infty = \operatorname{vrai\ sup}_{t \geqslant 0} \|u(t)\| . \tag{4.6}$$

The expression "essentially bounded on J" means that it is possible to find a constant $c > 0$ such that the set of points where the inequality $\|u(t)\| > c$ is fulfilled has degree zero; $\operatorname{vrai\ sup}_{t \geqslant 0} \|u(t)\|$ is the exact lower boundary of such numbers c.

We note that when $1 \leqslant p \leqslant \infty$ the following relation holds

$$\|u(t)\|_M \leqslant \|u(t)\|_{M_p} \leqslant \|u\|_p . \tag{4.7}$$

For $p = \infty$, inequality (4.7) is obviously true, since

$$\int_t^{t+1} \|u(\tau)\| \, d\tau \leqslant \|u(t)\|_\infty \,.$$

For $p < \infty$ the validity of (4.7) follows from the Houlder inequality ([71], p. 64)

$$\int_t^{t+1} \|u(\tau)\| \, d\tau \leqslant \left(\int_t^{t+1} \|u(\tau)\|^p \, d\tau \right)^{1/p} \leqslant \|u(t)\|_p \,.$$

If instead of the semi-axis J the interval $t_0 \leqslant t \leqslant t_1$ is taken, where $t_0 \geqslant 0$, then, defining the norm in a similar way, we obtain the space $B(t_0, t_1)$ (for example, $C(t_0, t_1)$, $L_p(t_0, t_1)$ and so on).

In future we shall assume that the function $x(t)$ defined by relation (4.2) always belongs to the space C. In this case formula (4.2) specifies a linear operator which translates the space B into the space C. If instead of the semi-axis J the interval $t_0 \leqslant t \leqslant t_1$ is considered, then the operator Φ is converted to the linear operator $\Phi(t_0, t_1)$ operating in the sub-space $B(t_0, t_1)$.

It is clear that the relation

$$\sup_{t_0 \leqslant t \leqslant t_1} \|x(t)\| \leqslant \|\Phi(t_0, t_1)\| \, \|u\|_{B(t_0, t_1)} \tag{4.8}$$

is true. Thus, knowing the magnitude of the norm of the operator $\Phi(t_0, t_1)$ or, in an extreme case, knowing the estimate of this norm, we can estimate the maximum deviation of $\|x(t)\|$ from zero due to the action of the function $u(t)$, which can be interpreted as an external disturbance causing a perturbation of the output signal $x(t)$.

The problem of perturbation build-up just formulated was first stated and solved in the finite-dimensional case by Bulgakov [96]. From the point of view of functional analysis, Bulgakov's problem reduces to a search for the exact value of the norm of the operator $\Phi(t_0, t)$. However, it is usually a difficult problem to calculate the value of the norm. An exception is the case when the functions of space B are functions with numerical values. In our problem this would correspond to a one-dimensional phase space E. However, it is not difficult to obtain an estimate of the operator $\Phi(t_0, t_1)$ in certain specific spaces. For example, these estimates can have the following form

(1)   In the space $C(t_0, t_1)$

$$\|\Phi(t_0, t_1)\| \leqslant \sup_{t_0 \leqslant t \leqslant t_1} \int_{t_0}^{t} \|W(t, \tau)\| \, d\tau \,. \tag{4.9}$$

(2)   In the space $L(t_0, t_1)$

$$\|\Phi(t_0, t_1)\| \leqslant \sup_{t_0 \leqslant \tau \leqslant t \leqslant t_1} \|W(t, \tau)\| \,. \tag{4.10}$$

(3)   In the space $L_2(t_0, t_1)$

$$\|\Phi(t_0, t_1)\| \leqslant \sup_{t_0 \leqslant t \leqslant t_1} \left(\int_{t_0}^{t} \|W(t, \tau)\|^2 \, d\tau \right)^{\frac{1}{2}} \,. \tag{4.11}$$

5. Problem of Perturbation Build-Up over an Infinite Interval of Time. Stability Theorems for the Zero Solution of a Homogeneous Linear Equation

1.   Let us consider now the problem in which perturbations build up over an infinite interval of time J, i.e. over the semi-axis $0 \leqslant t < \infty$. Suppose that the external perturbation $u(t)$ belongs to the space C. In that case, according to (4.9), we have

$$\|\Phi\| = \sup_{t \geqslant 0} \int_{0}^{t} \|W(t, \tau)\| \, d\tau \,, \tag{5.1}$$

where the operator Φ is given by the relation

$$\Phi u = \int_{0}^{t} W(t, \tau) u(\tau) d\tau \,.$$

Thus, if the quantity

$$\Phi_0 = \sup_{t \geqslant 0} \int_{0}^{t} \|W(t, \tau)\| \, d\tau \tag{5.2}$$

is finite the problem of build-up of perturbations has a solution. This means that to every function $u(t)$ bounded with respect to the norm of C there corresponds a bounded solution $x(t)$ of problem (4.1).
The following more profound result is true.

Lemma 5.1. *If the operator* $\Phi u = \int_0^t W(t, \tau) u(\tau) d\tau$ *translates a Banach space* B *of functions* $u(t)$ *into a space* C *of functions* $x(t)$, *then it is bounded. This means that a constant positive quantity* K *exists such that*

$$\|x\|_C \leqslant K \|u\|_B.$$

Indeed, we define the operator Φ_k which translates B into the space E by the relation $\Phi_k u = \int_0^{t_k} W(t_k \tau) u(\tau) d\tau$, where $\{t_k\}$ is a sequence of positive rational numbers enumerated in any order. If $u \subset B$, then the sequence $\Phi_k u$ is, according to our supposition, bounded and, consequently, according to theorem 1.1, there exists such a $K > 0$ that $\|\Phi_k u\| \leqslant K \|u\|_B$. Since for any real number $t \geqslant 0$ there exists a sequence of rational numbers t_m converging towards t then, by virtue of the last inequality, we obtain

$$\left\| \int_0^t W(t, \tau) u(\tau) d\tau \right\| \leqslant K \|u\|_B,$$

which is what we set out to prove.

Lemma 5.2. *If* E *is a finite-dimensional vector space and to every bounded perturbation* $u(t)$ *there corresponds a solution of* (4.1) *bounded on* J, *then the quantity* Φ_0 *specified by relation* (5.2) *is finite.*

In fact, in this case, the Cauchy operator $W(t, \tau)$ is transformed into a matrix with elements w_{ik}. For the sake of definiteness, we will assume that the norm of the vector and the norm of the matrix are defined as in (1.5) and (1.6).

Consider the vector function $u^i(\tau)$, which we shall define in the following way:

$$u_k^i(\tau) = \text{sign } w_{ik}(t, \tau),$$

where $u_k^i(\tau)$ is the k-th projection of the vector $u^i(\tau)$.
By virtue of lemma 5.1 a constant K exists such that

$$\left\| \int_0^t W(t, \tau) u^i(\tau) d\tau \right\| \leqslant K$$

for any $t \geqslant 0$, where $u^i(\tau)$ is treated as an element of the Banach space L_∞.
Thus for any i we have

$$\int_0^t \sum_{k=1}^n w_{ik} u_k^i \, d\tau = \int_0^t \sum_{k=1}^n |w_{ik}(t, \tau)| \, d\tau \leqslant K .$$

However, from this it follows that there exists a constant M (equal, for example to nK, where n is the dimensionality of space E) such that

$$\int_0^t \| W(t, \tau) \| \, d\tau \leqslant M \text{ for any } t .$$

Lemma 5.3. *If Φ_0 is finite, and if $\|A(t)\| \leqslant A < \infty$ on the semi-axis J, then a positive constant W_0 exists which is independent of t and t_0 such that $\|W(t, \tau)\| \leqslant W_0$ for $0 \leqslant \tau \leqslant t < \infty$.*

From the relation

$$\frac{d}{d\tau} U(\tau) U^{-1}(\tau) = U(\tau) \frac{dU^{-1}(\tau)}{d\tau} + \frac{dU(\tau)}{d\tau} U^{-1}(\tau) = 0$$

we have

$$\frac{dU^{-1}(\tau)}{d\tau} = -U^{-1}(\tau) \frac{dU(\tau)}{d\tau} U^{-1}(\tau) .$$

Since $W(t, \tau) = U(t) U^{-1}(\tau)$, where $U(t)$ is a fundamental operator, then

$$\frac{dW(t, \tau)}{d\tau} = -U(t) U^{-1}(\tau) \frac{dU(\tau)}{d\tau} U^{-1}(\tau) .$$

According to the definition of a fundamental operator, we have $dU(\tau)/d\tau = A(\tau) U(\tau)$, whence it follows that

$$\frac{dW(t, \tau)}{d\tau} = -W(t, \tau) A(\tau) .$$

Integrating the last relation with respect to τ between the limits t_0 and t, we obtain

$$W(t, \tau) - I = -\int_{t_0}^t W(t, \tau) A(\tau) d\tau .$$

Consequently,

$$\| W(t, \tau) - I \| = \left\| \int_{t_0}^t W(t, \tau) A(\tau) d\tau \right\| \leqslant A_0 \Phi_0 .$$

Whence it follows that $\| W(t, \tau) \| \leqslant A_0 \Phi_0 + 1$, so that one can set $W_0 = A_0 \Phi_0 + 1$.

Lemma 5.4 (Massera and Schäffer [94]). *Suppose $\psi(t)$ is a positive function and $\rho(t)$ is a continuous positive function for $t \geqslant 0$. If $\inf_{t \geqslant 0} \rho(t) < 1$, and if for all $t \geqslant t_0 \geqslant 0$ the inequality*

$$\psi(t) \leqslant \rho(t - t_0)\psi(t_0), \tag{5.3}$$

holds, then there exist positive numbers α, B which are independent of t_0 such that, for $t \geqslant t_0 \geqslant 0$, the following inequality is true

$$\psi(t) \leqslant B e^{-\alpha(t - t_0)}\psi(t_0). \tag{5.4}$$

A positive number τ does indeed exist such that $\rho(\tau) = \gamma < 1$. Let us set $\alpha = -\tau^{-1}\ln\gamma$ and $B = \max_{0 \leqslant t \leqslant \tau} e^{\alpha t}\rho(t)$. It is obvious that a number B with the above property exists by virtue of the continuity of $\rho(t)$. With $n = 0, 1, \ldots$ we have, by virtue of (5.3),

$$\psi(t_0 + n\tau) \leqslant \gamma^n \psi(t_0). \tag{5.5}$$

For any $t \geqslant t_0 \geqslant 0$ and for an integral positive value of n, the inequality $t + n\tau \leqslant t \leqslant t_0 + (n+1)\tau$ holds.
Thus, in accordance with (5.3) and (5.5), we obtain

$$\psi(\tau) \leqslant \rho(t - t_0 - n\tau)\psi(t_0 + n\tau) \leqslant \rho(t - t_0 - n\tau)\gamma^n \psi(t_0).$$

In addition, the inequality

$$\psi(t) \leqslant e^{\alpha(t - t_0 - n\tau)}\rho(t - t_0 - n\tau)\gamma^n e^{\alpha n\tau} e^{-\alpha(t - t_0)}\psi(t_0)$$

is valid. Since $e^{\alpha\tau} = \gamma^{-1}$ then, according to the choice of the number B, we obtain the required inequality (5.4).

Lemma 5.5. *If positive constants Φ_0 and W_0 exist such that*

$$\int_{t_0}^{t} \|W(t, \tau)\|\,d\tau \leqslant \Phi_0, \quad \|W(t, t_0)\| \leqslant W_0$$

for any $0 \leqslant t_0 \leqslant t < \infty$, then one can find positive constants α and B such that

$$\|W(t, t_0)\| \leqslant B e^{-\alpha(t - t_0)} \tag{5.6}$$

for any $0 \leqslant t_0 \leqslant t < \infty$.

Indeed, since $W(t, t_0) = W(t, \tau)W(\tau, t_0)$, we have

$$\left\| \int_{t_0}^{t} W(t, \tau) W(\tau, t_0) d\tau \right\| = \| W(t, t_0)\| (t - t_0) \leqslant \Phi_0 W_0 .$$

Making use of the supplementary inequality $\| W(t, t_0)\| \leqslant W_0$, we obtain

$$\| W(t, t_0)\| \leqslant \frac{W_0(1 + \Phi_0)}{1 + t - t_0} = \rho(t - t_0) .$$

In the general case we clearly have

$$\| W(t, t_0)\| \leqslant \| W(t, t_1)\| \, \| W(t, t_0)\| \leqslant \rho(t - t_1)\| \, W(t, t_0)\|$$

and we can apply lemma 5.4.

Definition. *The zero solution of the equation*

$$\dot{y} = A(t) y \tag{5.7}$$

is said to be exponentially stable if there exist positive constants α and B which are independent of t_0 and such that any solution of equation (5.7) satisfies the inequality

$$\| y(t)\| \leqslant B e^{-\alpha(t - t_0)} \| y(t_0)\| . \tag{5.8}$$

It is clear that an exponentially stable zero solution will be a uniformly asymptotically stable solution for any initial perturbations. This means that the zero solution will be stable and that for any positive numbers ε and δ one can find a number $T > 0$ such that from $\| y(t_0)\| < \varepsilon$ there follows $\| y(t)\| < \delta$ for $t \geqslant t_0 + T$.
If the operator function $A(t)$ is independent of t, exponential stability can occur if and only if the spectrum of the operator A lies inside the left-hand half-plane ([75]).

Theorem 5.1. *Let E be a finite-dimensional vector space and let $\| A(t)\|$ be bounded on J. In order that there shall be a bounded (uniformly with respect to t_0) solution of (4.1) corresponding to every function $u(t)$ bounded on J it is necessary and sufficient that the zero solution of equation (5.7) be exponentially stable.*

The necessity for the conditions attached to this theorem follows from lemmas 5.1, 5.3 and 5.5; the sufficiency of these conditions follows from formula (4.2).

Since, from (5.8) and (4.2), there follows the inequality $\|W(t, t_0)\| \leqslant B e^{-\alpha(t-t_0)}$ then, for $\|u(t)\| \leqslant c < \infty$, we have

$$\|x(t)\| \leqslant \int_{t_0}^{t} \|W(t, \tau)\| \, \|u(\tau)\| \, d\tau \leqslant \frac{Bc}{\alpha},$$

which is the result required.

The necessity for the conditions attached to theorem 5.1 was established by Madkin ([8], p. 367) who applied Lyapunov functions. Criterion (5.8) was first introduced by Persidskii; it plays an important part in future discussion.

In parallel with problem (4.1) let us consider the more general problem

$$\dot{x} = A(t)x + u(t), \quad x(t_0) = x_0. \tag{5.9}$$

Theorem 5.2 (Brigland [97]). *Let E be a finite-dimensional vector space and let $\|A(t)\|$ be integrable over any finite interval of the semi-axis J. If to every function $u(t)$ bounded on J there corresponds for any x_0 a bounded (uniformly with respect to t_0) solution $x(t)$ of problem (5.9), then the zero solution of (5.7) will be exponentially stable.*

Indeed, by setting $x_0 = 0$ we obtain problem (4.1) and therefore, by virtue of lemma (5.2), the inequality $\int_{t_0}^{t} \|W(t, \tau)\| \, d\tau \leqslant \Phi_0$ will be valid. Setting $u(t) \equiv 0$, we obtain the bounded function $y(t) = x(t) = W(t, t_0)x_0$ and therefore we obtain the inequality $\|W(t, t_0)\| \leqslant W_0$. The required result now follows from lemma 5.5.

It is clear that the inverse is also true.

Theorem. *If every solution of (5.7) satisfies the inequality (5.8), then to every bounded function $u(t)$ and to any initial point there will correspond a bounded solution of problem (5.9).*

This statement can be verified in exactly the same way as in the proof of the preceding theorem.

Theorem 5.2 is interesting because in formulating it no additional restrictions are imposed on the matrix $A(t)$, apart from those that ensure the existence of a solution of problem 4.1. Theorem 5.1 is true in the case when E is a Banach space. Theorem 5.6, which we shall meet later, considerably reinforces the result given in theorem 5.1. However, the method of proving theorem 5.1, and also the results and simple methods of proving the preliminary lemmas, are interesting in themselves from the view of perturbation build-up.

2. Let L_p^a denote the space of functions $u(t)$ defined on J with values in E such that

$$\int_0^\infty \|u(t)\|^p e^{apt}\, dt < \infty .$$

Let L_∞^a denote the space of functions for which

$$\text{vrai} \sup_{t \geqslant 0} \|u(t)\|\, e^{at} < \infty .$$

We introduce, respectively, the norms in the spaces L_p^a, L_∞^a.

$$\|u\|_{(p,\,a)} = \left(\int_0^\infty \|u(\tau)\|^p e^{ap\tau}\, d\tau \right)^{1/p} \qquad 1 \leqslant p < \infty ,$$

$$\|u\|_{(\infty,\,a)} = \text{vrai} \sup_{t \geqslant 0} \|u(t)\|\, e^{at} .$$

It is easy to see that the correspondence $\Omega u = e^{at} u(t)$ is a linear, mutually single-valued, correspondence between L_p^a and L_p^0 preserving the norm. Since the space $L_p^0 = L_p$ is a Banach space for any p, $1 \leqslant p \leqslant \infty$, then so also will be the spaces L_p^a.

By virtue of lemma 5.1, the operator $\Phi u = \int_0^t W(t,\tau) u(\tau) d\tau$, which translates the space L_p^a into the space L_∞^b, will be a bounded operator. This means that a positive constant K exists such that

$$\|\Phi u\|_{(\infty,\,b)} = \text{vrai} \sup_{t \geqslant 0} e^{bt} \left\| \int_0^t W(t,\tau) u(\tau) d\tau \right\| \leqslant K \|u\|_{(p,\,a)} . \tag{5.10}$$

Theorem 5.3 (Regis [98]). *Let the condition*

$$\int_t^{t+1} \|A(\tau)\|\, d\tau < \infty$$

be fulfilled for $t \geqslant 0$. If it is possible to find a p, $1 \leqslant p < \infty$ such that for every function $u(t) \subset L_p^a$ the solution of problem (4.1) belongs to L_∞^b, where $a > 0$, $b > 0$, then one can find a positive number N such that the inequality

$$\|W(t, t_0)\| \leqslant N e^{at_0} e^{-bt} \tag{5.11}$$

is fulfilled.

Proof. Assume $\sup_{t \geq 0} \int_t^{t+1} \|A(\tau)\| d\tau = A_1$. By virtue of (3.12) the following inequality holds for $|t - \tau| \leq 1$:

$$\|W(t, \tau)\| \leq e^{A_1} .$$

Later, we shall define the function for integral $m \geq 0$.

$$u_m(t) = \frac{W(t, m) x_0}{e^{at} \|W(t, m)\|}$$

for $m \leq t \leq m+1$, $\|x_0\| = 1$, $u_m(t) = 0$, everywhere at the remaining points. Clearly, $u_m \subset L_p^a$ since $\|u_m\|_{(p, a)} \leq 1$.
According to (5.10) we have

$$e^{bt} \left\| \int_0^t W(t, \tau) u_m(\tau) d\tau \right\| \leq K . \tag{5.12}$$

On the other hand

$$\left\| \int_0^t W(t, \tau) u_m(\tau) d\tau \right\| = \left\| \int_m^{m+1} W(t, \tau) \frac{W(\tau, m) x_0}{e^{a\tau} \|W(\tau, m)\|} d\tau \right\| =$$

$$= \|W(t, m)\| \int_m^{m+1} \frac{d\tau}{e^{a\tau} \|W(\tau, m)\|} \geq$$

$$\geq e^{-A_1} e^{-(m+1)a} \|W(t, m)\| .$$

According to (5.12), we obtain

$$\|W(t, m)\| \leq K e^{A_1} e^{(m+1)a} e^{-bt} .$$

If $m \leq \tau \leq m+1$, then

$$\|W(t, \tau)\| \leq \|W(t, m)\| \|W(m, \tau)\| \leq K e^{2A_1 + a} e^{a\tau} e^{-bt} ,$$

so that one can set $N = K e^{2A_1 + a}$.
We note that in proving Regis's theorem we have also somewhat reinforced it because instead of the requirement that $\|A(t)\|$ should be bounded over the whole semi-axis J, as in the formulation given in [98], we now have the requirement

$$\sup_{t \geq 0} \int_t^{t+1} \|A(\tau)\| d\tau = A_1 < \infty . \tag{5.13}$$

3.　In 1948 Krein [99] carried over theorem 5.1 to the case where the space E is a Banach space. Kucher [100] obtained a similar result for the case $u(t) \subset L_p$. Massera and Schäffer [94] investigated the corresponding theorems for the case of conditional stability. These authors removed the usual requirement that $\|A(t)\|$ should be bounded, requiring only that this function should be integrable over any finite interval. However, in order to obtain a result similar to that of theorem 5.1, they required that condition (5.13) be fulfilled. This condition provides for the uniformity of the asymptotic stability of the zero solution of equation (5.7), corresponding to the case when the quantity B in condition (5.8) is independent of t_0.

The formulation of the theorems given below and the proofs we give follow the work of Massera and Schäffer [94].

Theorem 5.4. *If for any function* $u(t) \subset L_p$, $1 < p < \infty$, *problem* (4.1) *has a bounded solution then a positive number* α *exists, and also a scalar positive function* $N(t)$, *such that any solution of equation* (5.7) *satisfies the inequality for* $t \geqslant t_0$:

$$\| y(t) \| \leqslant N(t_0) e^{-\alpha(t - t_0)^{1/q}} \| y(t_0) \| ,　\qquad (5.14)$$

where $(1/p) + (1/q) = 1$.

Proof. Let $y(t)$ be the non-zero solution of equation (5.7). Let us choose arbitrary numbers $\tau \geqslant t_0 > 0$ and define the function $\gamma(t)$ by assuming $\gamma(t) = 1$ for $t_0 \leqslant t \leqslant t_0 + \tau$ and $\gamma(t) = 0$ outside this interval. Clearly, the function

$$x(t) = y(t) \int_{t_0}^{t} \gamma(\tau) \| y(\tau) \|^{-1} d\tau$$

is a solution of problem (4.1) for $u(t) = \gamma(t) y(t) \| y(t) \|^{-1}$. Since $u(t) \subset L_p$ and $\|u\|_p = \tau^{1/p}$ then, according to the condition attached to the theorem, $x(t)$ will be a bounded solution of problem (4.1). By virtue of lemma 5.1 there exists a positive constant K_p such that

$$\| x(t) \| \leqslant K_p \| u \|_p = K_p \tau^{1/p} .$$

Putting

$$\varphi(t) = \int_{t_0}^{t} \| y(s) \|^{-1} ds ,　\qquad (5.15)$$

we obtain, for $\tau > 0$,

$$\| y(t_0 + \tau) \| \, \varphi(t_0 + \tau) \leqslant K_p \tau^{1/p} . \tag{5.16}$$

Since $\| y(t_0 + \tau) \|^{-1} = \dot{\varphi}(t_0 + \tau)$, it follows from (5.16) that

$$\dot{\varphi}(t_0 + \tau) \geqslant K_p^{-1} \tau^{-1/p} \varphi(t_0 + \tau) .$$

Integrating the last expression between the limits τ_0 and τ, we obtain

$$\varphi(t_0 + \tau) \geqslant \varphi(t_0 + \tau_0) \exp \left[q K_p^{-1} (\tau^{1/q} - \tau_0^{1/q}) \right] .$$

By virtue of (2.28), we have $\| y(t_0 + \tau) \| \leqslant \Delta(t_0, \tau) \, y(t_0)$ where

$$\Delta(t_0, \tau) = \exp \int_{t_0}^{t_0 + \tau} \| A(s) \| \, ds .$$

According to (5.15), we have

$$\varphi(t_0 + \tau_0) = \int_{t_0}^{t_0 + \tau_0} \| y(s) \|^{-1} ds \geqslant \| y(t_0) \|^{-1} \int_{t_0}^{t_0 + \tau_0} \frac{ds}{\Delta(t_0, s)} \geqslant$$

$$\geqslant \tau_0 (\| y(t_0) \| \, \Delta(t_0, \tau_0))^{-1} . \tag{5.17}$$

Thus, from (5.16) and (5.17) there follows

$$\| y(t_0 + \tau) \| \geqslant K_p \Delta(t_0, \tau_0) \tau_0^{-1} \exp(q K_p^{-1} \tau_0^{1/q}) \tau^{1/p} \times$$

$$\times \exp(-q K_p^{-1} \tau^{1/q}) \| y(t_0) \| .$$

Let α be an arbitrary positive number taken from the interval $0 < \alpha < q K_p^{-1}$. It is not difficult to convince oneself that

$$\max \tau^{1/p} \exp(\alpha - q K_p^{-1}) \tau^{1/q} = \left[epq^{-1} (q K_p^{-1} - \alpha) \right]^{-q/p} = \lambda(\alpha) .$$

Let

$$N(t_0) = N(\alpha, t_0, \tau_0) = \Delta(t_0, \tau_0) \exp(q K_p^{-1} \tau_0^{1/q}) \max(1, K_p \lambda(\alpha) \tau_0^{-1}) .$$

Clearly, for $\tau \geqslant 0$, we obtain

$$\| y(t_0 + \tau) \| \leqslant N(t_0) e^{-\alpha \tau^{1/q}} \| y(t_0) \| ,$$

which is equivalent to (5.14).

Theorem 5.5. *If for every function* $u(t) \subset C_0$ *of problem* 4.1 *there is a bounded solution, then there exists a constant* α *and a scalar pos'tive func-*

tion $N(t)$ such that any solution $y(t)$ of equation (5.7) satisfies the inequality

$$\| y(t) \| \leqslant N(t_0) e^{-\alpha(t-t_0)} \| y(t_0) \|$$ (5.18)

for $t \geqslant t_0 \geqslant 0$.

Proof. Let us define the function $\gamma(t)$ in the following way

$$\gamma(t) = \begin{cases} 1 & \text{for} \quad t \leqslant t_0 + \tau, \\ 1 - (t - t_0 - \tau) & \text{for} \quad t + \tau \leqslant t \leqslant t_0 + \tau + 1 \\ 0 & \text{for} \quad t_0 + \tau + 1 \leqslant t. \end{cases}$$

Consider the function $u(t) = \gamma(t) y(t) \| y(t) \|^{-1}$, where $y(t)$ is a non-zero solution of equation (5.7). Clearly, we have $\| u(t) \|_{c_0} = 1$. The function

$$x(t) = y(t) \int_{t_0}^{t} \gamma(s) \| y(s) \|^{-1} ds$$

is a solution of (4.1) for the chosen perturbation $u(t)$; therefore, by virtue of lemma 5.1, and for $t \geqslant t_0$, we have $\| x(t) \| \leqslant K$, where K is a positive number.

If we define function $\varphi(t)$ anew by relation (5.15), we obtain

$$\| y(t_0 + \tau) \| \varphi(t_0 + \tau) = \| y(t_0 + \tau) \| \int_{t_0}^{t_0 + \tau} \| y(s) \|^{-1} ds \leqslant K ,$$ (5.19)

whence it follows that

$$\dot{\varphi}(t_0 + \tau) \geqslant K^{-1} \varphi(t_0 + \tau) .$$

Integration of the last inequality between the limits τ_0 and τ, $\tau > \tau_0$, yields

$$\varphi(t_0 + \tau) \geqslant \varphi(t_0 + \tau_0) \exp K^{-1} (\tau - \tau_0) .$$ (5.20)

Thus, from (5.19), (5.17) and (5.20) we deduce that

$$\| y(t_0 + \tau) \| \leqslant K \exp(K^{-1} \tau_0) \tau_0^{-1} \Delta(t_0, \tau_0) \exp(-K^{-1} \tau) \| y(t_0) \|$$

and, introducing the function,

$$N(t_0) = \Delta(t_0, \tau_0) e^{K^{-1} \tau_0} \max(1, K\tau_0^-) ,$$

we obtain the required result

$$\| y(t_0 + \tau) \| \leqslant N(t_0) e^{-K^{-1} \tau} \| y(t_0) \| .$$

To obtain (5.18) it is sufficient to put $\alpha = K^{-1}$.

Since any function from C_0 may be considered as belonging to any of the spaces C, L_∞, M_p, theorem 5.5 will be true if it is re-formulated substituting any of these spaces for the space C_0.

Corollary. *If for $u(t) \subset C_0$ problem 4.1 has a bounded solution $x(t)$, then this solution possesses the property $\lim_{t \to \infty} x(t) = 0$.*

In fact, since $u(t) \subset C_0$, for any $\varepsilon > 0$ there exists a τ such that $\|u(t)\| \leqslant \varepsilon K^{-1}$ for $t \geqslant \tau$, where the constant K is taken from the proof of the preceding theorem.

Let us define the function $f(t)$ by setting $f(t) = u(\tau)$ for $t \leqslant \tau$, and $f(t) = u(t)$ for $t \geqslant \tau$. Clearly, the inequality $\|f(t)\| \leqslant \varepsilon K^{-1}$ is valid and, consequently, the problem $\dot{y} = A(t)y + f(t)$, $y(t_0) = 0$ has a bounded solution. In view of lemma 5.1 we also have $\|y(t)\| \leqslant K\|f(t)\| \leqslant \varepsilon$.

Let $z(t)$ be a solution of the problem $\dot{z} = A(t)z + u(t)$, $z(\tau) = y(\tau)$. Since $y(t) = z(t)$ for $t \geqslant \tau$, $\lim \sup_{t \to \infty} \|z(t)\| \leqslant \varepsilon$. If $x(t)$ is a solution of problem (4.1), then $x(t) - z(t)$ will be a bounded solution of equation (5.7) and, according to theorem 5.5, we will have $\lim_{t \to \infty} \|x(t) - z(t)\| = 0$. Consequently, we have also $\lim_{t \to \infty} \|x(t)\| \leqslant \varepsilon$ and, since ε is an arbitrary number, we obtain the required result.

Theorem 5.6. *Let $A(t)$ satisfy condition (5.13). If for every function $u(t) \subset B$ (where B is one of the spaces C_0, C, M_p, $1 \leqslant p < \infty$, L_p, $1 < p \leqslant \infty$) problem 4.1 has a bounded solution, then the zero solution of equation 5.7 is exponentially stable.*

Consider first the case $B = C_0$.
Let

$$\sup_{t \geqslant 0} \int_t^{t+1} \|A(s)\| \, ds = A_1 < \infty \, .$$

Using the same arguments as we used in proving theorem 5.5, we will assume that $\tau_0 = 1$. We then obtain

$$N(t_0) \leqslant \exp(A_1 + K^{-1}) \max(1, K) \, .$$

Thus, (5.8) will be valid. Clearly, the theorem can be shown to be valid in exactly the same way for $B = C$, $B = L_\infty$, $B = M_p$, $1 \leqslant p < \infty$.

Suppose now that $B = L_p$, $1 < p < \infty$. Repeating the proof of theorem 5.4, we assume $\tau_0 = 1$. By virtue of (5.13) we obtain

$$N(t_0) = \exp\left(A_1 + qK_p^{-1}\right) \max\left(1, K_p \lambda(\alpha)\right) = N \,,$$

whence, in accordance with (5.14), it follows that

$$\| y(t) \| \leqslant \rho(t - t_0) \| y(t_0) \| \,,$$

where

$$\rho(t) = N \exp\left(-\alpha t^{1/q}\right) \quad \text{and} \quad \lim_{t \to \infty} \rho(t) = 0 \,.$$

The result we require now follows from lemma 5.4.
Consider now the case when $u(t) \subset L$.

Theorem 5.7. *If for every function* $u(t) \subset L$ *problem* 4.1 *has a bounded solution, then any solution* $y(t)$ *of equation* (5.7) *satisfies the inequality*

$$\| y(t) \| \leqslant N \| y(t_0) \| \,, \tag{5.21}$$

where N *is independent of* t_0.

Let us choose numbers $0 \leqslant t_0 \leqslant t_1$ and $0 < \delta \leqslant t_1 - t_0$. We set $\gamma(t) = 1$ when $t_0 \leqslant t \leqslant t_0 + \delta$ and $\gamma(t) = 0$ outside this interval. Let $u(t) = \gamma(t) \| y(t) \|^{-1} y(t)$. It is clear that the function $u(t)$ belongs to L and $\| u \|_1 = \delta$. Consequently, according to the provisions of the theorem,

$$x(t) = y(t) \int_{t_0}^{t} \gamma(s) \| y(s) \|^{-1} ds$$

is a bounded function.
By virtue of lemma 5.1 we have

$$\| x(t) \| \leqslant N \| u \|_1 = N\delta \,.$$

Since

$$\| x(t) \| = \| y(t) \| \int_{t_0}^{t} \gamma(s) \| y(s) \|^{-1} ds =$$

$$= \| y(t) \| \int_{t_0}^{t_0 + \delta} \gamma(s) \| y(s) \|^{-1} ds$$

then, for $t > t_0 + \delta$, we have

$$\|x(t_1)\| = \|y(t_1)\| \int_{t_0}^{t_0+\delta} \gamma(s)\|y(s)\|^{-1} ds \leqslant N\delta .$$

For $\delta \to 0$ we obtain

$$\|y(t_1)\| \, \|y(t_0)\|^{-1} \leqslant N ,$$

whence, since t_1 is arbitrary, we arrive at the required result.
Clearly there is a converse to theorem 5.7. If condition (5.21) is fulfilled then, for $u(t) \subset L$, problem (4.1) will have a bounded solution.

4. We shall now give some examples.
Example 1 (Massera and Schäffer [94]). Consider the series of intervals $J_n = [n - e^{-n^2}, n + e^{-n^2}]$, $n = 1, 2, \ldots$ and let us define the function $\lambda(t)$ by setting $\lambda(t) = 1$ outside J_n, $\lambda(n) = e^{2n}$. We define the function $\lambda(t)$ on each of the intervals J_n such that the inequality $1 \leqslant \lambda(t) \leqslant e^{2n}$ is fulfilled. Clearly the function $\lambda(t)$ can be constructed so that it will be continuous and differentiable for $t > 0$.
Consider the linear homogeneous equation whose solution is the function $y(t) = e^{-t}(\lambda(t))^{-1}$. Since

$$y(n + e^{-n^2})(y(n))^{-1} = \exp(2n - e^{-n^2}) \to \infty ,$$

the solution $y(t)$ cannot satisfy an inequality of the type $|y(t)| \leqslant N|y(t_0)|$, where N is independent of t_0; moreover, $y(t)$ cannot be connected by an inequality of type (5.8).
If $u(t) \subset L_p$, $1 < p \leqslant \infty$, then the solution of the corresponding inhomogeneous equation

$$x(t) = \frac{e^{-t}}{\lambda(t)} \int_0^t e^s \lambda(s) u(s) ds$$

will be bounded.
In fact using Hölder's inequality, we obtain

$$|x(t)| \leqslant e^{-t} \int_0^t e^s |u(s)| ds + e^{-t} \sum_{n=1}^{\infty} \int_{J_n} e^s \lambda(s) |u(s)| ds \leqslant$$

$$\leqslant q^{-1/q} \|u\|_p + e^{-t} \|u\|_p \sum_{n=1}^{\infty} e^{2n} \exp(n + e^{-n^2})(2e^{-n^2})^{1/q} \leqslant$$

$$\leqslant \|u\|_p \left\{ q^{-1/q} + e \sum_{n=1}^{\infty} \exp(2n + e^{-n^2})(2e^{-n^2})^{1/q} \right\} .$$

Clearly $|x(t)|$ will be a bounded function since the last series converges for any q.

Thus, in formulating theorems 5.4 and 5.5, it is not possible to suppose that $N(t_0)$ is independent of t_0. To obtain the important property of independence, it is necessary either to impose a restriction of the type (5.13) on $A(t)$ (theorem 5.6) or to confine oneself to the case $p=1$, as was done in theorem 5.7.

Example 2 (Massera and Schäffer [94], Perron [101]). Consider the equation

$$\dot{x} + (a - \sin \ln (t+1) - \cos \ln (t+1))x = u(t), \tag{5.22}$$

where $1 < a < 1 + \tfrac{1}{2} e^{-\pi}$. Clearly, we have $|a - \sin \ln (t+1) - \cos \ln (t+1)| \leqslant a + \sqrt{2}$, so that $A(t)$ belongs to C. The solution of the homogeneous equation has the form

$$y(t) = y(0) e^a e^{-(a - \sin \ln (t+1))(t+1)}$$

and is bounded.

Since $|y(0)| e^a e^{-(a+1)(t+1)} \leqslant |y(t)| \leqslant y(0) e^a e^{-(a-1)(t+1)}$ then, when $t \geqslant t_0 \geqslant 0$, we have

$$|y(t)| \leqslant e^{2(t_0+1)} e^{-(a-1)(t-t_0)} |x(t_0)|.$$

Consequently equality (5.18) is fulfilled and moreover so is (5.14) for any $q < \infty$.

Consider next the corresponding inhomogeneous equation (5.22), setting $u(t) = e^{-a(t+1)}$. It is clear that $u(t) \subset L_p$ for $1 \leqslant p \leqslant \infty$ and $u(t) \subset C_0$. The solution of problem (4.1) has the form

$$x(t) = e^{-(a - \sin \ln (t+1))(t+1)} \int_0^t e^{-(s+1) \sin \ln (s+1)} ds.$$

We set $t_n = e^{(2n + \frac{1}{2})\pi}$, $n = 1, 2, \ldots$. If $t_n e^{-\pi} \leqslant s \leqslant t_n e^{-\frac{2}{3}\pi}$, then $-1 \leqslant \sin \ln s \leqslant -\tfrac{1}{2}$ and we have

$$\int_0^{t_n-1} e^{-(s+1) \sin \ln (s+1)} ds > \int_{t_n e^{-\pi}}^{t_n e^{-\frac{2}{3}\pi}} e^{-s \sin \ln s} ds > \int_{t_n e^{-\pi}}^{t_n e^{-\frac{2}{3}\pi}} e^{s/2} ds =$$

$$= 2 \exp\left(\tfrac{1}{2} t_n e^{-\pi}\right)\left\{\exp\left(\tfrac{1}{2} t_n (e^{-\frac{2}{3}\pi} - e^{-\pi})\right) - 1\right\}.$$

On the other hand $(a - \sin \ln t_n) t_n = (a-1) t_n$. Consequently, since $t_n \to \infty$

and $a < 1 + \frac{1}{2}e^{-\pi}$, we obtain

$$x(t_n - 1) > 2 \exp\left((1 + \tfrac{1}{2}e^{-\pi} - a)t_n\right)\{\exp(\tfrac{1}{2}t_n(e^{-\frac{3}{2}\pi} - e^{-\pi})) - 1\}$$

and, consequently, $x(t_n - 1) \to \infty$. Thus, the function $x(t)$ is unbounded and hence this example demonstrates that theorems 5.4 and 5.5 are, in the general case, irreversible.

5.   Let us consider how the results we have obtained bear upon automatic control theory. We saw in section 1 of Chapter 2 that any automatic system may be regarded as an assemblage of units each of which is characterised by an operator that translates an input signal into an output signal. It was noted that in the majority of cases the operator representing the action of a unit can be described with the help of a transfer function. If u is the input signal and x is the output signal, one can write $x = \Phi(u)$, where Φ is an operator which may be non-linear. Let us assume that the signal u changes for some reason and is converted to a new signal $u + \delta u$; in this case the signal x will also change and becomes the signal $x + \delta x$. Clearly, we shall have $x + \delta x = \Phi(u + \delta u)$, whence it follows that $\delta x = \Phi(u + \delta u) - \Phi(u)$.

A desirable property of any unit in a control system is insensitivity to the input signal, for that means that for any positive number $\varepsilon > 0$ it is possible to find such an $\eta > 0$ that from the inequality $\|\delta u\| < \eta$ there follows the inequality $\|\delta x\| < \varepsilon$.

Thus, the property of insensitivity (or, to use a frequently used phrase, the property of invariance with an accuracy up to ε) has to do with the fact that the operator Φ of the particular unit is continuous.

If the operator Φ is bounded, then in this case every bounded perturbation of the input signal u corresponds to a bounded perturbation of the output signal x. This is another interesting property that a unit can have.

For linear operators the properties of boundedness and continuity are equivalent. If $K = \|\Phi\|$ is the norm of a bounded linear operator, then $\|\delta x\| \leqslant K \|\delta u\|$.

Clearly the insensitivity of a unit increases as K, sometimes called the gain of the unit, decreases [102].

If the operator Φ is specified by the relation

$$x(t) = \Phi u = \int_0^t W(t, \tau) u(\tau) d\tau,$$

then the meaning of the theorems we have proved reduces to the following.

Consider as an input signal the function $u_0(t) = x_0 \delta(t - t_0)$, where $\delta(t - t_0)$ is a Dirac function. This gives $\Phi u_0 = W(t, t_0) x_0$. Consequently, the impulse response will in this case be a function which is a solution of $\dot{x} = A(t)x$, $x(t_0) = x_0$. The idea behind the above theorems is that the fact of boundedness of the operator associated with a particular unit permits us to make deductions about the asymptotic behaviour of the unit to an impulse provided certain additional restrictions are imposed on the operator function $A(t)$.

From the point of view of the logical neatness of the theory the most acceptable results would appear to be those derived from lemma 5.5 and theorems 5.2, 5.4, 5.5 (including the corollary), 5.7, since in these theorems no additional restrictions are imposed on the function $A(t)$ and the asymptotic behaviour of the response to an impulse is entirely determined by the reaction of the unit to actions belonging to one or other of the spaces, i.e. it is entirely determined by the properties of the Cauchy operator. Unfortunately, as the examples have shown, theorems 5.4 and 5.5 are irreversible.

Theorems 5.1, 5.2 and 5.6 yield conditions which are such that, when they are fulfilled, the boundedness of the operator Φ implies exponential stability of a free system. Exponential stability of a linear component is obviously equivalent to uniform asymptotic stability [8].

In theorems 5.3–5.5, the property of boundedness of the operator leads to the property of asymptotic stability, which may also be non-uniform. The importance of the property of boundedness of the operator Φ was first pointed out by James, Nichols and Phillips [103]. In their book these authors directly identified the stability of a filter with the boundedness of the corresponding operator. Various aspects of this new theory are discussed by Zadeh [104], Kalman [105] and Brigland [97].

In our view, the definition of the various kinds of component stability should be related to the asymptotic behaviour of the impulse response. This point of view corresponds to the classical representation of stability as an internal property of the system characterised by the behaviour of the system when acted upon by instantaneous perturbations. In addition, the behaviour of a system exposed to continuously acting perturbations is, of course, determined by the stability characteristics of the system; and the behaviour of a system exposed to instantaneous perturbations is determined by the way the system behaves under the action of continuously acting disturbances.

One other fact should be mentioned. We have supposed throughout that the linear operator $A(t)$ is a bounded operator. In essence this requirement was needed only for the purpose of ensuring the boundedness of the operator specified in formula (4.2), but nowadays many authors dispense with this requirement. The results obtained may be directly applied to the sudy of the stability of the solutions of equations in partial derivatives [106, 107].

6. Theorems about the Stability of Solutions of Non-Linear Equations

1. Consider the equation

$$\dot{x} = A(t)x + R(x, t), \qquad (6.1)$$

where $A(t)$ is a bounded linear operator which is continuous with respect to t, and the function $R(x, t)$ satisfies the condition

$$\|R(x, t)\| \leqslant L\|x\| \qquad (6.2)$$

in the region $D: \|x\| \leqslant H, 0 \leqslant t < \infty$.
Let $W(t, \tau)$ denote the Cauchy operator of the equation

$$\dot{x} = A(t)x, \qquad (6.3)$$

and let us suppose that the inequality

$$\| W(t, t_0)\| \leqslant B e^{-\alpha(t - t_0)} \qquad (6.4)$$

holds, where α, B are positive constants that are independent of t_0. We recall that condition (6.4) is the condition for exponential stability of the zero solution of equation (6.3).

Theorem 6.1 (stability with respect to the first approximation). *If conditions* (6.2) *and* (6.4) *are fulfilled, and if also the constants* α, B, L *satisfy the inequality*

$$\lambda = \alpha - BL > 0, \qquad (6.5)$$

the zero solution of equation (6.1) *will be exponentially stable.*

Making use of the Cauchy formula, we can write down an integral equation

$$x(t) = W(t, t_0)x_0 + \int_{t_0}^{t} W(t, \tau) R(x, \tau) d\tau \qquad (6.6)$$

equivalent to (6.1).

From conditions (6.2) and (6.4), we obtain the estimate

$$\|x(t)\| \leqslant B e^{-\alpha(t-t_0)} \|x_0\| + \int_{t_0}^{t} BL e^{-\alpha(t-s)} \|x(s)\| ds . \qquad (6.7)$$

Introducing the notation $\varphi(t) = e^{\alpha t} \|x(t)\|$, we see that from (6.7) it follows that

$$\varphi(t) \leqslant B e^{\alpha t_0} \|x_0\| + BL \int_{t_0}^{t} \varphi(s) ds ,$$

whence, according to lemma 1.1 of Chapter 1, we obtain

$$\varphi(t) \leqslant e^{BL(t-t_0)} B e^{\alpha t_0} \|x_0\| .$$

Thus, we have

$$\|x(t)\| \leqslant B e^{(BL-\alpha)(t-t_0)} \|x_0\| . \qquad (6.8)$$

Since $BL - \alpha < 0$, we obtain the required property of exponential stability. It is clear that (6.8) holds only for those x_0 that lie in the region $\|x\| \leqslant H$, i.e. in the region in which inequality (6.2) is fulfilled. By reducing H one can reduce the value of L entering into this inequality and by the same token one can ensure that condition (6.5) is fulfilled. Thus, the size of the region of attraction of the zero solution of equation (6.1) depends in the end on the magnitudes of α and B which enter into condition (6.4) for the exponential stability of equation (6.3).

Alongside the linear operator $A(t)$ let us consider now another linear operator, $F(t)$.

Corollary. *If condition* (6.4) *and the inequality*

$$\|F(t)\| \leqslant L \qquad (0 \leqslant t < \infty) ,$$

are fulfilled, and if in addition α, B, L, *satisfy condition* (6.5), *then the zero solution of the equation*

$$\dot{x} = (A(t) + F(t)) x \qquad (6.9)$$

is exponentially stable.

2. Let us consider now the stability of the zero solution of equation (6.1) in the presence of continuously acting perturbations. In conjunction with equation (6.1) let us consider also the equation

$$\dot{x} = A(t)x + R(x, t) + u(x, t).$$ (6.10)

As before, we shall assume that in region D conditions (6.2), (6.4) and (6.5) are fulfilled. In addition, let us suppose that in region D the function $u(x, t)$ satisfies the inequality

$$\|u(x, t)\| \leqslant r(t),$$ (6.11)

where $r(t)$ is a function which is integrable over any finite interval of time. The function $u(x, t)$ will be regarded as a continuously acting perturbation.

Let us introduce the notation

$$h_0 = \sup_{t \geqslant 0} r(t), \quad h_1 = \sup_{t \geqslant 0} \int_t^{t+1} r(\tau)d\tau, \quad h_2 = \sup_{t \geqslant 0} \left(\int_t^{t+1} r^2(\tau)d\tau\right)^{\frac{1}{2}}.$$

Definition. *Suppose that for any $\varepsilon > 0$ one can choose positive numbers h and δ such that for the solution of equation (6.10) the inequality $\|x(t)\| < \varepsilon$ holds for $t \geqslant 0$ provided only that $\|x(0)\| < \delta$ and one of the following conditions is fulfilled.*

(a) $h_0 \leqslant h$; (b) $h_1 \leqslant h$; (c) $h_2 \leqslant h$.

In this case we shall say that the zero solution of equation (6.1) is stable against continuously acting perturbations which are (a) bounded; (b) bounded on the average; (c) bounded in the mean square.

It is clear that cases (a), (b) and (c) correspond to estimates of continuously acting perturbations along the norm of the corresponding spaces L_∞, M, and M_2.

Lemma 6.1. *Every solution of equation (6.10) satisfies the estimate*

$$\|x(t)\| \leqslant B(\Phi_1(t) + \Phi_2(t)),$$ (6.12)

where

$$\Phi_1(t) = e^{-\lambda t}\|x_0\|, \qquad x_0 = x(0),$$ (6.13)

$$\Phi_2(t) = e^{-\lambda t} \int_0^t e^{\lambda s} r(s) \, ds \, , \tag{6.14}$$

$$\lambda = \alpha - BL \, .$$

In fact, making use of the Cauchy formula, we obtain

$$x(t) = W(t, 0)x_0 + \int_0^t W(t, s)(R(x, s) + u(x, s)) ds \, ,$$

whence it follows that

$$\|x(t)\| \le B e^{-\alpha t} \|x_0\| + B \int_0^t e^{-\alpha(t-s)} [L\|x(s)\| + r(s)] \, ds \, .$$

Introducing the notation $\varphi(t) = e^{\alpha t} \|x(t)\|$, we obtain

$$\varphi(t) \le B\|x_0\| + B \int_0^t [L\varphi(s) + e^{\alpha s} r(s)] \, ds \, ,$$

whence, according to lemma 2.3 (inequality (2.15)), there follows the inequality

$$\varphi(t) \le B e^{BLT} \left(\|x_0\| + \int_0^t e^{(\alpha - BL)s} r(s) \, ds \right) .$$

Thus, we obtain the estimate

$$\|x(t)\| \le B e^{-\lambda t} \left(\|x_0\| + \int_0^t e^{\lambda s} r(s) \, ds \right) ,$$

which is equivalent to the estimate (6.12)

Lemma 6.2. *For* $t \ge 0$, *the following estimates are valid*:

$$\Phi_2(t) \le \frac{h_0}{\lambda} \, , \tag{6.15}$$

$$\Phi_2(t) \le \frac{h_1 e^{\lambda}}{1 - e^{-\lambda}} \, , \tag{6.16}$$

$$\Phi_2(t) \le h_2 (1 - e^{-\lambda})^{-1} \left(\frac{e^{2\lambda} - 1}{2\lambda} \right)^{\frac{1}{2}} . \tag{6.17}$$

Indeed, estimate (6.15) follows directly from the inequalities

$$\Phi_2(t) \leqslant h_0 e^{-\lambda t} \int_0^t e^{\lambda s} ds \quad \text{and} \quad \int_0^t e^{\lambda s} ds \leqslant \frac{e^{\lambda t}}{\lambda}.$$

To obtain the estimate (6.16) we separate out from t the integral part k, we put in the form $t = k + \tau_0$, where $0 \leqslant \tau_0 < 1$. In that case, the following estimate is valid

$$\Phi_2(t) \leqslant e^{-k\lambda} \left[\sum_{m=1}^{k+1} \int_{m-1}^m e^{m\lambda} r(s) ds \right], \tag{6.18}$$

whence it follows that

$$\Phi_2(t) \leqslant h_1 e^{-k\lambda} \left[\sum_{m=1}^{k+1} e^{m\lambda} \right] \leqslant h_1 \frac{e^{\lambda}}{1 - e^{-\lambda}}.$$

We shall now prove that estimate (6.17) is true. Clearly, the inequality

$$\Phi_2(t) \leqslant e^{-k\lambda} \sum_{m=1}^{k+1} \int_{m-1}^m e^{\lambda s} r(s) ds \leqslant$$

$$\leqslant e^{-k\lambda} \sum_{m=1}^{k+1} \left(\int_{m-1}^m e^{2\lambda s} ds \right)^{\frac{1}{2}} \left(\int_{m-1}^m r^2(s) ds \right)^{\frac{1}{2}}$$

is true. Thus, we have

$$\Phi_2(t) \leqslant h_2 (2\lambda)^{-\frac{1}{2}} e^{-k\lambda} \sum_{m=1}^{k+1} (e^{2\lambda m} - e^{2\lambda(m-1)})^{\frac{1}{2}},$$

whence follows

$$\Phi_2(t) \leqslant h_2 (2\lambda)^{-\frac{1}{2}} (e^{2\lambda} - 1)^{\frac{1}{2}} (1 - e^{-\lambda})^{-1},$$

which proves the estimate.

Theorem 6.2 (concerning the stability of continuously acting perturbations). *If, in the ε-neighbourhood of the point $x = 0$, conditions* (6.2), (6.4), (6.5) *and* (6.11) *and one of the inequalities*

(A) $\quad h_0 < \dfrac{\varepsilon}{2B} \lambda,$

(B) $\quad h_1 < \dfrac{\varepsilon}{2B} e^{-\lambda} (1 - e^{-\lambda}),$

(C) $h_2 < \dfrac{\varepsilon}{2B}\left(\dfrac{2\lambda}{e^{2\lambda}-1}\right)^{\frac{1}{2}}(1-e^{-\lambda})$

are fulfilled, every solution of (6.10) *determined by the condition* $\|x_0\| < \varepsilon/2B$
will satisfy the inequality $\|x(t)\| < \varepsilon$ *for* $t \geqslant 0$.

Proof. From lemma 6.1 it follows that solution $x(t)$ satisfies (6.12).
The function $\Phi_1(t) = e^{-\lambda t}\|x_0\|$ obviously satisfies the condition $\Phi_1(t) <$
$\varepsilon/2B$ and, according to lemma 6.2, the function $\Phi_2(t)$ is related to it through
the similar inequality $\Phi_2(t) < \varepsilon/2B$ provided one of the conditions (A), (B)
or (C) is fulfilled.
From (6.12) it immediately follows that $\|x(t)\| < \varepsilon$.

3.   Let us now consider one more theorem, for which a suitable title
might be "the theorem of dissipative stability".

Theorem 6.3. *Assume that in the ε-neighbourhood of the point $x = 0$
conditions* (6.2), (6.4), (6.5), (6.11) *are fulfilled together with one of the
inequalities*

(a) $h_0 < \rho\,\dfrac{\delta}{B}\,\lambda\,,$

(b) $h_1 < \rho\,\dfrac{\delta}{B}\,e^{-\lambda}(1-e^{-\lambda})\,,$

(c) $h_2 < \rho\,\dfrac{\delta}{B}\left(\dfrac{2\lambda}{e^{2\lambda}-1}\right)^{\frac{1}{2}}(1-e^{-\lambda})\,,$

*where $0 < \rho < 1$ and $0 < \delta < \varepsilon/2B$. In that case there exists a positive num-
ber T such that for $t > T$ and $\|x_0\| < \delta$ a solution $x(t)$ of equation* (6.10)
satisfies the inequality $\|x(t)\| < \delta$.

Proof. Let T be a positive whole number such that $T > \lambda^{-1}\ln B/(1-\rho)$.
For $t > T$, we obtain the estimate $\Phi_1(t) = e^{-\lambda t}\|x_0\| < (1-\rho)(\delta/B)$. If one
of the conditions (a), (b), (c) is fulfilled then, according to lemma 6.2, we
obtain $\Phi_2(t) < \rho\delta/B$ from which it follows that a solution $x(t)$ of equation
(6.10) will satisfy the inequality $\|x(t)\| < \delta$ for $t > T$.

4.   Consider now the equation

$$\dot{x} = A(t)x + R(x, t) + u(t), \tag{6.19}$$

where the operator function $A(t)$, and the functions $R(x, t)$ and $u(t)$ are continuous and periodic in t. If the period is the same for all of these functions and equal to ω, the substitution $t = \tau\omega$ obviously leads us to the case where the period will be equal to unity. We shall therefore assume that $\omega = 1$. As before we shall suppose that the Cauchy operator $W(t, \tau)$ of equation (6.3) satisfies condition (6.4). Let us further suppose that in region D the function $R(x, t)$ satisfies the Lipschitz condition

$$\|R(x, t) - R(y, t)\| \leqslant L\|x - y\|. \tag{6.20}$$

Assuming that the condition $R(0, t) = 0$ is fulfilled for $t \geqslant 0$, we can regard condition (6.2) as satisfied. Now let us assume that the numbers α, B, L satisfy condition (6.5) and that the function $u(t)$ satisfies condition (6.11). Since, in condition (6.11), one can obviously put $r(t) = \|u(t)\|$, function $r(t)$ can be considered a periodic function of t.

Theorem 6.4. *Assume that for equation* (6.19) *the conditions enumerated above and one of the conditions* (a), (b) *or* (c) *of theorem* (6.3) *are fulfilled. In that case in the region* $\|x\| \leqslant H/2B$ *there exists a periodic solution* $z(t)$ *of equation* (6.19). *If* $x(t)$ *is any other solution of this equation such that* $\|x(0)\| \leqslant H/2B$, *then* $\|x(t) - z(t)\| \to 0$ *for* $t \to \infty$, *which means that the periodic solution* $z(t)$ *is asymptotically stable in the Lyapunov sense.*

To prove this theorem we note that from theorem 6.3 it follows that if $\|x(0)\| \leqslant \delta = H/2B$ then one can find a positive number T such that $\|x(T)\| \leqslant \delta$. This means that during the interval of time T the sphere $\|x\| \leqslant \delta$ passes along the trajectories of the equation into its part. We shall show that the mapping $x(0) \to x(T)$ satisfies the conditions of the principle of condensed mappings, i.e. the conditions of theorem 1.2. We note first that the number T was chosen in order to fulfil the inequality

$$T > \frac{1}{\lambda} \ln \frac{B}{1 - \rho} > \frac{1}{\lambda} \ln B. \tag{6.21}$$

If x_0 and y_0 are two elements of the δ-neighbourhood of the zero point then, according to the Cauchy formula, we obtain

$$x(T) = W(T, 0)x_0 + \int_0^T W(T, s)[R(x, s) + u(s)]\,ds\,,$$

$$y(T) = W(T, 0)y_0 + \int_0^T W(T, s)[R(y, s) + u(s)]\,ds\,,$$

which at once gives us the estimate

$$\|y(T) - x(T)\| \leqslant \|W(T, 0)\|\,\|y_0 - x_0\| +$$

$$+ \int_0^T \|W(T, s)\|\,\|R(y, s) - R(x, s)\|\,ds\,.$$

Taking conditions (6.4) and (6.20) into consideration, we obtain

$$\|y(T) - x(T)\| \leqslant B\,e^{-\alpha T}\|y_0 - x_0\| +$$

$$+ \int_0^T BL\,e^{-\alpha(T-s)}\|y(s) - x(s)\|\,ds\,.$$

Introducing the notation $\varphi(t) = e^{\alpha t}\|y(t) - x(t)\|$, we obtain

$$\varphi(t) \leqslant B\|y_0 - x_0\| + BL \int_0^T \varphi(s)\,ds\,,$$

whence, according to lemma 1.1, we get

$$\varphi(T) \leqslant B\,e^{BLT}\|y_0 - x_0\|\,,$$

i.e.

$$\|y(T) - x(T)\| \leqslant B\,e^{-\lambda t}\|y_0 - x_0\|\,. \tag{6.21'}$$

By virtue of condition (6.21) we have $B\,e^{-\lambda T} < 1$; this also demonstrates the possibility of applying the principle of condensed mappings.

Thus, in the sphere $\|x\| < \delta$, there exists a unique point $z(0)$ such that $z(T) = z(0)$. A periodic motion corresponds to this point and we shall say that the period associated with it is exactly equal to unity. Indeed, let us consider the point $z(1)$; clearly, in view of the periodic nature of the right-hand side of (6.19), we have $z(1) = z(T+1)$. Consequently $z(1)$ also is a fixed point of the mapping considered above. But since the fixed point must be unique, the inequality $z(0) = z(1)$ must be fulfilled.

The validity of the last part of the theorem now follows from inequality (6.21').

5. We shall now pass on to a discussion of theorems pertaining to stability in the presence of continuously acting perturbations, and theorems concerned with stability with respect to the first approximation, whose proofs do not fall within the scheme given earlier.

In conjunction with the equation

$$\dot{x} = X(x, t), \quad \text{where} \quad X(0, t) = 0 \tag{6.22}$$

let us consider the equation

$$\dot{y} = X(y, t) + R(y, t). \tag{6.23}$$

Assume that the conditions ensuring the existence and continuity of the solution of both these equations are fulfilled in a region D: $\|x\| \leqslant M, 0 \leqslant t < \infty$.

We give now some definitions that will be required later on.

(a) The equilibrium position $x = 0$ of equation (6.22) will be said to be uniformly stable in the Lyapunov sense if for any $\varepsilon > 0$ and $t_0 \geqslant 0$ it is possible to find a positive number δ depending only on ε such that from $\|x(t_0)\| < \delta$ it follows that $\|x(t)\| < \varepsilon$ for $t \geqslant t_0$.

(b) The equilibrium position $x = 0$ of equation (6.22) will be said to be uniformly asymptotically stable if it is uniformly stable in the Lyapunov sense and if, in addition, there exists an $\varepsilon > 0$ such that for any $\delta > 0$, $t_0 \geqslant 0$ it is possible to find a number $T > 0$ depending only on ε and δ such that from $\|x(t_0)\| < \varepsilon$ it follows that $\|x(t_0 + T)\| < \delta$. In the following definition, the point $x = 0$ is not assumed to be an equilibrium position.

(c) The point $x = 0$ is said to be ε-stable if it is possible to find a $\delta > 0$ such that, from $\|x(t_0)\| < \delta$, it follows that $\|x(t)\| < \varepsilon$ for $t \geqslant t_0$.

Hereafter it will be assumed everywhere that $x(t)$ denotes a solution of equation (6.22) and $y(t)$ a solution of equation (6.23).

Lemma 6.3. *Let the solution $x = 0$ of equation (6.22) be uniformly asymptotically stable. In accordance with (a) and (b) we shall define numbers $\delta < \varepsilon$ and $T >$ such that from $\|x(t_0)\| < \delta$ it follows that*

$$\|x(t)\| < \varepsilon/2 \quad \text{for} \quad t \geqslant t_0, \tag{6.24}$$

$$\|x(t_0 + T)\| < \frac{\delta}{2}. \tag{6.25}$$

Let $x(t_0) = y(t_0)$. If the inequality

$$\| y(t) - x(t) \| < \delta/2 \quad \text{for} \quad t_0 \leqslant t \leqslant t_0 + T , \tag{6.26}$$

is true, where t_0 is any positive number, then the point $x = 0$ will be ε-stable with respect to system (6.23).

Indeed, from the conditions (6.24) and (6.26) of the lemma, we obtain $\| y(t) \| < \varepsilon/2 + \delta/2 < \varepsilon$ for $t_0 \leqslant t \leqslant t_0 + T$. Moreover, from (6.24) and (6.25), it follows that $\| y(t_0 + T) \| < \delta$.

Thus, during the time interval $[t_0, t_0 + T]$, the point $y(t)$ does not pass outside the limits of the region $\| y \| < \varepsilon$, and at time $t = t_0 + T$, it will lie inside the region $\| y \| < \delta$.

Taking the time $t = t_0 + T$ as the initial instant of time, and pursuing similar arguments, i.e. by considering the solution $x(t)$ defined by the condition $x(t_0 + T) = y(t_0 + T)$, we can convince ourselves that the point $y(t)$ does not pass outside the limits of the region $\| y \| < \varepsilon$ for $t_0 + T \leqslant t \leqslant t_0 + 2T$ and, in addition, we obtain $\| y(t_0 + 2T) \| < \delta$.

Continuing further with this line of reasoning, we find that $\| y(t) \| < \varepsilon$ for $t_0 + (n-1)T \leqslant t \leqslant t_0 + nT$ and $\| y(t_0 + nT) \| < \delta$, which proves the lemma.

Let us call the equilibrium position $x = 0$ exponentially stable in the small if it is possible to find an $\varepsilon > 0$ such that, for $\| x(t_0) \| < \varepsilon$, $t \geqslant t_0$, any solution $x(t)$ of equation (6.22) satisfies the inequality

$$\| x(t) \| \leqslant B e^{-\alpha(t - t_0)} \| x(t_0) \| , \tag{6.27}$$

where $\alpha > 0$, $B > 0$ do not depend on t_0.

Lemma 6.4. *If the inequality*

$$\| x(t) - y(t) \| \leqslant \tfrac{1}{4} \| x(t_0) \| , \tag{6.28}$$

holds for $x(t_0) = y(t_0)$ and $t_0 \leqslant t \leqslant t_0 + T$, where t_0 is any positive number and the point $x = 0$ is exponentially stable in the small for equation (6.22), then this point will be exponentially stable in the small for equation (6.23) also.

Proof. Let $T = 1/\alpha \ln 4B$ and $\delta = \varepsilon/2B$, where ε is an arbitrary positive number for which inequality (6.27) is true.

If $\| x(t_0) \| < 0$, we have $\| x(t) \| < \varepsilon/2$ for $t_0 \leqslant t \leqslant t_0 + T$ and, in addition, $\| x(t_0 + T) \| < \delta/4$. From condition (6.28) it follows that $\| y(t) - x(t) \| < \delta/4$

for $t_0 \leqslant t \leqslant t_0 + T$, whence we obtain $\|y(t)\| < \varepsilon$ for $t_0 \leqslant t \leqslant t_0 + T$ and $\|y(t_0 + T)\| < \delta/2$.

Let us assume now that it has been demonstrated that $\|y(t)\| < \varepsilon/2^{n-1}$ for $t_0 + (n-1)T \leqslant t \leqslant t_0 + nT$, and $\|y(t_0 + nT)\| < \delta/2^n$. We shall show that the inequalities

$$\|y(t)\| < \varepsilon/2^n \quad \text{for} \quad t_0 + nT \leqslant t \leqslant t_0 + (n+1)T \tag{6.29}$$

and

$$\|y(t_0 + (n+1)T)\| < \delta/2^{n+1} \tag{6.30}$$

are true.

Indeed, from (6.27), it follows that if $\|x(t_0)\| < \delta/2^n$, then $\|x(t)\| < \varepsilon/2^{n+1}$ for $t_0 \leqslant t \leqslant t_0 + T$ and $\|x(t_0 + T)\| < \delta/2^{n+2}$. Condition (6.28) gives $\|x(t) - y(t)\| < \delta/2^{n+2}$ for $t_0 \leqslant t \leqslant t_0 + T$, whence it follows that $\|y(t)\| < \varepsilon/2^{n+1} + \delta/2^{n+2} < \varepsilon/2^n$ for $t_0 \leqslant t \leqslant t_0 + T$ and $\|y(t_0 + T)\| < \delta/2^{n+1}$.

If now, for the number t_0, we take $t_0 + nT$, we can convince ourselves of the validity of inequalities (6.29) and (6.30). From these equations it is easy to deduce the inequality

$$\|y(t)\| \leqslant 4B\delta \exp\left(-\alpha \ln 2/\ln 4B(t - t_0)\right),$$

which proves the assertion of our lemma.

Suppose now that in region D the function $X(x, t)$ satisfies the Lipschitz condition

$$\|X(x, t) - X(y, t)\| \leqslant L\|x - y\|, \tag{6.31}$$

and the function $R(x, t)$ satisfies the condition

$$\|R(x, t)\| \leqslant \eta, \tag{6.32}$$

where η is a positive number.

Theorem 6.5. (concerning stability in the presence of continuously acting perturbations). *If the zero solution of equation (6.22) is uniformly asymptotically stable, then, for any $\varepsilon > 0$, it is possible to find numbers $\delta > 0$ and $\eta > 0$ such that for any solution $y(t)$ of equation (6.23) the inequality*

$$\|y(t)\| < \varepsilon.$$

will follow, for $t \geqslant t_0$, from inequalities (6.32) and $\|y(t_0)\| < \delta$.

Indeed, in accordance with lemma 6.3, we must choose numbers $T > 0$

and $\delta > 0$ for a given $\varepsilon > 0$ such that inequalities (6.24) and (6.25) will be fulfilled. From theorem 2.6 we deduce the inequality

$$\|x(t) - y(t)\| \leqslant \int_{t_0}^{t_0 + T} e^{L(t-s)} \eta \, ds = \eta/L (e^{LT} - 1).$$

It is clear that if η is chosen initially in accordance with the inequality $\eta/L (e^{LT} - 1) < \delta/2$, all the conditions of lemma 6.3 will be fulfilled and we will obtain the required result.

Theorem 6.5 can be reinforced in the sense that in place of inequality (6.32) one can, as in the proof of lemma 6.2, require the fulfilment of the inequality $\|R(x, t)\| \leqslant \eta(t)$ with the estimate $\eta(t)$ along the norm in the spaces M, M_2.

Theorem 6.6. *Assume that condition* (6.31) *and the condition*

$$\|R(x, t)\| \leqslant M \|x\| \tag{6.33}$$

are fulfilled in region D. If the zero solution of equation (6.22) *is exponentially stable in the small then, for a sufficiently small value of M, the zero solution of equation* (6.23) *will also be exponentially stable in the small.*

To prove this theorem let $T = (1/\alpha) \ln 4B$, where α and B are taken from condition (6.27). Taking into account conditions (6.31), (6.33) and the inequality $\|x(t)\| \leqslant \delta B$ ensuing from (6.27) we can derive, for $t_0 \leqslant t \leqslant t_0 + T$, the inequality

$$\|x(t) - y(t)\| \leqslant \frac{MB\delta}{M+L} (e^{(M+L)(t-t_0)} - 1), \tag{6.34}$$

which we established when proving lemma 4.4 of Chapter 2. By choosing M to be small enough, we can make the value of the right-hand side of (6.34) smaller than $\delta/4$. We then apply lemma 6.4.

6.   We will mention now work by other authors who have investigated the problems we have been discussing in the context of a finite-dimensional phase space.

The earliest papers devoted to the study of stability in the presence of bounded, continuously acting perturbations are due to Gorshin [108] and Malkin ([8], p. 308). Stability of motion in the presence of perturbations which are bounded on the average has been investigated by Germaidze and Krasovskii [109]. An investigation of the stability of a periodic motion in the presence of bounded continuously acting perturbations has been made by Artem'ev [110].

Problems concerned with the existence, preservation and stability of a periodic motion in the presence of external perturbations which are bounded in accordance with some model have been discussed by Krasovskii [111] and by Antosiewicz [12] on the basis of the method of Lyapunov functions.

Barbashin [113] has investigated the effect of perturbations bounded in the mean square, and has also studied periodic motions in the presence of perturbations bounded on the average and in the mean square. These ideas provided a basis for a study of the action of random perturbations [114] and for studying the stability of solutions of integro-differential equations [85, 91].

Lemmas 6.3 and 6.4 are from reference [115] where a more general case is investigated, namely one which does not require uniqueness of the solutions; in addition, the stability of the set was studied. Theorem 6.6 was published in a paper by Barbashin and Skalkina [116].

The ideas behind lemmas 6.3 and 6.4 provided a basis for a whole series of papers on theories of difference equations [117, 118], equations with delays [77], integro-differential equations [84] and equations in Banach space [119].

7. Stability with Respect to Impulse Perturbations

1. A case of particular interest arises when the perturbations acting on the system are in the form of a step-function. In particular, as an example of a step-function or impulse perturbation, consider the function $u(t) = x_0 \delta(t - t_0)$, where x_0 is a fixed element of the space E, $t_0 \geqslant 0$ and $\delta(t - t_0)$ is the Dirac function.

If the condition $x(t) = 0$ is fulfilled for $t < t_0$, it is not difficult to see that after such a perturbation has acted on the system the solution of the problem

$$\dot{x} = A(t)x + u(t), \quad x(0) = 0 \tag{7.1}$$

for $t > t_0$ will have the form

$$x(t) = W(t, t_0)x_0 . \tag{7.2}$$

This means that at time $t = t_0$ the perturbation $u(t)$ causes an instantaneous transition of the zero point to the point x_0.

Consider the function $e(t)$ (a unit jump function) defined in the following way:

$$e(t) = 0 \quad \text{for} \quad t < t_0,$$
$$e(t) = 1 \quad \text{for} \quad t \geqslant t.$$

It is easy to see that solution (7.2) can be represented by the formula

$$x(t) = \int_0^t W(t, s) x_0 \, de(s), \tag{7.3}$$

where the integral should be regarded as a generalised Stieltjes integral. If one regards the function $e(t)$ as an input distribution then relation (7.3) shows how this distribution is transformed into the new distribution $x(t)$ during its passage through a unit of the automatic system described by equation (7.1). Thus, if we adopt the point of view that equation (7.1) describes the law for transforming the input distribution into the output distribution, an interesting new problem presents itself which has to do with the theory of generalised functions. Because of limitations of space, however, we are unable to give a full description here of the transformation of generalised input signals into output signals.

By using the simple device of the Stieltjes integral, which we discussed briefly in section 1, it is not difficult to investigate the important class of impulse perturbations of the form

$$u(t) = u_0(t) + \sum_{i=1}^{\infty} a_i \delta(t - t_i), \tag{7.4}$$

where the function $u_0(t)$ is integrable over any finite interval, and the a_i are elements of space E.

2. Consider first the equation

$$x(t) = \int_0^t W(t, s) \, dg(s), \tag{7.5}$$

corresponding to problem (7.1).

Theorem 7.1. *For a function $x(t)$ bounded along the norm L_∞ to correspond, by virtue of (7.5), to every function $g(t)$ of the bounded variation over the set*

$0 \leqslant t < \infty$, it is necessary and sufficient that the inequality

$$\| W(t, t_0) \| \leqslant W_0 < \infty$$

be fulfilled for any $0 \leqslant t_0 \leqslant t < \infty$.

Indeed, to demonstrate the necessity of the above condition it is sufficient to take a function $g(t)$ in the following form:

$$g(t) = \int_0^t u(t) dt ,$$

where $u(t)$ belongs to the space **L**. Thus the quantity

$$\int_0^\infty \| u(t) \| dt$$

is finite and $g(t)$ will be a function of the bounded variation over the set $t \geqslant 0$. According to the condition attached to the theorem, the function $x(t)$ should be bounded whereupon, using theorem 5.7, we obtain the inequality we need: $\| W(t, t_0) \| \leqslant W_0 < \infty$ for $0 \leqslant t_0 \leqslant t < \infty$.

The sufficiency of the condition follows from inequality (1.9). From this inequality it follows that

$$\| x(t) \| \leqslant W_0 \bigvee_0^\infty g(t) ,$$

whence we obtain the boundedness of $x(t)$.

Consider now a space **U** whose elements are functions $g(t)$ such that

$$\| g(t) \|_U = \sup_{t>0} \bigvee_t^{t+1} g(t) < \infty .$$

Theorem 7.2. *Assume the condition*

$$\sup_{t>0} \int_t^{t+1} \| A(t) \| dt < \infty .$$

is fulfilled. For the bounded function $x(t)$ to correspond by virtue of (7.5) to every function $g(t) \in U$ it is necessary and sufficient that the inequality

$$\| W(t, t_0) \| \leqslant B e^{-\alpha(t - t_0)} , \tag{7.6}$$

be fulfilled, where $\alpha > 0$, $B \geqslant 1$ are independent of t_0.

Indeed, to prove the necessity of the condition we consider a sub-space of space U consisting of all functions of the form $g(t) = \int_0^t u(t)\,dt$ where $u(t)$ belongs to the space M. This corresponds to the condition

$$\sup_{t \geqslant 0} \int_t^{t+1} \|u(t)\|\,dt < \infty \,.$$

Since

$$\bigvee_t^{t+1} g(t) \leqslant \int_t^{t+1} \|u(t)\|\,dt \,,$$

then $g(t)$ belongs to U.
Clearly, in this case we have

$$x(t) = \int_0^t W(t, s) u(s)\,ds \,.$$

However, since $u(s) \in M$ and $x(t)$ is a bounded continuous function, the validity of (7.6) follows from theorem 5.6.
Let us prove the sufficiency of the condition. According to (7.6) and (1.10) we have

$$\|x(t)\| \leqslant B\,e^{-\alpha t} \int_0^t e^{\alpha s}\,dv(s) \,, \tag{7.7}$$

where $v(s) = \bigvee_0^s g(s)$.
We will now evaluate the quantity

$$\Phi(t) = e^{-\alpha t} \int_0^t e^{\alpha s}\,dv(s) \,.$$

To do this we separate out the whole number part of t, i.e. we represent t in the form $t = k + \tau$, $0 \leqslant \tau < 1$. Following the line of reasoning used in proving lemma 6.2, we have

$$\Phi(t) \leqslant e^{-k\alpha} \left[\sum_{m=1}^{k+1} \int_{m-1}^m e^{\alpha m}\,dv(s) \right] \,.$$

If

$$\sup_{t \geqslant 0} \bigvee_t^{t+1} g(t) = \sup_{t \geqslant 0} \int_t^{t+1} dv(s) = h < \infty \,,$$

we obtain

$$\Phi(t) \leqslant h\,e^{-k\alpha} \sum_{m=1}^{k+1} e^{\alpha m} \leqslant \frac{h\,e^{\alpha}}{1 - e^{-\alpha}} \,. \tag{7.8}$$

Thus, our evaluation of (7.7) assumes the form

$$\|x(t)\| \leqslant \frac{Bh\,e^{\alpha}}{1-e^{-\alpha}},$$

which yields the required result.

3. Consider now the non-linear problem.
Suppose the law of transformation of the input is given by the formula

$$x(t) = \int_0^t W(t,s)R(x,s)\,ds + \int_0^t W(t,s)\,dg(s). \tag{7.9}$$

It is easy to see that in the case of a differentiable function $g(s)$ problem (7.9) is equivalent to the problem

$$\dot{x} = A(t)x + R(x,t) + u(t), \qquad x(0) = 0, \tag{7.10}$$

where $u(t) = \dot{g}(t)$.
Let us suppose that conditions (7.6) are fulfilled and

$$\|R(x,t)\| \leqslant L\|x\| \tag{7.11}$$

in the region $D: \|x\| \leqslant H, 0 \leqslant t < \infty$.
We shall suppose, in addition, that the inequality

$$\lambda = \alpha - LB > 0 \tag{7.12}$$

is true.

Theorem 7.3. *Assume*

$$\sup_{t \geqslant 0} \bigvee_{t}^{t+1} g(t) = h.$$

If conditions (7.6), (7.11) *and* (7.12) *are fulfilled then the estimate*

$$\|x(t)\| \leqslant B\,\frac{h\,e^{\lambda}}{1-e^{-\lambda}}$$

is valid.

In fact, we have

$$\|x(t)\| \leqslant BL\,e^{-\alpha t}\int_0^t e^{\alpha s}\|x(s)\|\,ds + B\,e^{-\alpha t}\int_0^t e^{\alpha s}\,dv(s),$$

where

$$v(s) = \bigvee_0^s g(s).$$

For the function $\varphi(t) = \|x(t)\| \, e^{\alpha t}$ the inequality

$$\varphi(t) \leqslant BL \int_0^t \varphi(s) \, ds + B \int_0^t e^{\alpha s} \, dv(s)$$

holds and, by virtue of lemma 2.3 (inequality (2.14)), we have

$$\varphi(t) \leqslant B \, e^{BLt} \int_0^t e^{\lambda s} \, dv(s),$$

whence we obtain

$$\|x(t)\| \leqslant B \, e^{-\lambda t} \int_0^t e^{\lambda s} \, dv(s).$$

Making use now of estimate (7.8), we get the required result.
Theorem 7.3 is a theorem about stability with respect to perturbations which may, in a particular case, be instantaneous.

4. Consider the equation

$$x(t) = W(t, 0)x_0 + \int_0^t W(t, s) R(x, s) \, ds + \int_0^t W(t, s) \, dg(s), \quad (7.13)$$

where $R(x, t)$ has the property $R(0, t) = 0$, $g(-0) = g(+0)$. This equation corresponds to problem (7.10) but with the difference that $x(0) = x_0$. We assume that the Cauchy operator satisfies the condition

$$W(t+1, s+1) = W(t, s) ; \qquad (7.14)$$

and, in addition, we assume that $R(x, s)$ and $g(s)$ are also periodic functions with period 1. Condition (7.4) is obviously equivalent to the requirement that the operator function $A(t)$ appearing in equation (7.10) should be periodic.
As before, let us assume in addition that conditions (7.6) and (7.12) are fulfilled. In place of (7.11) we require that the Lipschitz condition be fulfilled in region $D_{\scriptscriptstyle .}$

$$\|R(x, t) - R(y, t)\| \leqslant L \|x - y\| . \qquad (7.15)$$

Theorem 7.4. *Suppose* $\|x_0\| \leqslant \delta$, *where* $\delta = H/2B$ *and*

$$\sup_{t \geqslant 0} \bigvee_t^{t+1} g(t) = h \leqslant \rho \frac{\delta}{B} e^{-\lambda}(1 - e^{-\lambda}), \qquad 0 < \rho < 1 . \tag{7.16}$$

For the solution of (7.13) *the estimate* $\|x(t)\| \leqslant H$ *is valid. In addition, it is possible to find an* x_0, $\|x_0\| \leqslant \delta$ *such that the corresponding solution* $x(t)$ *will be periodic and asymptotically stable. Every other solution determined by an initial point from the region* $\|x\| \leqslant \delta$ *will be attracted towards this periodic solution.*

To prove this theorem we repeat the proof of lemma 6.1 and use lemma 2.3 once more (inequality (2.14)). In this way we find that

$$\|x(t)\| \leqslant B e^{-\lambda t}\|x_0\| + B e^{-\lambda} \int_0^t e^{\lambda s} dv(s) .$$

Using the estimate of the previous theorem, we obtain

$$\|x(t)\| \leqslant B e^{-\lambda t} \delta + B \frac{h e^{\lambda}}{1 - e^{-\lambda}} ,$$

whence, by virtue of (7.16), it follows that

$$\|x(t)\| \leqslant B e^{-\lambda t} \delta + \rho \delta < (B + \rho)\delta < H .$$

On the other hand, for integral $T > \lambda^{-1} \ln B/(1 - \rho)$, we obtain $|x(T)\| \leqslant \delta$ and, consequently, the point x_0 again moves into the δ-neighbourhood of the point $x = 0$. It is not difficult to see that in this case the transformation $x_0 \rightarrow x(T)$ is continuous and unique. Repeating now the proof of theorem 6.4, one can show that this transformation satisfies the conditions of the condensed mapping principle, whence follows the existence and uniqueness of the periodic motion, which, however, may have a denumerable number of discontinuities. The asymptotic stability of the periodic solution is established in exactly the same way as in the proof of theorem 6.4.

The finite-dimensional case of the last theorem is discussed in reference [113].

8. Problem of Realising a Motion along a Specified Trajectory

1. Let us consider now the problem of finding an equation which will

ensure the exact or approximate realization of a given process. The problem can be stated as follows. Suppose we are given the differential equation

$$\dot{x} = X(x, \eta, t) + u(y, t), \tag{8.1}$$

where $x(t)$, $\eta(t)$, $y(t)$ are functions with values in the Banach space E, and $\eta(t)$ is, in general, a random function. Suppose that in the phase space E, and for $0 \leqslant t < T$ $(0 < T \leqslant \infty)$, a certain trajectory $x = \psi(t)$ is specified. We assume that certain information is arriving about the variation of the function $\eta(t)$ which plays the part of a background noise. It is required to select a control by choosing such a $y(t)$ that a certain solution of equation (8.1) will exactly or approximately realise the motion along the trajectory $x = \psi(t)$ during the specified interval of time. The problem may be complicated by the existence of a restriction on the set of possible values of the function $y(t)$; for example the set could be bounded, compact, have finite dimensionality, *etc.*

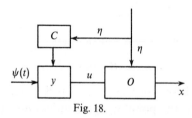

Fig. 18.

The block diagram of the corresponding automatic system is given in Fig. 18. In this diagram 0 is the object of control, the purpose of which is to obtain a specified mode of behaviour $x = \psi(t)$. To do this, we add unit y which generates a control signal u. In generating this signal, use is made of information about the required behaviour $\psi(t)$ and about the noise $\eta(t)$. For a number of reasons this information about the noise arrives in a distorted form. For example, distortion might arise as a result of delays, inertia in the connecting line C, errors of measurement, random errors, *etc.*

Since the equation for this automatic control system varies in accordance with a previously specified function of time $\psi(t)$, the system is a programmed automatic system.

If the programmed control problem when formulated in this way has an exact solution, the control we are seeking is found from the equation

$$u(y(t), t) = \psi(t) - X(\psi(t), \eta(t), t) . \tag{8.2}$$

In many cases, however, equation (8.2) is unsolvable with respect to the controlling function $y(t)$. The insolubility of this equation may be a consequence of the restrictions imposed on the norm of the function $y(t)$, restrictions on the dimensionality $y(t)$, the presence of incomplete or distorted information about the external action $\eta(t)$. It can also happen that the control can be selected only from a restricted class of functions, for example, from step-functions, trigonometrical polynomials *etc.*

2. In equation (8.1) let us make the substitution $z = x - \psi(t)$; the new equation will have the form

$$\dot{z} = Z(z, \eta, t) + \Delta(y, \psi(t), \eta(t), t) \tag{8.3}$$

where

$$Z(z, \eta, t) = X(z + \psi(t), \eta(t), t) - X(\psi(t), \eta(t), t) ,$$
$$\Delta(y, \psi(t), \eta(t), t) = X(\psi(t), \eta(t), t) - \psi(t) + u(y, t) = \Delta(t) .$$

In the equation for the perturbed motion, the function $\Delta(t)$ determines the error of the approximation to the programming function; the deviation of the solution $z(t)$ of equation (8.3) from zero coincides with the deviation of the solution $x(t)$ of equation (8.1) from the specified function $\psi(t)$. The principal problem here is to evaluate $\|z(t)\|$ as a function of $\|\Delta(t)\|$. We considered this problem in a general form in section 2; it was also solved in section 4 for the case when Z is a linear operator with respect to Z where it appeared as a problem about the build-up of perturbations.

In cases where the problem is to realise a given form of behaviour in an infinite time interval $0 \leqslant t < \infty$, then it is easy to see that an approximate solution to the problem is possible if the zero solution of the equation

$$\dot{z} = Z(z, \eta, t) \tag{8.4}$$

is stable with respect to continuously acting perturbations which are bounded with respect to the same metric in which the error of the approximation $\Delta(t)$ is estimated. Theorems 6.2 and 6.3 permit an estimate to be made of the accuracy of the approximation $\|z(t)\|$ of the behaviour being programmed with the help of the norm $\varDelta(t)$ taken in the spaces C, M, M_2. Theorem 6.4 permits us to obtain the corresponding result when the specified behaviour is periodic.

If the behaviour being programmed is discontinuous then the estimates of the errors should be made with the help of the theorems of section 7.

Finally, if we wish to realize a random behaviour by stressing the stochastic nature of the equations, we should take into account example 5 of section 3. The arguments presented there allow the problem to be reduced to a determinate case [114].

From theorem 6.5 it follows that stability in the presence of continuously acting perturbations guarantees uniform asymptotic stability of the zero solution of equation (8.4). This gives rise to an interesting problem.

We shall say that the behaviour $\psi(t)$ of a system is stable with respect to equation $\dot{x} = X(x, t)$ if the zero solution of the equation $z = X(z + \psi(t), t) - X(\psi(t), t)$ is uniformly asymptotically stable. From the preceding discussion it is clear that only stable behaviours can claim to be a good approximation for all $t \geqslant 0$.

In the case when the operator $X(x, t)$ is linear with respect to x it is obvious that any behaviour will be stable if the zero solution of the equation $\dot{x} = X(x, t)$ is uniformly asymptotically stable.

The systems investigated by Krasovskii [120] have the same property. These systems are identified by the fact that for each of them it is possible to find a constant symmetrical matrix A having positive eigenvalues such that the symmetrized matrix

$$\{B\}_{ik} = \left\{ \left(A \frac{\partial X}{\partial x} \right)_{ik} + \left(A \frac{\partial X}{\partial x} \right)_{ki} \right\},$$

where

$$\left(\frac{\partial X}{\partial x} \right)_{ik} = \frac{\partial X_i}{\partial x_k},$$

has negative eigenvalues μ_i satisfying the inequality $\mu_i < -\alpha, \alpha > 0$ at all points of space, $-\infty < x_i < \infty$, $i = 1, 2, ..., n$, $0 \leqslant t < \infty$. Here X_i is the projection of the vector function $X(x, t)$.

3. Consider now in the n-dimensional linear vector space E_n the differential equation

$$\dot{x} = X(x, t) + \sum_{k=1}^{m} c_k y_k(t) . \tag{8.5}$$

Here x, c_k are n-dimensional vectors and the y_k are scalar functions. If the problem at hand is the realization of the process $x = \psi(t)$ in the interval $0 \leqslant t \leqslant T$, then the substitution $z = x - \psi(t)$ reduces equation (8.5) to the equation

$$\dot{z} = Z(z, t) + \varDelta(t) , \tag{8.6}$$

where

$$Z(z, t) = X(z + \psi(t), t) - X(\psi(t), t) ,$$

$$\varDelta(t) = X(\psi(t), t) - \dot{\psi}(t) + \sum_{k=1}^{m} c_k y_k(t) .$$

Assume that in the region $\|z\| \leqslant H, 0 \leqslant t \leqslant T$ the function $Z(z, t)$ satisfies the Lipschitz condition

$$\|Z(z_1, t) - Z(z_2, t)\| \leqslant L\|z_1 - z_2\| .$$

Then, according to theorem 2.6, the solution $z(t)$ of equation (8.6) may be estimated in the following way:

$$\|z(t)\| \leqslant \int_0^T e^{L(t-s)} \varDelta(s) ds .$$

It is clear that to solve the problem of realising the process $z = 0$ approximately we must make the vector function $\varDelta(s)$ sufficiently small with respect to one of the metrics by suitably choosing either the vectors c_k, or the functions $y_k(t)$, or both these quantities.
Let

$$r(t) = \dot{\psi} - X(\psi(t), t) ,$$

then we will have

$$\varDelta(t) = \sum_{k=1}^{m} c_k y_k(t) - r(t)$$

and consequently the problem reduces to one of approximating the function $r(t)$ by the linear aggregate $y(t) = \Sigma_{k=1}^{m} c_k y_k(t)$. The problem is obviously a problem in approximation theory. The simplest procedure is to solve such problems in the metric L_2, i.e. in terms of the theory of mean square approximations. Let us now recall some of the basic statements of this theory [121].

In the linear space H we associate with each pair of elements x, y a certain number (x, y) which we shall call the scalar product. Assume that the following conditions are fulfilled:

(a) $(x, y) = (y, x)$,
(b) $(\alpha x + \beta y, z) = \alpha(x, z) + \beta(y, z)$,
(c) $(x, x) \geqslant 0$
(d) $(x, x) = 0$ if, and only if, $x = 0$.

We will introduce the norm in space H in accordance with the rule

$$\|x\|^2 = (x, x).$$

We shall call the space H a Hilbert space. If $(x, y) = 0$, then the elements x and y will be said to be orthogonal.

We shall say that the system of elements $x_1, \ldots, x_m$ of H is linearly independent if, from

$$\alpha_1 x_1 + \ldots + \alpha_m x_m = 0,$$

where α_k are real numbers, it follows that $\alpha_k = 0$ for any value of k. We shall say that the system of elements $x_1, \ldots, x_m$ is orthogonalised if $(x_i, x_k) = 0$ for $i \neq k$, $(x_i, x_i) = 1$ for $i = 1, 2, \ldots, m$.

If $x_1, \ldots, x_m$ is a system of linearly independent elements of the space H then one can construct an orthogonalised system $y_1, \ldots, y_m$ whose elements are linear combinations $x_1, \ldots, x_m$, and *vice versa*.

Let H_m be an m-dimensional sub-space of the space H, i.e. a sub-space generated by the m linearly independent elements $h_1, \ldots, h_m$, and let f be an arbitrary element of space H. We set ourselves the problem of choosing numbers $\alpha_1, \ldots, \alpha_m$ such that the quantity

$$\|f - \alpha_1 h_1 - \ldots - \alpha_m h_m\|$$

is minimized.

Such a problem always has a solution, and this solution is unique. If

$$h_0 = \sum_{k=1}^{m} \alpha_k h_k$$

is the best approximation in the above sense, then the equality

$$(f - h_0, h) = 0,$$ (8.7)

is valid, where h is any element of H_m.

Equality (8.7) means that the element $f - h_0$ is orthogonal to any element h of H_m. This fact obviously admits of a simple, straightforward interpretation: if H is a finite-dimensional vector space, then h_0 is the projection of vector f onto the hyper-plane H_m.

If for h we take any of the generating elements h_i from (8.7), we deduce

$$\left(f - \sum_{k=1}^{m} \alpha_k h_k, h_i \right) = 0,$$

whence it follows that

$$\sum_{k=1}^{m} \alpha_k (h_k, h_i) = (f, h_i), \qquad i = 1, 2, \ldots, m.$$ (8.8)

System (8.8) enables us to find the numbers $\alpha_1, \ldots, \alpha_m$. The determinant of this system

$$\Gamma(h_1, \ldots, h_m) = \begin{vmatrix} (h_1, h_1) \ldots (h_1, h_m) \\ \ldots\ldots\ldots\ldots\ldots \\ (h_m, h_1) \ldots (h_m, h_m) \end{vmatrix}$$

is called a Gram determinant. If the elements $h_1, \ldots, h_m$ are linearly independent, the Gram determinant is always positive. With the help of the Gram determinant one can find the error of the approximation, i.e. the quantity

$$\delta = \| f - h_0 \|.$$

The formula

$$\delta^2 = \frac{\Gamma(h_1, \ldots, h_m, f)}{\Gamma(h_1, \ldots, h_m)}$$ (8.9)

is valid.

If the system $\{h_i\}$ is orthonormalised, we have

$$\delta^2 = (f, f) - \sum_{i=1}^{m} \alpha_i^2.$$ (8.10)

If the system $\{h_i\}$ of orthonormalised vectors is infinite, then the series

$$\sum_{i=1}^{\infty} \alpha_i \mathbf{h}_i \,,$$

where $\alpha_i = (f, \mathbf{h}_i)$ is called a Fourier series. An infinite orthonormalised system is said to be complete if no non-zero element exists which is orthogonal to each element of the system.

If the space H is separable, i.e. if there is a denumerable set of elements in it, which is everywhere dense, then in H there always exists a denumerable and completely orthonormalised system of elements. In this case, from (8.10), there follows the Bessel inequality

$$\sum_{i=1}^{\infty} \alpha_i^2 \leqslant \|f\|^2 \,.$$

If the space H is separable and complete, the Fourier series of any element f with respect to a complete orthonormalised system converges towards f and the Parseval inequality holds:

$$\sum_{k=1}^{\infty} \alpha_k^2 = \|f\|^2 \,.$$

4.   Let us return now to our problem, i.e. to the problem of approximating the vector function $r(t)$ by the linear aggregate

$$\sum_{k=1}^{m} c_k y_k(t) \,.$$

Problem A. *Choose vectors c_k in such a way that the error*

$$\delta = \left(\int_0^T \|\Delta(t)\|^2 \, dt \right)^{\frac{1}{2}}$$

is minimised.

Here

$$\|\Delta(t)\|^2 = \sum_{i=1}^{n} \left(\sum_{k=1}^{m} c_{ik} y_k(t) - r_i(t) \right)^2 \,,$$

and c_{ik} are the projections of the vector c_k. We have

$$\delta^2 = \sum_{i=1}^{n} \delta_i^2 \,,$$

where

$$\delta_i^2 = \int_0^T \left(\sum_{k=1}^m c_{ik} y_k(t) - r_i(t) \right)^2 dt$$

and the problem reduces to one of minimising each of the partial errors δ_i. This partition can be made in such a way that the choice of c_{ik} for one value of i has no effect on the choice of these quantities for the other value of i.

Consider a space H whose elements are functions $f(t)$ with an integrable square over the interval $[0, T]$. We will introduce the scalar product in H in accordance with the rule

$$(f_1, f_2) = \int_0^T f_1(t) f_2(t) dt .$$

The sub-space H_m will now be a sub-space generated by the functions $y_1(t), ..., y_m(t)$. Thus, one is faced with the problem of finding the best mean square approximation of the function $r_i(t)$ by the linear aggreagate

$$\sum_{k=1}^m c_{ik} y_k(t) .$$

In accordance with (8.8), we have the following system for determining the quantities c_{ik} for a given value of i.

$$\sum_{k=1}^m c_{ik}(y_k, y_j) = (r_i, y_j) , \qquad j = 1, 2, ..., m . \tag{8.11}$$

To determine the vectors c_k in accordance with (8.11) we can obtain the system

$$\sum_{k=1}^m c_k(y_k, y_j) = (r, y_j) , \qquad j = 1, 2, ..., m . \tag{8.12}$$

The square of the error of the approximation in the given case will be equal to

$$\delta^2 = \sum_{i=1}^n \frac{\Gamma(y_1, ..., y_m, r_i)}{\Gamma(y_1, ..., y_m)} .$$

Problem B. *For given vectors c_k, find a system of functions $y_1(t), ..., y_m(t)$, $m \leqslant n$ which will minimise δ.*

As before, we should note that the choice of values of the functions $y_k(t)$ at a given instant t does not affect the choice of values for these functions at any other instant of time. Consequently, the problem reduces to one of minimising the quantities

$$\|\varDelta(t)\|^2 = \sum_{i=1}^{n} \left(\sum_{k=1}^{m} c_{ik} y_k(t) - r_i(t) \right)^2 .$$

It is already clear that one should identify the space of n-dimensional vectors c_k with the Hilbert space H while the sub-space generated by the vectors $c_1, \ldots, c_m$ will play the part of the sub-space H_m.
In accordance with (8.8) we obtain a system for defining $y_k(t)$:

$$\sum_{k=1}^{m} y_k(t)(c_k, c_j) = (r(t), c_j), \qquad j = 1, 2, \ldots, m .$$

Here the expressions (c_k, c_j), $(r(t), c_j)$ denote the scalar products of the corresponding vectors in the customary sense.
In accordance with (8.9), we obtain

$$\delta^2 = \int_0^T \|\varDelta(t)\|^2 dt = \frac{1}{\Gamma(c_1, \ldots, c_m)} \int_0^T \Gamma(c_1, \ldots, c_m, r(t)) dt .$$

The problem has a simple geometric interpretation. Let H_m denote the plane generated by the vectors $c_1, \ldots, c_m$. In the n-dimensional space H let the curve $z = r(t)$ be given; it is required to find a curve

$$z = \sum_{k=1}^{m} c_k y_k(t) ,$$

which has the least mean-square deviation from the given curve. The problem is solved by obtaining each point of the curve being sought as a projection on the plane H_m of the corresponding point of the first curve $z = r(t)$. Whence it follows that the problem is not altered if we take as our generating system of vectors $c_1, \ldots, c_m$ an orthonormal system which is equivalent to it. In this case we obtain

$$y_j(t) = (r(t), c_j) , \tag{8.13}$$

$$\delta^2 = \int_0^T r^2(t) dt - \sum_{j=1}^{m} (r(t), c_j)^2 dt . \tag{8.14}$$

Problem C. *Find the optimum system of vectors c_k and functions $y_k(t)$ which will minimise δ.*

Consider a matrix B whose elements have the form

$$b_{ik} = \int_0^T r_i(t) r_k(t) \, dt \, ,$$

where $r_i(t)$ is the projection of vector $r(t)$.
Since B is a symmetric matrix it has real eigenvalues; moreover its eigenvalues are non-negative. In fact, B is a matrix of positive terms having the quadratic form

$$I(x) = \sum_{i,k=1}^n b_{ik} x_i x_k = \int_0^T \left(\sum_{k=1}^n r_k(t) x_k \right)^2 .$$

From which, in accordance with section 10 of Chapter 1, we deduce that the smallest eigenvalue λ_n, as the minimum of the form $I(x)$ on the unit sphere, must be non-negative. Let us arrange the eigenvalues of matrix B in decreasing order

$$\lambda_1 \geqslant \lambda_2 \geqslant \ldots \geqslant \lambda_n \geqslant 0 \, .$$

To each eigenvalue λ_k there corresponds at least one eigenvector c_k. Now a system of eigenvalues can be orthonormalised (see Reference [5], p. 20) and in this way we can obtain an orthonormalised system of eigenvectors of matrix B.

Theorem 8.1. *An orthonormalised system of eigenvectors $c_1, \ldots, c_m$ of a matrix B is the optimum system of control vectors and if the system of control functions $y(t)$ is chosen in accord with (8.13), then*

$$\delta^2 = \sum_{k=m+1}^n \lambda_k \, . \tag{8.15}$$

Indeed, if the system of vectors $c_1, \ldots, c_m$ is orthonormalised then, according to (8.14), we have

$$\delta^2 = \int_0^T r^2(t) \, dt - \sum_{k=1}^m \int_0^T (c_k, r(t))^2 \, dt \, .$$

It is necessary to choose the system of vectors in such a way that the sum

$$\sum_{k=1}^{m} \int_{0}^{T} (c_k, r(t))^2 \, dt$$

is maximised. Consider the first term of this sum

$$I_1 = I(c_{1i}) = \int_{0}^{T} (c_1, r(t))^2 \, dt =$$

$$= \sum_{i,k=1}^{n} \left(\int_{0}^{T} r_i(t) r_k(t) \, dt \, c_{1k} c_{1i} \right) = \sum_{i,k=1}^{n} b_{ik} c_{1i} c_{1k} \,.$$

Here, c_{ik} are the projections of the vector c_i. The problem reduces to one of finding the maximum quadratic form $I(c_{1i})$ with the condition

$$\sum_{i=1}^{n} c_{1i}^2 = 1 \,.$$

According to section 10 of Chapter 1, the maximum we are seeking is equal to the largest eigenvalue λ_1 and it is attained for the eigenvector c_1 corresponding to this value. In order to maximise the next term

$$I_2 = \int_{0}^{T} (c_2, r(t))^2 \, dt = I(c_{2i})$$

with the additional conditions $(c_1, c_2) = 0$, $c_2^2 = 1$, it is necessary to take the eigenvector c_2 corresponding to the next eigenvalue. According to the theory of extremals of quadratic forms ([5]), the maximum I_2 will be equal to λ_2. If $\lambda_1 = \lambda_2$, then for c_2 one should choose a vector orthogonal to c_1 from amongst the infinite set of eigenvectors of the square root of λ_1. Using similar arguments we obtain a complete solution to our problem. Since

$$\int_{0}^{T} r^2 \, dt = \sum_{i=1}^{n} c_{ii} = \sum_{i=1}^{n} \lambda_i$$

is the invariant of the quadratic form I, then formula (8.15) follows directly from formula (8.14).

We should note that the realisation of a trajectory by way of choosing an optimum system of control functions and control vectors is possible for $m \leqslant n$ only in the case when

$$\lambda_{m+1} = \lambda_{m+2} = \ldots = \lambda_n = 0 \,.$$

This means that the equation

$$D(\lambda) = |B - \lambda E| = 0 \quad (E- \text{ unit matrix})$$

has a zero root of multiplicity $n - m$. The conditions for existence of such a root have the form $D(0) = D'(0) = \ldots = D^{(n-m+1)}(0) = 0$. Geometrically these conditions mean that the curve $z = r(t)$ lies in an m-dimensional linear sub-space of the space E_n. If the quantity

$$\delta^2 = \sum_{k=m+1}^{n} \lambda_k$$

is not equal to zero, then it is equal to the minimum of the root mean square deviation of the curve $z = r(t)$ from the m-dimensional hyperplane of the space E_n

Thus, in the given case, the quantity δ is the m-th diameter of the curve $z = r(t)$ in the space E_n [122].

To calculate δ^2 from formula (8.15), it is not absolutely necessary to know the roots $\lambda_{m+1}, \ldots, \lambda_n$. Lavrent'ev and Shabat ([123], p. 80) have shown that

$$\delta^2 = \frac{1}{2\pi i} \int_R z \, \frac{D'(z)}{D(z)} \, dz \,,$$

where R is any contour of the plane of the complex variable enclosing only those roots of the equation $D(\lambda) = 0$ indicated above. In particular, R can be the circumference of radius ε with centre at the coordinate origin if it is known that $\lambda_{m+1} < \varepsilon < \lambda_m$. To find the minimum number of control functions that will permit a trajectory to be realised with a given accuracy it is helpful to use some argument, or any other well-known method (for example, Sturm's method), for finding the number of roots of the equation $D(X) = 0$ lying in the interval $(0, \varepsilon)$. If this number is equal to l then $n - l$ control functions and $n - l$ control vectors can be chosen such that the inequality $\delta < \varepsilon l$ holds. The best estimate of the accuracy of the approximation in this case is again given by formula (8.15). It is in any case useful to remember that an approximation based on the use of m control functions will be more accurate the lower the absolute magnitude of the coefficients of the equation $D(\lambda) = 0$, for powers of λ not exceeding $m - n$.

5. In the case in which the time interval required to realise the given process is semi-infinite, i.e. when the inequality $0 \leqslant t < \infty$ applies, it is

necessary to appeal to lemma 6.2 (inequality (7.17)) and to theorem 6.5. If we wish to estimate the quantity $\varDelta(t)$ along the norm M_2 we can choose the control vector c_k so as to minimise

$$\|r(s) - \sum_{k=1}^{m} c_k y_k(s)\| \quad \text{over the interval } t \leqslant s \leqslant t+1 .$$

In this case it is obvious that for variable t the vectors c_k transform into the vector functions $c_k(t)$. The vector functions can be replaced by step-functions if the minimisation is carried out only over intervals $k \leqslant t \leqslant k+1$, where k is an integer. The problem of the best approximation in M_2 cannot be solved exactly in either of these cases although the equation that is found may turn out to be satisfactory in practice.

6. It can happen that certain restrictions are imposed upon the magnitude of the control vectors. The author has given a method for solving the problem in such a case elsewhere [124]. Various other approaches to the problem considered here can be found in the literature [125–131]. In discussing the problem of realising a given process we have been assuming all along that the initial point of the actual trajectory coincides with that of the trajectory one wishes to realise. If the initial state does not correspond to the desired state then one must first induce a transient process [124]. However, a more perspective method is to arrange that the transient process and the process that realises a given trajectory occur simultaneously. In this case it is necessary to specify a family of transient curves defining a field of directions in phase space. This family can also be specified by differential equations. The given system of differential equations also defines a certain field of directions which depends on the equation. The equation is found from the condition for minimising at each instant of time the squared deviation between the vectors representing the various directions [130].

One should note, however, that a similar result is obtained if the equation is chosen by starting out from the requirement of maximum rate of decrease of a Lyapunov function set up for the equations of the perturbed motion.

REFERENCES

Chapter 1

[1] A. M. Lyapunov, The general problem of stability of motion, *Fitmatgiz* (1959).
[2] R. Bellman, *Theory of the stability of the solutions of differential equations*, McGraw Hill (1953).
[3] V. V. Nemitskii and V. V. Stepanov, *Qualitative theory of differential equations*, Gostekhizdat (1949).
[4] J. L. Massera, On Lyapunov's condition of stability, *Ann. of Math.*, Vol. 50, No. 3 (1949).
[5] F. R. Gantmakher, *Matrix theory*, N.Y. Chelsea Publishing Co., (1949).
[6] E. A. Barbashin and N. N. Krasovskii, Stability on the whole, *Dokl. Akad. Nauk SSSR*, Vol. 86, No. 3 (1952).
[7] N. N. Krasovskii, Some problems concerning the theory of stability of motion, *Fizmatgiz* (1959).
[8] I. G. Malkin, *Theory of stability of motion*, Gostekhizdat (1952).
[9] Yu. I. Alimov, The construction of Lyapunov functions for linear differential equations with constant coefficients, *Sib. matem. zhurnal*, Vol. 2, No. 1 (1961).
[10] N. G. Chetaev, On the choice of stability parameters for a mechanical system, *Prikl. Mat. Mekh.*, Vol. 15, No. 2 (1951).
[11] J. La Salle and S. Lefshets, *Investigation of stability by Lyapunov's direct method*, Academic Press, Inc., New York (1961).
[12] M. A. Aizerman, On a problem concerning stability in the large of dynamical systems, *Uspekh. Matem. Nauk*, Vol. 4, No. 4 (1949).
[13] N. N. Krasovskii, Theorems of stability of motions determined by two equations, *Prikl. Mat. Mekh.*, Vol. 16, No. 5 (1952).
[14] V. A. Pliss, *Some problems concerning the theory of stability of motion in the large*, Leningrad State University (1958).
[15] I. G. Malkin, On the stability of automatic control systems, *Prikl. Mat. Mekh.*, Vol. 16, No. 4 (1952).

[16] N. P. Erugin, On a problem concerning the theory of the stability of automatic control systems, *Prikl. Mat. Mek.*, Vol. 16, No. 5 (1952).

[17] N. N. Krasovskii, On a problem concerning stability of motion on the whole, *Doklad. Akad. Nauk SSSR*, Vol. 88, No. 3 (1953).

[18] E. A. Barbashin, On the construction of Lyapunov functions for non-linear systems, *Proceedings of the First International Congress of the International Federation for Automatic Control, Akad. Nauk SSSR*, pp. 742–751 (1961).

[19] N. N. Krasovskii, On the stability of motion on the whole in the presence of continuously acting perturbations, *Prikl. Mat. Mekh.*, Vol. 18, No. 1 (1954).

[20] E. A. Barbashin, On the stability of the solution of a third order non-linear equation, *Prikl. Mat. Mekh.*, Vol. 16, No. 3 (1952).

[21] E. I. Zheleznov, On the stability on the whole of a non-linear system of three equations, *Proceedings of the Urals Polytechnic Institute, Collect.* 74 (1958).

[22] A. I. Lur'e, *Some non-linear problems in automatic control theory*, Gostekhizdat (1951).

[23] A. M. Letov, The stability of non-linear control systems, *Fizmatgiz* (1962).

[24] M. A. Aizerman and F. R. Gantmakher, Absolute stability of control systems, *Akad. Nauk SSSR* (1963).

[25] E. A. Barbashin, Method of sections in the theory of dynamical systems, *Matem. Collect.*, Vol. 29, No. 2 (1951).

[26] N. G. Chetaev, *Stability of motion*, Gostekhizdat (1956).

Chapter 2

[27] Yu. V. Dolgolenko, Sliding conditions in indirect control relay systems. *Proceedings of the Second All-Union Conference on Automatic Control Theory, Moscow-Leningrad State Publishing House, Akad. Nauk SSSR*, 1.

[28] Yu. I. Neimark, On the sliding condition of automatic control relay systems. *Avtom. i. telemekh.*, Vol. 18, No. 1, pp. 27–33 (1957).

[29] J. Flugge–Lotz, *Discontinuous automatic control*, Princeton (1953).

[30] A. M. Letov, Conditionally stable control systems (concerning one

class of optimum control systems), *Avtom. i telemekh.*, Vol. 18, No. 7 (1957).

[31] E. A. Barbashin, I. N. Pechorina and R. M. Eidinov, Application of automatic control systems with variable structure to the control of one class of linear static objects, *Avtom. i telemekh.*, Vol. 24, No. 1 (1963).

[32] E. A. Barbashin and V. A. Tabueva, On a method of stabilising high-gain third order control systems, I. *Avtom. i telemekh.*, Vol. 23, No. 10 (1962).

[33] E. A. Barbashin and V. A. Tabueva, On a method of stabilising high-gain third order control systems, II. *Avtom. i telemekh.*, Vol. 24, No. 5 (1963).

[34] E. A. Barbashin, V. A. Tabueva and R. M. Eidinov, On the stability of a control system with variable structure when sliding conditions are violated, *Avtom. i telemekh.*, Vol. 24, No. 7 (1963).

[35] E. A. Barbashin and V. A. Tabueva, Stability theorem for the solution of a third order differential equation with a discontinuous characteristic, *Prikl. Mat. Mekh.*, Vol. 27, No. 4 (1963).

[36] E. A. Barbashin and V. A. Tabueva, Theorems about the asymptotic stability of the solutions of certain third order differential equations with discontinuous characteristics, *Prikl. Mat. Mekh.*, Vol. 28, No. 3 (1964).

[37] E. A. Barbashin and E. I. Gerashchenko, On the stabilisation of control systems, *Prikl. Mat. Mekh.*, Vol. 28, No. 4 (1964).

[38] V. M. Badkov and E. A. Barbashin, On a method of stabilising control systems in the presence of bounded permissible values of the controller parameters, *Izv. Akad. Nauk SSSR, Tekhnicheskaya Kibernetika*, No. 2 (1964).

[39] E. I. Gerashchenko, On the stability of motion in the sliding hyper-plane for certain automatic control systems with a variable structure (with additions by S. V. Emel'yanov and V. A. Taran), *Izv. Akad. Nauk SSSR, Tekhnicheskaya Kibernetika*, No. 4 (1963).

[40] E. I. Gerashchenko, On the degree of stability of non-linear systems operating under sliding conditions. *Izv. Akad. Nauk SSSR, Tekhnicheskaya Kibernetika*, No. 2 (1964).

[41] E. A. Barbashin and E. I. Gerashchenko, On the focussing of sliding conditions. *Differential Equations*, Vol. 1, No. 1 (1965).

[42] E. A. Barbashin and E. I. Gerashchenko, On a principle for use in

the design of servo-systems, *Avtom. i Telemekh.*, Vol. 26, No. 6 (1965).

[43] E. A. Barbashin, E. I. Gerashchenko, V. A. Tabueva and R. M. Eidinov, Some aspects of the theory of the design of automatic control systems with variable structure, *Proceedings of the Third All-Union Conference on Automatic Control*, 1965.

[44] E. I. Gerashchenko, The design of relay systems, *Avtom. i telemekh.*, Vol. 26, No. 10 (1965).

[45] E. I. Gerashchenko and A. F. Kleimenov, Analysis of a non-linear system by the method of separating the motions, *Differential Equations*, No. 10 (1965).

[46] E. I. Gerashchenko and L. V. Kiselev, On the stability of a control system under focussed sliding conditions, *Differential Equations*, No. 12 (1965).

[47] R. M. Eidinov, Estimating the speed of transient response in automatic control systems with variable structure, *Izv. Akad. Nauk SSSR. Tekhnicheskaya Kibernetika*, No. 5 (1965).

[48] V. A. Tabueva, Quality study of a second order differential equation in control theory, *Differential Equations*, No. 12 (1965).

[49] S. V. Emel'yanov and A. I. Fedotova, Construction of optimum second order control systems using limiting values for the gains of the control circuit components, *Avtom. i telemekh.*, Vol. 21 No. 1 (1960).

[50] S. V. Emel'yanov and V. A. Taran, A class of automatic control systems with variable structure, *Izv. Akad. Nauk SSSR, Energetika i Avtomatika*, No. 3 (1 62).

[51] S. V. Emel'yanov and V. I. Utkin, Applications of automatic control systems with variable structure to the control of objects whose parameters vary over wide limits, *Dokl. Akad. Nauk SSSR*, Vol. 152, No. 2 (1963).

[52] S. V. Emel'yanov and N. E. Kostileva, On certain peculiarities of motion in automatic control systems with variable structure possessing discontinuous switching functions, *Doklad. Akad. Nauk SSSR*, Vol. 153, No. 4 (1963).

[53] B. N. Petrov and S. V. Emel'yanov, Principle of construction of combined automatic control systems with variable structure, *Doklad. Akad. Nauk SSSR*, Vol. 153, No. 5 (1963).

[54] B. N. Petrov, G. M. Ulanov and S. V. Emel'yanov, Optimisation

and invariance in automatic control systems with rigid and variable structure. *Proceedings of the Second International Congress of the International Federation for Automatic Control, Theory of continuous automatic systems, "Nauka"*, 1965.

[55] A. V. Bakakin, M. A. Bermant and V. B. Eserov, Application of systems with variable structure to the stabilisation of an object with varying parameters in the presence of restrictions on the movement of the controlling device, *Avtom. i telemekh.*, Vol. 25, No. 7 (1964).

[56] B. N. Petrov, S. V. Emel'yanov and N. E. Kostileva, On the control of linear objects with variable structure, *Doklad. Akad. Nauk SSSR*, Vol. 155, No. 1 (1964).

[57] B. N. Petrov, S. V. Emel'yanov and V. I. Utkin, Principle of construction of invariant automatic control systems with variable structure, *Doklad. Akad. Nauk SSSR*, Vol. 154, No. 6 (1964).

[58] M. A. Bermant and S. V. Emel'yanov, On the stability of a class of automatic control systems with variable structure, *Izv. Akad. Nauk. SSSR, Tekhnicheskaya Kibernetika*, No. 6 (1964).

[59] S. V. Emel'yakov and V. A. Taran, Stabilisation of an automatic control system with variable structure with the help of inertial units having a variable time constant, *Avtom. i Telemekh.*, Vol. 25, No. 6 (1964).

[60] S. V. Emel'yanov and V. I. Utkin, On the stability of motion of a class of automatic control systems with variable structure, *Izv. Akad. Nauk SSSR, Tekhnickeskaya Kibernetika*, No. 2 (1964).

[61] V. I. Utkin, Application of automatic control systems with variable structure to the compensation of perturbations applied to different points of the object, Symposium *"Theory and application of automatic systems"*, Moscow "Nauka" (1964).

[62] S. I. Garret, A linear switching condition for a third order positive-negative feedback control system, *Applic. and Industry*, Vol. 7, No. 54 (1961).

[63] M. A. Aizerman and F. V. Gantmakher, Some aspects of the theory of non-linear control systems with discontinuous characteristics, *Proceedings of the First International Congress of the International Federation for Automatic Control, Theory of continuous systems, Akad. Nauk SSSR* (1961).

[64] Yu. I. Alimov, The application of the direct method of Lyapunov

to differential equations with non-homogeneous right-hand sides, *Avtom. i telemekh.*, Vol. 22, No. 7 (1961).

[65] J. Andre and P. Zeibert, Motion after an end-point and the analysis of its stability for the general case of discontinuous control systems. *Proceedings of the First International Congress of the International Federation for Automatic Control, Theory of continuous systems, Akad. Nauk SSSR* (1961).

[66] N. N. Krasovskii, Second method of Lyapunov in the theory of stability of motion, *Proceedings of the All-Union Congress on Theoretical and Applied Mechanics, Akad. Nauk SSSR* (1962).

[67] V. I. Zubov, *Oscillations and non-linear control systems.* Sudprom-giz (1962).

[68] E. A. Barbashin, E. I. Gerashchenko, V. A. Tabueva and R. M. Eidinov, Methods of analysing automatic control systems with variable structure, *Report of the Third International Congress on Automatic Control,* London (1966).

[69] E. A. Barbashin, V. A. Tabueva and R. M. Eidinov, Stability of control systems with variable structure. *Proceedings of the second All-Union Congress on Theoretical and Applied Mechanics,* No. 2, "Nauka", pp. 7–14 (1965).

Chapter 3

[70] R. Bellman, On the application of a Banach-Steinhaus theorem to the study of the boundedness of solutions of non-linear differential and difference equations, *Ann. of Math.*, Vol. 49, pp. 515–522 (1948).

[71] L. V. Kantorovich and G. P. Akilov, Functional analysis in normalised spaces, *Fizmatgiz* (1959).

[72] M. A. Krasnosel'skii, *Topological methods in the theory of non-linear integral equations,* Gostekhizdat (1956).

[73] E. Hille and R. S. Phillips, Functional analysis and semi-groups, *American Math. Soc.,* Providence (1957).

[74] M. A. Krasnosel'skii and S. G. Krein, Non-local existence and uniqueness theorems for systems of ordinary differential equations, *Doklad. Akad. Nauk SSSR,* Vol. 101, No. 1 (1955).

[75] M. G. Krein, Lectures on the theory of the stability of the solutions

of differential equations in Banach space, *Akad. Nauk Ukr. SSR*, Institute of Mathematics, Kiev (1964).

[76] S. G. Mikhlin, *Integral equations*, Pergamon, 1957.

[77] Yu. M. Repin, On the stability of the solutions of equations with a retarded argument, *Prikl. Mat. Mekh.*, Vol. 21, No. 2 (1957).

[78] N. P. Erugin, Linear systems of differential equations *Akad. Nauk Belorusskaya SSSR*, Minsk (1963).

[79] N. P. Erugin, Guiding systems, *Nauki i Tekhnika*, Minsk (1966).

[80] K. P. Persidskii, On the stability of solutions of an infinite system of equations, *Prikl. Mat. Mekh.* Vol. 12, No. 5 (1948).

[81] K. P. Persidskii, On characteristic numbers, *Izv. Akad. Nauk Kazakhstan SSR*, Vol. 116, No. 1 (6) (1952).

[82] E. A. Barbashin, On the conditions for preserving the stability of solutions of integro-differential equations, *Izv. Vuzov, Matem.*, No. 1 (1957).

[83] E. A. Barbashin, On the stability of the solutions of integro-differential equations, *Proceedings of the Urals Polytechnic Institute*, No. 74 (1958).

[84] L. Kh. Liberman, On the stability of the solutions of integro-differential equations, *Izv. Vuzov, Matem.*, No. 3 (4) (1958).

[85] E. A. Barbashin and L. P. Bisyarina, On the stability of the solutions of integro-differential equations, *Izv. Vuzov, Matem.*, No. 3 (34) (1963).

[86] Ya. V. Bikov, The analytical theory of linear integro-differential equations of the Barbashin type, *Issled. po Integro-Differensial'nim Uravneniyam v Kirgizii, Frunze*, No. 2 (1962).

[87] E. Ya. Bikova, On the stability of the solutions of integro-differential and integro-difference equations of the Barbashin type, *Issled. po Integro-Differentsial'nim Uravneniyam v Kirgizii, No. 3 (1962).

[88] Kh. M. Salpagarov, On the stability of integro-differential equations of the Barbashin type, *Issled. po Integro-Differentsial'nim Uravneniyam v Kirgizii, Frunze*, No. 2 (1962).

[89] E. A. Barbashin and L. Kh. Liberman, On the stability of the solutions of integro-differential equations in total differentials, *Dokl. Visshei shkoli*, No. 3 (1 58).

[90] L. P. Bisyarina, On the stability of solutions of integro-differential equations in partial derivatives, *Izv. Vuzov, Matem.*, No. 2 (39) (1964).

[91] L. P. Bisyarina, On the existence of a periodic solution of an integro-differential equation, *Matemat. zap.*, Urals Institute, Sverdlovsk, Vol. 4, No. 2 (1963).

[92] E. A. Barbashin and Yu. I. Alimov, Dynamical systems with ambiguous characteristics, *Doklad. Akad. Nauk SSSR*, Vol. 140, No. 1 (1961).

[93] E. A. Barbashin and Yu. I. Alimov, The theory of relay differential equations, *Izv. Vuzov, Matem.*, No. 1 (26) (1962).

[94] J. L. Massera and J. L. Schäffer, Linear differential equations and functional analysis, I. *Ann. of Math.* Vol. 57, No. 3 (1958).

[95] J. L. Massera and J. L. Schäffer, Linear differential equations and functional analysis, II. *Ann. of Math.*, Vol. 69, No. 1 (1959).

[96] B. V. Bulgakov, On the build-up of perturbations in linear oscillatory systems with constant parameters, *Dokl. Akad. Nauk SSSR*, Vol. 51, No. 5 (1946).

[97] T. F. Brigland, Some remarks on the stability of linear systems, *J.E.E.E. Trans., Circuit Theory*, CT-10, No. 4 (1963).

[98] A. Halanay, *Teoria calitativa a equatiilor differentiale*, Academie PRP (1963).

[99] M. G. Krein, On certain problems connected with the ideas of Lyapunov in stability theory, *Uspekh. Matem. Nauk*, Vol. 3, No. 3 (25) (1948).

[100] D. L. Kucher, On certain boundedness criteria for the solutions of a system of differential equations, *Dokl. Akad. Nauk SSSR*, Vol. 59, No. 5 (1949).

[101] O. Perron, Die Stabilitatsfräge bei Differentialgleichungen, *Math. Zeit*, p. 32 (1930).

[102] Ya. Kudrevich, Stability of non-linear negative feedback systems, *Avtom. i telemekh.*, Vol. 25, No. 8 (1964).

[103] H. N. James, N. Nichols and R. Phillips, *Theory of servo-systems*, McGraw Hill, 1947.

[104] L. A. Zadeh, On stability of linear varying-parameter systems, *J. Appl. Phys.*, Vol. 22, No. 4 (1951).

[105] R. E. Kalman, On the stability of time-varying linear systems, *JRE Trans., Circuit Theory*, CT-9, No. 4 (1962).

[106] P. E. Sobolevskii, On equations of the parabolic type in Banach space. *Trud. Mosk. matem. Obshchestvo* (Trans. Moscow Math. Soc) Vol. 10 (1961).

[107] Z. I. Khalilov, On the stability of the solutions of equations in Banach space, *Dokl. Akad. Nauk SSSR*, Vol. 137, No. 4 (1961).

[108] S. I. Gorshin, On the stability of motion with continuously acting perturbations, *Izv. Akad Nauk Kazakhstan SSR*, No. 56 (1948).

[109] V. E. Germaidze and N. N. Krasovskii, On stability with continuously acting perturbations, *Prikl. Mat. Mekh.*, Vol. 21, No. 6 (1957).

[110] N. A. Artem'ev, *Foundations of the qualitative theory of ordinary differential equations*, Leningrad State University (1941).

[111] N. N. Krasovskii, On periodic solutions of differential equations with time delays, *Dokl. Akad. Nauk SSSR*, Vol. 114, No. 2 (1957).

[112] N. N. Antosiewicz, Forced periodic solutions of systems of differential equations. *Ann. of Math.*, Vol. 57, No. 2 (1953).

[113] E. A. Barbashin, On the structure of periodic motions, *Prikl. Mat. Mekh.*, Vol. 25, No. 2 (1961).

[114] E. A. Barbashin, Programmed control of systems with random parameters, *Prikl. Mat. Mekh.*, Vol. 25, No. 5 (1961).

[115] E. A. Barbashin, Two proofs of theorems of stability in the first approximation, *Dokl. Akad. Nauk SSSR*, Vol. 111, No. 1 (1956).

[116] E. A. Barbashin and M. A. Skalkina, The problem of stability in the first approximation, *Prikl. Mat. Mekh.*, Vol. 19, No. 5 (1955).

[117] M. A. Skalkina, On the connexion between the stability of the solutions of differential and finite difference equations, *Prikl. Mat. Mekh.*, Vol. 19, No. 3 (1955).

[118] M. A. Skalkina, On the preservation of asymptotic stability during the transition from differential equations to the corresponding differences, *Dokl. Akad. Nauk SSSR*, Vol. 104, No. 4 (1955).

[119] R. Gabasov, On the stability of the solutions of differential equations with continuously acting perturbations, *Izv. Vuzov, Matem.*, No. 5 (30) (1962).

[120] N. N. Krasovskii, On stability in the presence of large initial perturbations, *Prikl. Mat. Mekh.*, Vol. 21, No. 3 (1957).

[121] N. I. Akhiezer, *Lectures on the theory of approximations* Gostekhizdat (1947).

[122] A. Kolmogoroff, Über die beste Annäherung von Funktion einer gegeben Funktionsklassen, *Ann. of Math.*, Vol. 37 (1936).

[123] M. A. Lavrent'ev and B. V. Shabat, *Methods of the theory of functions of a complex variable*, Gostekhizdat (1951).

[124] E. A. Barbashin, On a problem concerning the theory of dynamic

programming, *Prikl. Mat. Mekh.*, Vol. 24, No. 6 (1960).

[125] E. A. Barbashin, On estimating the mean square value of the deviation from a given trajectory, *Avtom. i telemekh.*, Vol. 21, No. 7 (1960).

[126] E. A. Barbashin, On estimating the maximum deviation from a given trajectory, *Avtom. i telemekh.*, Vol. 21, No. 10 (1960).

[127] E. A. Barbashin, Programme control and the theory of optimum systems. *Proceedings of the Second International Congress of the International Federation for Automatic Control, Optimum Systems, Statistical Methods*, "Nauka", pp. 221–230 (1965).

[128] E. A. Barbashin, The structure of periodic motion as a problem in the theory of programme control. *Proceedings of the International Symposium on Non-linear Oscillations*, Vol. III, Akad. Nauk. Ukrainian SSR, Kiev (1963).

[129] E. A. Barbashin, The realization of processes and the design of system output signals, *Proceedings of the Fourth All-Union Mathematical Congress*, Vol. II, "Nauka" (1964).

[130] G. N. Mil'shtein, On the approximate realisation of processes using transient curves, *Prikl. Mat. Mekh. Vol.* 26 (1962).

[131] L. Kh. Liberman, On some problems concerning the theory of approximations of solutions of differential operator equations in Hilbert space, *Izv. Vuzov. Matem.*, No. 3 (40) (1964).

[132] K. A. Karacharov and A. G. Pilyutik, Introduction to the technical theory of stability of motion, *Fizmatgiz* (1962).

[133] N. P. Erugin, Qualitative study of integral curves of systems of differential equations, *Prikl. Mat. Mekh.*, Vol. 14, No. 6 (1950).

[134] N. P. Erugin, On some problems pertaining to stability of motion and the qualitative theory of differential equations, *Prikl. Mat. Mekh.*, Vol. 14, No. 5 (1950).

[135] N. P. Erugin, Qualitative methods and the theory of stability, *Prikl. Mat. Mekh.*, Vol. 19, No. 5 (1955).

[136] V. A. Pliss, *Non-local problems concerning the theory of oscillations*, "Nauka" (1964).

[137] W. Hahn, *Theorie und Anwendung der Direkten Methode von Lyapunov*, Springer–Verlag, Berlin (1959).

[138] V. I. Zubov, *The methods of A. M. Lyapunov and their application*, Leningrad State University (1957).

[139] J. L. Massera and J. J. Schäffer, Linear differential equations and functional analysis, III, *Ann. of Math.*, Vol. 69, No. 3 (1959).

[140] J. L. Massera and J. J. Schäffer, Linear differential equations and functional analysis—IV, *Math. Annalen*, Vol. 139 (1960).

[141] K. P. Persidskii, On a theorem of Lyapunov, *Dokl. Akad. Nauk SSSR*, Vol. 14, No. 9 (1937).

[142] I. G. Malkin, The problem of inverting the asymptotic stability theorems of Lyapunov, *Prikl. Mat. Mekh.*, Vol. 18, No. 2 (1954).

ADDITIONAL BIBLIOGRAPHY

M. A. Aizerman and F. R. Gantmacher, *Absolute stability of control systems*, Holden-Day, San Francisco (1963).

J. Auslanden and P. Seibert, Prolongations and generalised Lyapunov functions: in *International symposium on non-linear differential equations*, Ed. by J. F. de Salle and S. Lefshetz, p. 454, Academic Press, New York, 1963.

A. V. Balakrishnan, On the state space theory of linear systems. *J. Math. Anal. Appl.*, 14 (1966) 371.

A. Blaquiere, Stabilité des systèmes: Deuxième method de Lyapunov, *Rev. Cethedec* (1966) 5, 1.

T. F. Bridgland, Jr., Stability of Linear Transmission Systems. *Soc. Indust. Appl. Math. Rev.* (1963) 5, No. 1, 7.

V. A. Brusin, Absolute stability of a class of control systems with a distributed component *Izv. Vys. Ucheb. Zav. Radiofizika*, (1966) 9, 810.

L. Cesari, *Asymptotic Behaviour and Stability Problems in ordinary differential equations*, Springer-Verlag O.H.G. Berlin, (1959).

J. Devooght, The problem of Lurie in automatic control. *Acad. Roy. Belg. Bull. U. Sci.* (5), 51 (1965) 76.

R. E. Kalman, Lyapunov functions for the problem of Lurie in automatic controls. *Proc. Nat. Acad. Sci. U.S.A.* 49, 201 (1963).

R. E. Kalman and J. Betram, Control system design via the second method of Lyapunov. *Trans. A.S.M.E. Ser. D.* (1960) 82, 371.

Wei-Pin Kao, On the absolute stability and degree of absolute stability of non-linear control systems, *Sci. Sinica*, (1966), 15, 107.

F. Kozin, On relations between moment properties and almost sure

Lyapunov stability for linear stochastic systems, *J. Math. Anal. Appl.*, (1965) 10, 342.

M. J. Kushiner, Stability of stochastic dynamical systems. *Advances in Control Systems*, (1966) 4, 73. (Academic Press, New York).

M. J. Kushiner, Converse theorems for stochastic Lyapunov functions, *S.I.A.M. J. Control* (1967) 5, 22.

J. P. La Salle, Applications of Lyapunov stability theory to control systems. *Proc. J.B.M. Sci. Comput. Symp. Control Theory Appl.*, (Yorktown Heights, N.Y., 1964) 61–75. I.B.M. Data Process. Div., White Plains, New York (1966).

J. P. La Salle, Complete stability of a non-linear control system, *Proc. Nat. Acad. Sci. U.S.A.* (1962) 48 600.

S. Lefshetz, *Stability of non-linear control systems*, Academic Press (New York) (1965).

S. H. Lehnig, *Stability theorems for linear motion with an introduction to Lyapunov's direct method*, Printice-Hall Inc., Engewood Cliffs, N.J., 1966.

A. M. Letov, *Stability of non-linear control systems*, Princeton University Press, N.J. (1961).

A. M. Lyapunov, Problème général de la stabilité du mouvement, *Annals of Math. Studies* No. 17. Princeton Univ. Press, Princeton, New Jersey, (1967).

L. Marcus, Continuous matrices and stability of differential systems, *Math. Z.* (1955) 62, 310.

R. A. Nesbit, General applications of the direct method of Lyapunov, *Advances in Control Systems* (1965) 2, 269. Academic Press, New York.

M. B. Nevelson and R. Z. Has'minskii, Stability of stochastic systems, *Problem Peredaci Informacii*, (1966), 2 76.

T. Pavlidis, Stability of systems described by differential equations containing impulses, *I.E.E. Trans Automatic Control*, (1967). AC12, 43.

M. M. Power, The companion matrix and Lyapunov functions for linear multi-variate time invariant systems, *J. Franklin. Inst.* (1967) 283, 214.

I. W. Sandberg, Some stability results related to those of V. M. Popov, *Bell Syst. Tech. J.*, (1965) 44, 2133.

D. G. Schultz, The generation of Lyapunov functions, *Advances in Control Systems* (1965) 2, 1. (Academic Press, New York).

W. G. Vogt, and J. M. George, On Aizerman's conjecture and boundedness, *I.E.E. Trans. Automatic Control*, (1967) AC 12, 338.

T. Yoshizawa, Lyapunov's function and boundedness of solutions, *Funcal. Ekvac.* (1959) 2, 95.

R. I. Zarosskii, Stability of solution of a functional equation of dynamic programming, *Z. Vycisl. Mat. i Fiz.* (1967) 7, 199.